DICTIONARY OF WORD ORIGINS

Linda Flavell completed a first degree in modern languages and has subsequent qualifications in both secondary and primary teaching. She has worked as an English teacher both in England and overseas, and more recently as a librarian in secondary schools and as a writer. She has written three simplified readers for overseas students and co-authored, with her husband, *Current English Usage* for Papermac and several dictionaries of etymologies for Kyle Cathie.

Roger Flavell's Master's thesis was on the nature of idiomaticity and his doctoral research on idioms and their teaching in several European languages. On taking up a post as Lecturer in Education at the Institute of Education, University of London, he travelled very widely in pursuit of his principal interests in education and training language teachers. In more recent years, he was concerned with education and international development, and with online education. He also worked as an independent educational consultant. He died in November 2005.

By the same authors

Dictionary of Idioms and their Origins

Dictionary of Proverbs and their Origins

Dictionary of English down the Ages

Dictionary of Word Origins

Linda and Roger Flavell

Kyle Books

This edition printed in Great Britain in 2016 by
Kyle Books, an imprint of Kyle Cathie Ltd.
192–198 Vauxhall Bridge Road
London, SW1V 1DX
general.enquiries@kylebooks.com
www.kylebooks.co.uk

First published in Great Britain in 1995 by Kyle Cathie Limited
Completely revised, updated and expanded in 2006

ISBN: 978 0 85783 410 2

A Cataloguing in Publication record for this title is available from the British Library.

Printed and bound at Gopsons Papers Ltd., Noida

Main Essays

Introduction

With a book of this kind it is always tempting to ignore the introduction. The browser plunges into the text at random while the reference reader confines his or her reading to the index and the relevant entries. In this case we hope that both types of reader will take a moment to read these few pages. They provide background information about the development of the English language that will increase your enjoyment and understanding of the rest of the book.

Indo-European

Nearly all European languages, some languages spoken in the Middle East and northern India, and the ancient tongues of Greek, Latin and Sanskrit show a number of striking similarities which point to a common prehistoric source. This is assumed to be a language spoken thousands of years ago, possibly in central Europe, which is now referred to as Proto-Indo-European. Languages deriving from it belong to the Indo-European family. The term Indo-European describes the extent of the geographical distribution of the different languages.

The dispersal of the people who spoke Proto-Indo-European caused various linguistic branches to spring from the parent stock. One of these was Germanic. The original prehistoric tongue, now referred to as Proto-Germanic, eventually divided into North Germanic, East Germanic and West Germanic. Modern Scandinavian languages developed from North Germanic. English, along with Fresian, Flemish, German and Dutch, is of West Germanic origin.

Old English

During the fifth and sixth centuries Britain was invaded and settled by the Angles, the Saxons and the Jutes, Germanic peoples from the Jutland region of northern Europe. In Britain these peoples were soon collectively known as the Angles. The Germanic dialects they spoke were very similar to each other and from them the English language (*Englisc*) evolved. (The name of the language comes from *Engle*, the Old English word for 'Angle'.) This initial period of the

English language, which is now known as Old English, lasted until the Norman invasion of 1066.

During these centuries Old English was considerably enriched by the vocabulary of Christian mission (see **Early Latin influences**, page 86) and by a stock of Old Norse words that it absorbed during the Viking invasions (see **Viking conquests**, page 263).

Middle English

English changed considerably as a result of the Norman Conquest. During the Middle English period, which lasted from about 1100 to 1500, French was the language of the upper classes. The French spoken in England developed from the northern French dialect of the conquerors and is known as Anglo-Norman or Anglo-French. English survived as the language of the uneducated masses but naturally absorbed a large number of Anglo-French words. After about 1250, however, there was an increasing tendency for upper-class French speakers to express themselves in English. In doing so, they made use of French words that were familiar to them, many of them borrowed from Old French, so that an even greater influx of foreign words poured into every area of English vocabulary. Where an Old English word and a French word had the same meaning, the Old English was often discarded in favour of the French. Nevertheless, in its grammatical structure and with its important core of basic vocabulary (*house, meat, drink, work, sleep, sing,* etc.) which remained unchanged, English was still a Germanic language.

(It is perhaps worth noting that the Romance languages – French, Italian, Spanish, Portuguese and Romanian – also belong to the Indo-European family, through their Latin origins.)

Modern English

Modern English, which we date from about 1500, continued to assimilate a huge number of foreign terms. The Renaissance excited the spirit of discovery. The invention of printing with movable type sparked the desire to break the restriction of Latin as the language of scholarship and to communicate in the vernacular to a wider readership. Where English was inadequate for this purpose, classical terms were naturalised. Translations were made from modern languages such as French and Italian, as well as classical Greek and Latin, thus introducing further foreign words into English. New continents and people were discovered and English vocabulary extended through the adoption of strange terms descriptive of exotic landscapes, life and customs. (Some of the essays in this book explore borrowings from individual languages such as Malay, Chinese, Hindi and Arabic.) Trade flourished and new commodities were made available, from different fabrics to beverages such as tea and cocoa. Medical and scientific knowledge increased and were expressed in terms coined from Latin and Greek.

English continues to grow and change rapidly as it reflects the concerns, interests and needs of its speakers. Technological advances in the twentieth century, for instance, have introduced a wealth of new terms while, at the close of the century, the adjective *green* has developed a new meaning which reflects present-day preoccupation over the welfare of our planet.

How to use this book

This dictionary seeks to trace the origins of particular words and to provide a historical context for them. These 'headwords' are arranged in alphabetical order. Often, however, words from the same source are referred to in the entries and so, for ease of reference, a comprehensive index has been included. Here headwords appear in *italic* type while their etymological relatives, together with words which feature in the essays, are printed in plain type. The essays and boxes scattered throughout the book expand on themes which are relevant to a number of entries or are of general interest in the development of our language.

It is rarely possible to be exact about when a word appeared in English. *Serendipity* and *robot* are exceptions. Where a word is set in a particular century it usually means only that the first known written record of the term appeared then. There is no way of knowing how long a word featured in spoken English before it occurred in written form.

Sometimes a word is traced back to an unattested term or root. This means that although there is no written evidence that the particular form ever existed, linguistic scientists have been able to draw upon their understanding of how words in that family develop and are confident that it did.

In selecting words for inclusion, we have chosen those which have a story to tell. While we have striven for scholarly accuracy (without, we hope, falling into academic pedantry), we have also aimed to show something of the richness and diversity of the English language, and to include sufficient that is plain curious to satisfy the browser motivated by nothing more than a quest for knowledge and a love of words.

accolade

1. the conferment of a knighthood
2. an expression of praise or high honour

'So you like it here,' I prompted Mum as we walked, microphones down our bras and cameramen backing down the street before us, towards the sea front.

'Oh, it's fabulous,' she beamed, 'what a wonderful spot. Who'd have thought it? I mean I've never heard of it before . . . and isn't it CLEAN!' (Mum's greatest accolade, *a sort of Egon Lipman, highly polished, 5 stars.) 'You could eat off the streets . . . '*
(Maureen Lipman, GOOD HOUSEKEEPING, October 1994)

The project was the dream of the previous transport minister Hanja Maij Weggen, who has since departed the government to take up a European MEP seat. She has the dubious accolade *of having been the least popular transport minister in recent Dutch history.*
(1994 ANNUAL REVIEW, 3 January 1995)

Knighthoods were a practical arrangement. A medieval ruler would grant lands to faithful noblemen in exchange for a certain number of mounted men-at-arms to be supplied in times of conflict. The noblemen, in turn, secured the services of such men by granting them a portion of their lands on condition that they pledged themselves to be available for military duties when required. Nevertheless this businesslike arrangement was based on trust and knighthoods were an honour which elevated the beneficiaries to the ranks of the lesser nobility. Ideally knighthoods were solemnly conferred in church where candidates had spent the night in vigil. In practice they were often speedily bestowed in a baronial hall or even on the battlefield. The name of the ceremony, an *accolade*, reflects its earliest form. Originally, especially on the Continent, the king or a great lord embraced the knight about the neck, hence the French *accollade* (from the Italian *accollata* , from Vulgar Latin *accollāre*, 'to embrace round the neck', from Latin *ad*, 'about' and *collum*, 'neck'). Then the ceremony evolved whereby the sovereign or lord touched the candidate on both shoulders with the flat of a sword-blade before girding him with the weapon. The present-day British monarch still confers knighthoods upon servants of the realm by means of a sword.

The customs and ceremonies attached to the British monarchy ensure that *accolade* is still used in this sense, but it is more often found today as an expression of great honour or praise in other areas; an actor might receive an *accolade* for an outstanding performance, for instance, or a particular award might be considered the highest *accolade* in a profession.

◆ *Accolade* is made up of three elements. The final part, the suffix *-ade*, is interesting in this case as it shows the different times and paths by which words were borrowed into English. The root is the Latin *-āta*, the feminine past participle of one class of verbs. This regularly became *-ee* in Old French from where a word might be borrowed into English. This is exactly what happened to *accolade*: it is found in fifteenth century English in the form *acolee*, after the French *acolee*. Meanwhile, the Latin suffix *-āta* took on other characteristic forms in other Romance languages – usually *-ada* or *-ata*. In a borrowing of the sixteenth century, the Italian *accollata* gave *accolade* in French, supplanting the earlier *acolee*. This led English to borrow the same word from

French a second time in the early seventeenth century in the form of our current *accolade*, which then supplanted the earlier English *acolee*.

Latin *collum*, 'neck', is related to a number of English words, the most common of which are the medical term *torticollis* and *collar*. The latter has been in the language since before 1300.

The third element is the common Latin prefix *ac-*, from *ad-*, meaning 'to, towards'. It forms the initial part of many English words.◆

aftermath

1. a second crop of hay
2. the consequences of an event or action

Italy, in fact, had another serious bout with a rabid dog population in the aftermath *of the Second World War.*
(James Hansen, NEW SCIENTIST, 1983)

Patrick stared at the ceiling. A vein in his throat pumped wildly. They lay in companionable silence and for a while their breathing was in time, as in the aftermath *of gratified desire.*
(Alan Judd, SHORT OF GLORY, 1984)

Several hundred people sat on the sea wall, staring south into the late afternoon sky. It was a bruised, feverish red, flaring like the aftermath *of an explosion, and it induced a sombre mood among the spectators.*
(Alexander Frater, CHASING THE MONSOON, 1990)

The story is told of a teacher of mathematics who called his retirement home *Aftermath*. Strictly, *aftermath* is an agricultural term, still used in some rural communities, to refer to the cutting of a second crop of hay in the same season. The word is composed of *after* and *math*, from an Old English word *mæth*, 'to mow'. (*Aftercrop* follows the same pattern.) By extension it is now more commonly applied to the unpleasant consequences that are reaped after a disaster, a second crop of misery.

agnostic

someone who claims the existence of God cannot be known

If I am asked, as a purely intellectual question, why I believe in Christianity, I can only answer, 'For the same reason that an intelligent agnostic *disbelieves in Christianity.' I believe in it quite rationally upon the evidence.*
(G K Chesterton, ORTHODOXY, 1909)

There are Hindus and Moslems in every corner of Ceylon, but neither of these orthodoxies seems fitting for the place. Hinduism is too fanciful and chaotic, Islam too puritanical and austere. Buddhism, with its gentle agnosticism *and luxuriant sadness, is so right in Ceylon that you feel it could have been born here, could have grown up out of the soil like the forest.*
(Paul Bowles, THEIR HEADS ARE GREEN, 1963)

If it were an attempt to prove the existence of God, the book would be a failure. But the book can't be an attempt at evangelisation because it includes, in very English fashion, agnostics *and professional doubters as well.*
(THE TIMES, 3 March 1994)

The miracle was repeated many times over the following months. Padre Cicero was unsure how to react to events and his bishop in the state capital of Fortaleza ignored them, hoping they would cease. But a prominent doctor, allegedly agnostic, *published a newspaper article agreeing that the host had changed to blood, 'a supernatural fact for which it is impossible to find a scientific explanation'.*
(WEEKEND FINANCIAL TIMES, 14 January 1995)

Strictly, an agnostic is not simply someone who doubts the existence of God but one who believes that only the finite can be known and made sense of, so that God and the infinite are consequently unknowable. The word was coined in 1869 by Thomas Henry Huxley, a biologist and vigorous exponent of Darwin's evolutionary theory. In the February 1889 issue of the NINETEENTH CENTURY, Professor Huxley explained the reasoning behind the new word:

When I reached intellectual maturity and began to ask myself whether I was an atheist, a theist, or a pantheist, a materialist or an idealist, a Christian or a free-thinker, I found that the more I learned and reflected, the less ready was the answer, until at last I came to the conclusion that I had neither art nor part with any of these denominations except the last. The one thing in which most of these good people agreed was the one thing in which I differed from them. They were quite sure they had attained a certain 'gnosis,' had more or less successfully solved the problem of existence; while I was quite sure I had not, and had a pretty strong conviction that the problem was insoluble . . . This was my situation when I had the good fortune to find a place among the members of that remarkable confraternity of antagonists, long since deceased, but of green and pious memory, the Metaphysical Society. Every variety of philosophical and theological opinion was represented there, and expressed itself with entire openness; most of my colleagues were ists *of one sort or another; and, however kind and friendly they might be, I, the man without a rag of a label to cover himself with, could not fail to have some of the uneasy feelings which must have beset the historical fox when, after leaving the trap in which his tail remained, he presented himself to his normally elongated companions. So I took thought, and invented what I conceived to be the appropriate title of* 'agnostic.' *It came into my head as suggestively antithetic to the 'Gnostic' of Church history who professed to know so much about the very things of which I was ignorant, and I took the earliest opportunity of parading it at our society, to show that I, too, had a tail like the other foxes. To my great satisfaction, the term took; and when the* Spectator *had stood godfather to it, any suspicion in the minds of respectable people that a knowledge of its parentage might have awakened was, of course, completley lulled.*

Other accounts as to exactly when the professor announced his new word differ slightly. According to R H Hutton, editor of the SPECTATOR and fellow founder member of the Metaphysical Society, Huxley aired it not after debate with the Society's members but at a party held previous to its formation, at James Knowles's house on Clapham Common on 21 April 1869. The first written record of the word occurred just a few weeks later in Hutton's SPECTATOR of 29 May 1869. Perhaps the professor already felt at sea without a label and used the party as an opportunity to test the waters with his new tag.

As for the form of the word, Hutton claimed it was from St Paul's mention in Acts, Chapter 17, verse 23 of the altar to the Unknown God: in Greek *agnostō theō.* Whether this account is true or not, gnostic as a noun and adjective, meaning 'known, relating to knowledge', had been in use in English for over two hundred years before Huxley's time; the negative prefix *a-* was also familiar to him. *Agnostic* therefore was a simple coining. It does not, however, fully respect its Greek roots, in that the ending *-ikos* (giving *-ic* in English) could not co-occur with *a-* in that language.

Today the scope of the word has

been extended to refer to someone who questions the wisdom of an opinion or course of action.

For another word where the precise time of its coining can be fixed, see **ammonia** and **Precise Timing** (page 219). See **amethyst** for a classical Greek example of the prefix *a-*.

agony

1. acute mental or physical torment
2. a deep feeling of pleasure or pain

This night as I was in my sleep, I dreamed, and behold the heavens grew exceeding black; also it thundered and lightened in most fearful wise, that it put me into an agony; *so I looked up in my dream, and saw the clouds rack at an unusual rate, upon which I heard a great sound of a trumpet, and saw also a man sit upon a cloud, attended with the thousands of heaven; they were all in flaming fire: also the heavens were in a burning flame. I heard then a voice saying, 'Arise, ye dead, and come to judgement'.*

(John Bunyan, THE PILGRIM'S PROGRESS, 1678)

Cramp seized her tired feet, knotting her toes into twisted shapes, moving up to her calves until she gasped with pain. Stamping and trying to tread away the agony, *she drew the curtains, switched on the light. There was no river, no fish, no child.*

(Mary Wesley, AN IMAGINATIVE EXPERIENCE, 1994)

On the surface, Dorothea is a prim heroine, a goody-two-shoes borrowed from Dickens to resolve the plot and release its victims with dollops of inherited wealth. But her appeal to the modern reader lies with her inner doubts and agonies.

(THE TIMES, 22 January 1994)

The word has its origin in a Greek verb *agein*, 'to drive, to lead, to celebrate'. This was the root of *agōn*, 'a gathering or an arena', where combatants, athletes and spectators came together to enjoy the competition. From this came *agōnia*, the word for the struggle or contest itself. Gradually the term was used more generally to refer firstly to wrestling against severe physical pain, then against mental anguish.

The word did not come directly into English from Greek. *Agōnia* was borrowed into Latin and from there into Middle English, possibly through Old French *agonie*. The OED, however, suggests that Wycliffe may have coined it from the Latin of the Vulgate. He is known to have been a strong influence on Chaucer, who used the word to mean 'mental distress' in the 'Miller's Tale' (c.1387). Wycliffe himself used *agonye* in a passage that is better known in the later rendering of the Authorised Version of 1611:

'*And being in an* agony, *he prayed more earnestly; and his sweat was, as it were, great drops of blood falling down to the ground'* (Luke 22:44).

Christ's Agony became a general term to refer to this major episode in his life, of the same order as his Birth, Baptism and Transfiguration. As this episode in his life is closely linked to his imminent death, it is not surprising that the physical and mental torment of *agony* is prominent in the sixteenth century extension of meaning to refer to death throes.

The eighteenth century saw the emergence of a new sense where the word was used to describe any intense sensation of either delight or anguish. Then, at times, both emotions might co-exist:

Then he thought of his flower. He got it out, rumpled and wilted, and it mightily increased his dismal felicity. He wondered if she would pity him if she knew? Would she cry? . . . This picture brought such an agony *of pleasurable suffering that he worked it over and over again in his mind and set it up in new and varied lights, till he wore it threadbare.* (Mark Twain, THE ADVENTURES OF TOM SAWYER, 1876)

Pain and pleasure may well be the reverse side of the same coin; current usage, none the less, emphasises the former over the latter. The agony wins out over the ecstasy.

See **excruciating.**

From all points of the compass

English collects words from other languages like a magpie. Apart from very obvious sources such as Latin, Greek, Arabic and the Romance languages of western Europe, just in this book are included:

Chinese:	tea, kowtow
Czech:	robot
Tahitian:	tattoo
Tongan:	taboo

Even a cursory glance at a large dictionary shows how many other languages from around the world have enriched English over the centuries. The biggest of them all, the OXFORD ENGLISH DICTIONARY, lists over 500 foreign languages and dialects that have influenced its entries, from Abnakei and Aboriginal to Zulu and Zuñi.

See also **Words from Malay** (page 56), **Words from Chinese** (page 153), **Words from Arabic** (pages 10–11), **A taste of India** (page 243).

alarm

1. call to arms
2. a warning
3. a feeling of fear or anxiety
4. a type of clock

'Why, Dodo, you never told me that Mr Ladislaw was come again!'

Dorothea felt a shock of alarm*: every one noticed her sudden paleness as she looked up immediately at her uncle, while Mr Casaubon looked at her.*
(George Eliot, MIDDLEMARCH, 1872)

The whole First Act of Coriolanus *is so full of* alarms *and excursions and hand-to-hand fighting, with hard blows given and taken, that it is tedious to Shakespeare's modern admirers, but it gave keen pleasure to the patrons of the Globe.*
(Walter Raleigh, SHAKESPEARE, 1907)

Although our bonfire burnt the year round . . . it was at about this time of year that it became the focus of the garden. We would be sent, in the middle of a wholly unconnected activity, to 'check the bonfire'. We were expected to react like a fireman answering a call. The alarm *was always prompted by flames seen from a window. Flames meant the fire was taking matters too liberally into its own hands and had to be damped down with more weeds . . .*
(Life, THE OBSERVER MAGAZINE, 27 November 1994)

'Alarme! Alarme!' was originally a warning cry meaning 'To arms!' which has been in use since medieval times. It was borrowed into English from Old French *alarme* and Italian *allarme*, a contraction of *all'arme*, literally 'To (the) arms!'. Its ultimate source is probably the Late Latin phrase *ad illas armas*, 'to those arms'. Before long the interjection itself had become the term by which the call to arms was known, whether it was the shout '*alarme!*', a

blast on a horn or a clanging bell.

In the sixteenth century the word was applied to a loud noise made to alert people to imminent danger of any kind. It was also applied to mechanisms which sounded an alarm. This sense is best noted today in the *alarm clock*, with its warning that it's time to get up.

Modern use stresses the feelings of the person who hears the alarm, fear or at least disquiet at the approach of danger or uncertainty. This application dates back to the second half of the sixteenth century. Today one increasingly finds signs on doors that say, *This door is alarmed.* Clearly, doors are not being given animate abilities to feel fear. 'Equipped with a burglar alarm' is its new meaning.

An alternative spelling *alarum* dates from medieval times. It probably arose through the very marked pronunciation of the letter *r* in a drawn out last syllable when the call to arms was made. It is only found very occasionally today, principally for the sense 'alarm clock'.

album

1. a book with blank pages for the collection of like items: stamps, photographs, etc
2. a collection of songs on a CD, cassette or record

Dined at Hay Castle. Mrs Bevan and the girls gave me a splendid photograph album . . .
(Francis Kilvert, DIARY, Wednesday 28 August 1872)

KERRANG!: The Album
The first half of this double album *features 15 tracks of up to date mayhem, and is sub-titled KONTEMPORARY KAOS! The second half, KERRANG! KLASSIX! includes as many all-time monsters which are similarly favourites with readers of the world's greatest heavy metal magazine, and as the sleeve note suggests, 'This cacophonous collection will make yer ears bleed! You have been warned. . .'. Maybe not the right choice for your granny's birthday — but the most Kranium Krunchin'* album *of the century!*
(BRITANNIA MUSIC CATALOGUE, Music News 10, 1994)

The [friendship] book is a small album, *exquisitely contained in an elegant 18th century green morocco binding with typically restrained gilding and decoration. On its spine are the words 'Sacred to Friendship' . . . There are over 100 signed contributions . . . many by eminent artists, sculptors and writers . . .*
(DAILY TELEGRAPH, 4 March 1995)

Album is the neuter form of *albus*, a Latin adjective meaning 'white'. In ancient Rome an *album* was a white board upon which public notices were written. Boards were displayed in public places such as the Forum and information inscribed on them might include the praetor's edicts or the chronicles compiled by the chief priest.

Since the seventeenth century, English has used *album* for a book with blank pages to be filled with verses, drawings or autographs of friends or prominent people. According to Dr Johnson, this was a foreign custom of long-standing. Certainly it was common in Germany, where friends' signatures were collected in an *album amicorum*. The Victorians applied the word to any blank-leaved book which was used to collect like items together; photographs or pressed flowers, for instance. In the 1960s the word was taken up by the world of recorded music, when a collection of songs on a long-playing record became known as an *album*, a term which is now similarly applied to a CD.

alcohol

spirits, strong drink, ethanol

Tony Williams: How was New York?
Richard Merton: Alcoholic.
Tony Williams: Did you sell any books?
Richard Merton: At the cost of cirrhosis, yes.
Tony Williams: You look well enough.
(Robin Maugham, THE SERVANT, 1972)

Those early birds at breakfast television are obviously having trouble rousing experts to appear at ungodly hours to comment on the morning's news. One of our hacks reeled home the other week after a particularly intensive study of the behavioural effects of alcohol *at the 'Three Compasses'. He passed out, fully clothed, on his sofa.*
(NEW SCIENTIST, 1983)

Imperial Water, a wrinkle potion from the 18th century, was composed of 'five quarts of brandy into which you put frankincense, mastic, benjamin, gum arabic, cloves, nutmeg, pine nuts, sweet almonds and musk, all bruised and distilled'. This may sound more like a knock-out punch, but alcohol *is, of course, something we still put on our skin.*
(New Zealand WOMAN'S WEEKLY, 14 January 1991)

THE GOODY-GOODY FACTOR.
All BYU students sign pledges not to drink alcohol, *tea or coffee, use recreational drugs, smoke, swear or engage in premarital sex. They didn't use to be able to wear blue jeans.*
(SPORTS ILLUSTRATED, 31 August 1992)

Few would guess the connection between this word and the make-up box. The root is Arabic: *al-* meaning 'the' and *kohl*, an extremely fine black, metallic powder used to stain the eyelids. George Sandys, writing in 1615 of his travels in Palestine, says that the women '*put betweene the eye-lids and the eye a certaine black powder . . . made of a minerall brought from the kingdome of Fez, and called Alcohole*'. (Kohl pencils are still used to define the eyes today.) This was a very old practice indeed in the region. In the Old Testament of the Bible, Ezekiel (born around 621 BC) gives God's judgement on Oholah and Oholibah: *You bathed yourself, you painted your eyelids, and put on your finest jewels for them.* (THE LIVING BIBLE TRANSLATION, Ezekiel 23:40)

In Arabic as well as sixteenth-century English, the word was used to refer to any impalpable powder. Europeans parted company from the Arabic by applying the term not only to fine powder but also to pure distilled liquids. (Distillation, coincidentally, was a skill which they had learnt from Arab alchemists several centuries earlier.) Wine was commonly subjected to this process, which yielded its very essence, *alcool vini*, spirit of wine. Edward Phillips, Milton's nephew, clearly shows the development of the word in his THE NEW WORLD OF ENGLISH WORDS (1658):

Alcahol *or* Alcool, *the pure Substance of anything separated from the more Gross. It is more especially taken for a most subtil and highly refined Powder, and sometimes for a very pure Spirit: Thus the highest rectified Spirit of Wine is called* Alcohol Vini.

By the end of the eighteenth century the word *alcohol* was firmly fixed as the term for a liquid converted to its essence. By the mid-nineteenth century, by association with spirit of wine, it was also more loosely applied to any inebriating fermentation or brew. Indeed the temperance movement of the period even asserted that the source of *alcohol* was the Arabic *al gul*, 'the devil' or 'demon' – the demon drink.

◆ There are quite a number of other

loans from Arabic that begin with *al*. This is the Arabic definite article which is borrowed into most European languages along with the following noun. It is obviously present in *alchemy*, *algebra*, *almanac* and a number of other words, and less clearly so in *azimuth* and *lute*. (For a fuller discussion, see **Words from Arabic**, pages 10–11).◆

See **teetotaller**.

ale

a fermented, intoxicating drink, beer

To make Cock Ale. *Take eight gallons of* Ale; *then take a March Cock and boil him well; and take four pounds of raisins well stoned, two or three nutmegs, three or four flakes of mace and half a pound of dates. Beat all these in a mortar, and put to them two quarts of the best sherry-sack. Put all this into the* Ale, *with the Cock, and stop it close six or seven days, and then bottle it: and after a month you may drink it.*
(The Closet of Sir Kenelm Digby Opened, 1669)

J D Wetherspoon stands out among the specialist pub companies. Its pubs are often conversions from banks or old supermarkets, have no-smoking areas, ban jukeboxes and offer real ale *at 99p a pint.*
(Daily Telegraph, 5 January 1995)

[The Lady of Traquair's] special interest is running the 200-year-old brewery, revived by her father in 1965, which each year produces 100,000 bottles of strong ale – *'very strong, I grew up on it'.*
(Daily Telegraph, 5 January 1995)

A Germanic root, *alut-*, gave rise to the Old English *ealu*, 'ale', and related words in Scandinavian languages. The Old English word *bēor*, 'beer', also existed and sprang from an unidentified Germanic root from which German and Dutch also derived their words for beer. In medieval England the two words were synonymous, although *ale* was much more commonly used, *beer* being reserved for more formal poetical contexts. In the Middle Ages wood sage, alecost and ground-ivy (alehoof) were used to preserve and flavour ale but in the sixteenth century Flemish immigrants introduced the practice of adding hops to malted grain and this drink was called *beer* to distinguish it from *ale*. In his *Dyetary* (1542) Andrew Boorde describes the brew and laments the harmful effects of its popularity: *Bere is made of malte, of hoppes, and water: it is a naturall drynke for a Dutche man. And nowe of late dayes it is moche used in Englande to the detryment of many Englysshe men.*

But just under a century later in John Gerard's revised *Herbal* (1633) beer is found to be a nourishing beverage: *The manifold virtues of Hops so manifestly argue the wholesomeness of beer above ale: for the hops rather make it a physical drink to keep the body in health, than an ordinary drink for the quenching of our thirst.*

In the Middle Ages and through to the seventeenth century, ale was not only a drink but a term given to a festivity where ale was drunk. Sometimes this was a family occasion such as a wedding (*bride ale*) or funeral (*dirge ale*). Often an ale would be held on a saint's day or Christian festival (*Whitsun ale*) to benefit church funds. The congregation would donate malt, from which the church wardens brewed ale to sell back to them at the celebration. Or an ale might mark out the agricultural or working year (*lamb ale, scythale*). These were sometimes at the expense of the lord of the manor but often peasants were ordered to contribute malt and then forced to buy the brew (L F Saltzman, ENGLISH LIFE IN THE MIDDLE AGES, 1926). Whatever the excuse for the *ale*, it was generally marked by revelry and drunkenness.

For an unlikely word in which *ale* is a major constituent, see **bridal**. See also **dirge**.

algebra

a generalised type of arithmetic that uses letters and symbols to represent numbers

A bomb, thought to have been planted by the IRA nearly two years ago, has been discovered at a branch of Dillons bookshop, apparently behind some shelves in the mathematics section. This has caused some amusement about the slow stock-turn of books on algebra.

(DAILY TELEGRAPH, 4 March 1995)

In a well-meaning effort to make mathematics more accessible to most pupils, school algebra *has been gradually transformed in the pre-16 curriculum to the point where most mathematicians would not recognise it as* algebra . . . *Under GCSE, more emphasis is placed on solving practical problems related to everyday life; but* algebra *is hardly ever useful in everyday life. Even when a problem looks like an* algebraic *one (because x is being used), pupils are now learning to use a method called 'trial and improvement' which involves trying out numbers until a solution is found. This is an eminently practical way of solving equations but it fails to teach pupils the important* algebraic *idea of manipulating abstract objects.*

(DAILY TELEGRAPH, 8 March 1995)

The Arabic term *al-jebr* meant 'the bringing together or reunion of broken parts' and referred to the setting of fractured bones. It came from the verb *jabara* which meant 'to reunite, to restore'. The word was taken into Italian, Spanish and medieval Latin as *algebra* and was borrowed into English from one of these in the sixteenth century as a medical term. It was, however, short-lived in this sense, unlike Spanish which, according to John Minsheu's DICTIONARY IN SPANISH AND ENGLISH (1623), had: *Algébra, bone-setting. Algebrísta, a bone-setter.*

In Arabic *al-jebr* was also found in the phrase *'ilm al-jebr wa'l-muqābalah.* This was a mathematical term meaning 'the science of restoration and equation' and denoted algebraic calculation. In this mathematical sense *al-jebr* was borrowed into Italian as *algebra* at the turn of the thirteenth century, and came into English in the mid-sixteenth century, with the spelling *algeber.* This was possibly influenced by the French *algèbre* and certainly confused with the name of the Arab chemist Geber, who was erroneously held by some to be its inventor. By the late sixteenth century, however, the Italian spelling had become the accepted form.

See **Words from Arabic** (pages10–11).

alibi

1. evidence to demonstrate the accused was not present at a crime
2. an excuse or justification for an action of any sort

As to the arrest of John Mitton, the valet, it was a council of despair as an alternative to absolute inaction. But no case could be sustained against him. He had visited friends in Hammersmith that night. The

Words from Arabic

Arabic has provided English with a store of common words. Some of them are listed here, others are given fuller treatment as separate entries (see **algebra, alcohol, assassin, coffee, giraffe, hazard** and **magazine**). There are also entries for several words which were strongly influenced by Arabic (see **apricot, chemist, chess** and **serendipity**).

A number of the words begin in *al-*. This is the definite article 'the' which, in Arabic, is not easily separated from its noun, so that the whole is often borrowed as a single item. In the following list *alcove, alkali,* and *lute* show this tendency; see also the entries for **alcohol, algebra, apricot,** and **chemist.**

In some instances (see **chemist**), the prefix *al-* was lost. This was doubtless because there was a growing etymological awareness that *al-* was simply the definite article in Arabic. The effects were patchy, however. For example, the English *magazine,* originally meaning 'storehouse, depot', and Spanish *almacén,* with the same meaning, share the one Arabic root; yet only the latter shows evidence of the definite article. The same is true for the English/Spanish pairs *mattress* and *almadraque* and *cotton* and *algodón.* The reasons why the definite article is lost in some cases and not in others are as obscure as the reasons why, out of several hundred words in English from Arabic sources, only a relatively small percentage were borrowed with the article integrated in the first place.

alcove (17th cent): from French *alcôve,* from Spanish *alcoba,* 'a recess for a bed', from Arabic *al-qobbah,* 'the vault'.

alkali (14th cent): Middle English *alcaly,* from Medieval Latin *alcali,* from Arabic *al-qualīy,* 'the ashes (of the saltwort plant)', from *qalay,* 'to fry'. The original alkaline was lye, obtained from the ashes of the saltwort.

camel (late Old English): from Latin *camēlus,* from Greek *kamēlos,* from Semitic *gāmāl* or Arabic *jamal.*

carafe (18th cent): from French *carafe,* from Italian *caraffa,* from Arabic *gharrāffa,* from *gharafa,* 'to draw water'.

cipher (14th cent): Middle English *cifre,* 'zero', from Old French, from Medieval Latin *cifra,* from Arabic *sifr,* 'empty', the adjective being used as a noun. Originally, then, *cipher* meant 'nought', but by the sixteenth century was freely applied to any numeral and then to codes, many of which substituted numbers for letters.

cotton (14th cent): Middle English *cotoun,* from Old French, from Spanish-Arabic dialect *qoton,* from Arabic *qutn.* The Spanish-Arabic *alqoton,* which is prefixed by the definite article *al-,* is responsible for modern Spanish *algodón* and Portuguese *algodão.*

crimson (15th cent): Middle English *cremesin,* from Old Spanish, from Arabic *qirmazī,* 'red colour, crimson', from *qirmaz,* 'kermes', a species of scale insect from which the dye was made.

gazelle (16th cent): from Old French *gazel*, from Spanish *gacela*, from Arabic *ghazāl*.

jar (16th cent): from French *jarre*, from Provençal *jarra*, from Arabic *jarrah*, 'earthenware water pot'.

lime (17th cent): from French *lime*, from Provençal *limo*, from Arabic *līmah*.

lute (14th cent): from Middle French *lut* (earlier *leut*), from Old Provençal *laut*, from Arabic *al-'ud*, 'the oud' (literally 'the wood') where *al-* is the definite article. The article is still present in the Romance borrowing, being represented by the initial *l*. The *lute* was descended from a similar Arabic instrument.

mask (16th cent): from French *masque*, from Italian *maschera*, probably from Arabic *maskharah*, 'buffoon, laughing-stock'.

mattress (13th cent): Middle English *materas*, from Old French, from Italian *materasso*, from Arabic *al-matrah*, 'place where something is thrown down', hence 'mat or cushion', from *taraha*, 'to throw'.

monsoon (16th cent): from early modern Dutch *monssoen* (now obsolete), from Portuguese *monção*, from Arabic *mausim*, 'season' and hence 'monsoon season'.

racket (16th cent) [tennis]: through French *raquette*, from Italian *racchetta*, from Arabic *rāhat*, 'palm of the hand'. Tennis was originally played with the hand.

safari (19th cent): Arabic *safarīy*, a 'journey', from *safara*, 'to travel'.

sash (16th cent): Originally *shash* in English, from Arabic *shāsh*, 'turban' and also the 'band of fabric', such as muslin, from which the turban was made.

sequin (17th cent): from French *sequin*, from Italian *zecchino*, from *zecca*, 'the mint', from Arabic *sikkah*, 'die for stamping coins'. The *zecchino* was a Venetian gold coin and *sequin* was originally used in this sense in English. The term was applied to an 'ornamental spangle' in the last quarter of the nineteenth century.

sofa (17th cent): from Arabic *suffah*, applied to a raised part of the floor scattered with carpets and cushions. Originally used in this sense in English but then, from the early eighteenth century, to denote a piece of drawing-room furniture.

syrup (14th cent): Middle English *sirop*, from Old French, from Medieval Latin *siropus*, from Arabic *sharāb*, 'beverage' (heavily sweetened). Used since medieval times in cookery as a sweetener or preservative and in medicine as a vehicle for remedies.

tariff (16th cent): from French *tarif*, from Italian *tariffa*, from Turkish *ta'rifa*, from Arabic *ta'rīf*, 'notification, explanation', from *'arafa*, 'to notify'. Originally an 'arithmetical table', then a 'list or table of customs duties' and finally, from the mid-eighteenth century, a 'list of charges'.

alibi *was complete. It is true that he started home at an hour which should have brought him to Westminster before the time when the crime was discovered, but his own explanation that he had walked part of the way seemed probable enough in view of the fineness of the night.*
(Sir Arthur Conan Doyle, THE RETURN OF SHERLOCK HOLMES, 1905)

Imogen was staring as if she could see the only happy days of her childhood breaking and reshaping into a new pattern, a pattern of betrayal. Days in which she had not been the centre of love, but had been a diversion or, even worse than that, an alibi. *A totally innocent chaperone whose presence had made an adultery possible.*
(Philippa Gregory, 'The Playmate', GOOD HOUSEKEEPING, March 1994)

The first step is to compartmentalise your life so that each separate section of it – work, home, other people's homes, recreation – is kept as far apart from the others as is possible. The rule being that the more discrete your life the more discreet you can be about its complications and contradictions. To put it another way, you maximise your potential alibis.
(OBSERVER MAGAZINE, 29 January 1995)

The word is a Latin locative adverb and means 'elsewhere'. It is a combination of *alius*, 'other', and *ubī*, 'where'. It has been used in English law since the eighteenth century, originally in a sense very like the Latin: *We, the jury, find that the accused was* alibi.

By the the late eighteenth century *alibi* was accepted as a noun. An *alibi* was evidence offered by the accused that he was somewhere else when the crime took place. It has retained that sense ever since.

Twentieth-century developments in America make the word a synonym for excuse: *Low spirits make you seem complaining. . . I have an* alibi *because I'm going to have a baby.* (L P Hartley, FELLOW DEVILS, 1951)

Still later it fell victim to the American habit of creating verbs out of nouns, so that there is now a verb *to alibi* someone, meaning 'to provide an excuse or alibi'. There is also the rather neat expression an *alibi artist*, someone who is an expert at getting out of uncongenial mundane tasks.

◆ The component elements of *alibi* are found in other English words. *Alias* in Latin signifies 'otherwise'; it was borrowed into sixteenth century legal English, meaning 'also called or named'. It subsequently became a noun, with the connotation that alternative names were adopted for nefarious purposes. *Alien* also contains the same root. Latin *alienus* meant 'belonging to another person or place', a sense it retained when it was borrowed into Middle English through Old French in the fourteenth century. The word's use in science fiction dates from just before the mid-twentieth century.

Ubī is hardly *ubiquitous* as it is found in this word and just a few others (from New Latin *ubīquitas*, from Latin *ubīque*, 'everywhere').◆

See **altruism** for words stemming from the related *alter*.

alligator

a large reptile

'Surely these are only crocodiles?'

'Alligators! Alligators! *There is hardly such a thing as a true crocodile in South America . . .'*
(Sir Arthur Conan Doyle, THE LOST WORLD, 1912)

I regret I did not take part in the flash-light alligator *hunt but I heard about it from an old New Yorker who had found one: 'It was four feet long and not at all slimy. Just kinda cute.'*
(WEEKEND TELEGRAPH, 11 February 1995)

Early Spanish explorers in the Americas, struck by the *alligator's* similarity to the lizards in their homeland, referred to the creature as *el lagarto*, 'the lizard', a word derived from the Latin *lacertus* (feminine form *lacerta*). The English borrowed the term and modified it, running the two words into one and substituting English vowel sounds. The English naval commander, Sir John Hawkins, who led expeditions to the Spanish American coast in the second half of the sixteenth century, came close to the Spanish using *alagartoes* in his descriptions of his voyages. But Shakespeare's ROMEO AND JULIET shows how the word was evolving. While the First Quarto of 1597 has:

> *And in his needy shop a tortoyrs hung,*
> *An* Aligarta *stuft* (Act 5 scene 1)

the First Folio of 1623 has *allegater*. Ben Jonson favoured the spelling *alligarta* and, according to Nares, in a still credulous age seems to hint at a superstition that the reptile would make any plant it urinated upon poisonous: *And who can tell, if before the gathering and making up thereof, the* alligarta *hath not piss'd thereon.* (BARTHOLOMEW FAYRE, 1614)

Aligator, *alegator* and *allegator* are other seventeenth-century forms but the spelling had more or less settled into *alligator* by the eighteenth century. The word has the distinction of being one that was borrowed from English into French, rather than the other way round.

To discover how *alligator* ultimately means 'forearm' see **lizard**. For the etymology of its relative **crocodile**, see under that entry.

aloof

withdrawn, reserved, keeping at a distance

The women are less surefooted, perhaps because Eliot was herself ambivalent towards them. One moment she is Dorothea, Mary Garth, even Rosamund, the next she is an aloof *commentator, mother superior to a turbulent convent.*
(THE TIMES, 22 January 1994)

Alan Bennett still really is an academic in his serious, disciplined, bookish, conscientious approach to his writing; in staying aloof *from showbiz he has avoided the fleshpots, and has built up a remarkable corpus of lasting work to prove it.*
(DAILY TELEGRAPH, 25 March 1995)

The Dutch, like the English, were a great seafaring nation and many nautical terms used in English were borrowed from these near-neighbours. *Aloufe* was one of these from the sixteenth century. The word may be split into two parts, *a* and *loufe*. *A* is an Old English prefix meaning 'on' and is found in other words such as *asleep*, *aloft*, *afoot*, *aground*, etc. *Loufe* is a borrowing of the Dutch *loef*, 'windward'. (It is unclear whether it came direct into early Middle English or via Old French.) Put together *aloufe* was a command to 'put the boat's helm down and sail closer to the wind'. It is obsolete in this sense today, supplanted by *to luff*, another word that comes from the Dutch *loef*.

Almost immediately *aloof* was used outside its seafaring context. Early senses, which persisted well into the nineteenth century, were not nautical commands but terms stressing physical distance. Shakespeare in ROMEO AND JULIET (1597) had Paris command his page, '*Give me thy torch, boy. Hence, and stand* aloof' (Act 5, scene 3). Milton uses the word in similar fashion, as the context he gives the word in PARADISE REGAINED (1671) shows:

> *They at his sight grew mild,*
> *Nor sleeping him nor waking harmed;*
> *his walk*
> *The fiery serpent fled and noxious worm;*
> *The lion and fierce tiger glared* aloof.

'*The lion and fierce tiger glared* aloof' means 'from a distance'. And in the last quarter of the sixteenth century a figurative application began to emerge, so that *aloof* also came to mean 'detached, uninvolved, unsympathetic'. After all, a vessel can only make progress windward if the helmsman steers slightly away from the wind. Thus *aloof* was applied to a person who remains with the company and yet holds back, keeping himself to himself.

The original morphological division of the word is at odds with the humourous efforts of one folk etymologist. A well-known grafitto begins with *Be alert!* Underneath another hand had written: *No, don't be a lert, be a loof. We've got enough lerts.*

altruism

having consideration and regard for others

'I genuinely believed in my naivety that once it was understood that over a thousand people, mostly young, would be destined to spend the remainder of their lives on dialysis unless a donor kidney was made available to them, everyone would carry one [a donor card]. How wrong I was.'

In fact, only 18 per cent of adults carry donor cards, although according to annual Gallup surveys ... 74 per cent of the adult population are willing to become organ donors after their death. There appears to be a huge gap between our altruistic *intentions and the reality of carrying a card that is a constant reminder of our own mortality.*
(THE TIMES, 8 February 1994)

Some [animals] are even capable of altruism*: when one researcher was following a group of chimpanzees he discovered he had forgotten his lunch. Watching him trying to knock fruit down from the trees, 'an adolescent male chimpanzee, Sniff, collected some fruit, climbed down the tree and gave it to him.'*
(DAILY TELEGRAPH, 25 February 1995)

Like *agnostic*, the word was invented to encapsulate a philosophical principle, that of seeking to promote and taking satisfaction from the well-being of others. It was coined by the French philospher Auguste Comte, in his COURS DE PHILOSOPHIE POSITIVE (1830–42), as the antithesis of *egotism*, the principle of self-advancement. Where *egotism* has its roots in Latin *ego*, meaning 'I', *altruism* is derived from Italian *altrui* (French *autrui*), meaning 'belonging to others'. This in turn derives from Latin *alter*, meaning 'other'. Inspiration for the word is believed to have come from the French law-terms *le bien d'autrui*, 'the good of others', and *le droit d'autrui*, 'the right of others'. *Altruism* was readily embraced in Europe and America by those who, having reasoned themselves out of belief in God, found in the philosophy a motive for practising unselfish morality. But many a promising philosophy has foundered on the sharp rock of basic human nature. Walsh quotes the following New York newspaper report on the demise of the Altruist Society of St Louis:

Those to whom experiments for a remodelling of society appeal must be saddened by the last phase in the history of the Altruist *Community of St. Louis. 'We find it necessary,' says Mr. Alcander Longley, its late president, in the columns of its organ, the* Altruist, *'to announce to our readers that the* Altruist *Community is dissolved by mutual consent of all the members. The reasons for the dissolution are some of them as follows. Since Mr. Smith withdrew, late last fall, there have been but two male members of the community, George E. Ward and myself, and our natures and our methods of doing things are so different that there has been more or less discord at different times since, and not at any time real harmony.' One of the causes of disagreement was Mr. Ward's ambition to be 'appointed or elected as one of the editiors and managers of the Altruist', which Mr. Longley had decided views about controlling himself, 'saying that he would not own and manage a paper with Mr. Ward or any one else.' This led to the calling of a special meeting to elect a president in Mr. Longley's place, and the success of Mr. George E. Ward and two Mrs. Wards, who formed a majority of the community. Meanwhile, Mr. Longley admits, 'I have, during our dissensions, said some very uncomplimentary and disrespectful things to Mr. Ward, for which I have told him I am sorry. Among them was, I charged him with being an anarchist and with bullying his wife to get her to vote as he desired in the community, and with having acted fraudulently in keeping the record of the community as secretary and in the election of himself as president, all of which I hereby retract and apologize for.' Mr Longley and the remaining members of the pentagonal community, except Miss Travis, withdrew when Mr. Ward's journalistic aspirations were about to be gratified.*
(NATION, April 10, 1890)

See **alibi** for words from the related Latin *alius*.

◆ Latin *alter* surfaces today in Cicero's Latin words *alter ego* and a little more obliquely in a number of English words, such as *to alter* ('to make something other, different'), *altercation* ('dispute with another'), *alternate* ('do one thing after another by turns').◆

ambition

a strong desire to reach a goal, often of money or power

The devil speed him! No man's pie is freed
From his ambitious *finger.*
(Shakespeare, KING HENRY VIII, 1613)

Posy was in disgrace. Sylvia and Nana were horrified to find her, as they considered, selfish and hard-hearted. It was all very well to be ambitious, *but* ambition *should not kill the nice qualities in you.*
(Noel Streatfeild, BALLET SHOES, 1936)

. . . George V was a model constitutional monarch. His ambitions *did not soar beyond his stamp collection and his shoots. He was a country gent whose tastes were lower-middle-class and who preferred the workers to the aristocracy.*
(Paul Johnson, WAKE UP, BRITAIN!, 1994)

This word is one which rests easily on a politician's shoulders and, indeed, its origins are political. It derives from the Latin *ambitio*, meaning 'a going round' (from the verb *ambīre*; *ambi-*, 'about' and *īre*, 'to go'), a word which was particularly applied to political candidates doing the rounds in Rome to solicit support. Not surprisingly the word gradually came to mean 'a driving desire to achieve honour or success'. *Ambicious* and the noun *ambicioun* came into English in the fourteenth century from Latin, possibly through Old French. Until at least the second half of the seventeenth century, *ambition* had negative connotations and was classed as a vice. Only then did an inordinate desire for preferment moderate to a strong (and more acceptable) urge. The form too changed. Probably through the general move to regularise spellings on the Latin originals (see **crocodile** and **amethyst**), the sixteenth century saw the rise of *ambition* in preference to *ambicioun*.

◆ The two Latin root elements of *ambition* are quite productive in English. There are nearly 20 words (most of them obscure) that contain *ambi-*, such as *ambidextrous*, *ambiguous*, and more than twice as many with *ire*. These include *circuit*, *exit*, *perish*, *preterite*, *sedition*, *transit*. Just *ambit* and *ambient* contain both roots. The former made its appearance at the end of the fourteenth century, the latter two hundred years later.◆

For another word arising from Roman elections, see **candidate**.

ambrosia

delectable food; anything of fine taste or flavour

When Jill complains to Jack for want of
meate,
Jack kisses Jill, and bids her freely eate:
Jill sayes, of what? sayes Jack, on that
sweet kisse,
Which full of Nectar and Ambrosia *is,*
The food of poets; so I thought sayes Jill,
That makes them looke so lanke, so
Ghost-like still.
Let Poets feed on aire, or what they
will;
Let me feed full, till that I fart, sayes
Jill.
(Robert Herrick, 1591–1674)

Then, in a flowery valley, set him
down
On a green bank, and set before him
spread
A table of celestial food, divine
Ambrosial *fruits fetched from the Tree of*
Life,
And from the Fount of Life ambrosial
drink,
That soon refreshed him wearied, and
repaired
What hunger, if aught hunger, had
impaired,
Or thirst.
(John Milton, PARADISE REGAINED, 1671)

Anne's hungry guests, however, did not seem to think anything was lacking and they ate the simple viands with apparent enjoyment... Mrs. Pendexter said little; she merely smiled with her lovely eyes and lips, and ate chicken and fruit cake and preserves with such exquisite grace that she conveyed the impression of dining on ambrosia *and honeydew.*
(Lucy Maud Montgomery, ANNE OF AVONLEA, 1925)

NAUGHTY BUT NICE
From the Esher News & Mail: 'Ambrosia *is the food of gods, said to bestow immorality.*'
(DAILY TELEGRAPH, 25 February 1995)

According to Greek and Roman mythology, *ambrosia* was the food of the gods, and was thought to make those who ate it immortal. It derives from the Greek *a*, 'not', and *mbrotos*, 'mortal'. In sixteenth-century English, when the word was first used, there are references to the classical *ambrosia* which encompassed food, drink and even anointing oil. All these positive connotations produced a figurative range of senses. Swift charmingly describes his heroine in STREPHON AND CHLOE (1734) thus:

Venus-like her fragrant skin
Exhal'd ambrosia *from within.*

In modern usage, the word can be applied to anything which tastes or smells particularly delicious – a brand of creamed rice, for instance, is called Ambrosia. Perhaps it makes those who eat it wax lyrical, in line with the rather poetic feel of the word.

Interestingly, Sanskrit has a parallel formation to the Greek. *Amrita* is an adjective used in nineteenth century literary language by both Southey and Moore, meaning 'immortal, ambrosial'. Its root lies in Sanskrit *a*, 'not,' plus *m'rta*, 'dead'. The Sanskrit and the Greek both go back to the common pre-Germanic root *mer-* or *mor-*, 'to die', from which comes the English *murder*.

Ambrosia takes care of the gods' food. For what they drank see **nectar**.

ambulance

vehicle to transport injured people

In the flats below people came in from work, turned on their televisions, cooked their suppers, talked loudly, slammed doors, ran baths and subsided into bed as night closed in, not to silence but the muted roar of a vast city interrupted by occasional police sirens and the distant sound of tugs hooting on the river. Sometime in the night an ambulance *raced fast through the street, bell ringing.*
(Mary Wesley, AN IMAGINATIVE EXPERIENCE, 1994)

The earliest *ambulances* were horse-drawn carts used to carry wounded soldiers off the battlefield. The Spaniards apparently used them at the siege of Malaga in 1487 to bring swift relief to the wounded. Possibly the wagons came under heavy attack and the idea was judged impractical for it did not catch on. In the centuries which followed, the wounded were left where they fell until after the battle.

Three hundred years and many casualties later the French revived the concept and called the battlefield wagon the *hôpital ambulant*, 'walking hospital' (from Latin *ambulāre*, 'to walk'), soon to be abbreviated to *ambulant* and finally to *ambulance*. The usefulness of the vehicles was especially recognised during the Crimean War (1854–56). Until then the term *ambulance*, though known, had not been in general use, for even in the mid-nineteenth century the service still lacked proper organisation. Gradually, other countries began similar immediate relief for their war wounded and in 1864 the Geneva Convention agreed that *ambulances* serving in a war zone should not come under attack. The first public *ambulance* service in Britain began in 1878 and was manned by drivers who had been trained in basic first aid. By this time the emphasis was less on being a kind of field hospital, more on the rapid removal of the wounded from the scene of battle or from an accident, or the sick from their home to a better equipped treatment centre.

◆ The Latin *ambulāre* is the root of *amble* and *perambulate*, both clearly connected with the basic sense of 'to walk'. The Latin *somnus*, 'sleep', has combined with the same verb to produce a family of related terms, such as *somnambulist*, *somnambulation*, *somnambulism*.◆

amethyst

a stone of purple quartz

The casket was soon open before them, and the various jewels spread out, making a bright parterre on the table. It was no great collection, but a few of the ornaments were really of remarkable beauty, the finest that was obvious at first being a necklace of purple amethysts *set in exquisite gold work, and a pearl cross with five brilliants in it.* (George Eliot, MIDDLEMARCH, 1872)

According to Dr Brewer in DICTIONARY OF PHRASE AND FABLE, Roman ladies of a certain age treasured this gemstone in the belief that it would prevent their husbands' affections from wandering. The stone was chiefly prized, however, by those who loved carousing for it was believed that it had the power to prevent intoxication. A classical myth tells how Bacchus, the god of wine, was angry with the goddess Diana. He directed his fury against Amethyst, a young girl who was worshipping in Diana's temple, whereupon the protective goddess swiftly changed the girl into a statue. Baccus, feeling somewhat remorseful, poured wine over it so that the statue was stained the colour of the grape and Amethyst was freed from the effects of wine. The fortunate possessor of a charm or drinking vessel fashioned in the beautiful purple quartz could drink as much as he liked and feel no ill effects at all. That, at least, was the theory – the learned Greek biographer and moralist, Plutarch, knew better, it seems:

As for the amethyst, *as well the herb as the stone of that name, they who think that both the one and the other is so called because they withstand drunkennesse, miscount themselves, and are deceived.* (MORALIA, tr. Philemon Holland, 1603)

The ancient belief is reflected in the word itself which is derived from Greek *a-*, meaning 'not' and *methuskein*, 'to intoxicate' (from *methu*, 'wine'). The Greek adjective *amethustos*, 'anti-intoxicant', was applied to both the gemstone and a herb that was thought to possess the same qualities. From this came the Latin name for the quartz, *amethystus*. Old French borrowed the word *asametiste*, variants of this (*ametist, amatist, amatyst*) are found in Middle English from the thirteenth century onwards. It was only in the sixteenth century that the *-th-* was re-introduced, after the Latin.

For an unusual example of the negative Greek prefix *a-*, see **agnostic**.

ammonia

a colourless, pungent gas

Shamlegh's summer population is only three families – four women and eight or nine men. They were all full of tinned meats and mixed drinks, from ammoniated *quinine to white vodka, for they had taken their full share in the overnight loot.* (Rudyard Kipling, KIM, 1901)

Some countries now plan to make their own fertilisers. For example, Indonesia and Malaysia propose to make ammonia *and urea. But developing a large chemical industry needs capital, and to run it needs energy.* (NEW SCIENTIST, 1983)

The origin of this word is both heavenly and very down-to-earth. The supreme Egyptian god, *Amen*, was known as *Ammon* by the Greeks, who recognised him as Zeus. He was worshipped at his desert oracle which was situated by the oasis of *Jupiter Ammon* in Lybia. It was at this same oasis that a substance the Romans called *sal ammōniacus*, meaning 'salt of Ammon', was processed from the dung and urine of camels (collected, presumably, while they were watered there). *Ammonia*, the term for the colourless gas obtained from *sal ammoniac* (better known today as *ammonium chloride*), derives its name from that of the compound. This pseudo-Latin term was coined by the Swede Torbern Bergman in 1782.

Today *ammonia* is obtained through the Haber-Bosch process in the gas and coke industry, for ultimate use in fertilisers, explosives and nitric acid. This is a far cry from earlier practices when organic matter such as hoof and horn were used. The powdered antler of a hart served as smelling salts, the sharp, pungent smell of ammonia being very efficacious in bringing young ladies who had swooned back to their senses. It had already been called the *spirit of hartshorn* for a hundred years before Bergman's more scientific neologism.

For another word where the precise time of its coining can be fixed, see **agnostic** and **Precise Timing** (page 219). For other nineteenth-century scientific terms that find their origins in myths of the ancient world, see **tantalise**.

ampersand

an abbreviation denoting 'and'

I told all this to Tallulah, the former Injun maiden who had as little English as I had Athapaskan when I met and wooed her, and who, by dint of the tough, real instructions of secretarial school—the shorthand and the Palmer and the formal business letters and 70 to 80 and more words per minute without mistakes and without looking, the mastery, I mean, of that infinite keyboard (or, at Taloo's level, even palette) of the 100 different numerals, characters, punctuation marks, underscore keys, percentage, dollar and ampersand *signs and all the uppercase, lowercase conditions—was as savvy and street-smart as someone who had never even seen a reservation.*

(Stanley Elkin, PLAYBOY, January 1994)

There was Sonny: With his hair ('Your haircut is almost Shakespearean,' Jackie Kennedy observed, fumbling for something flattering to say after the duet performed for her in New York), his bell-bottoms, his lambskin vests, and his mopey affect, he looked like a cossack playing Ringo in the stage version of Help! Then there was the ampersand *of Sonny's eye, Cher: a confluence of Beat-generation bohemia, glam rock, and white trash.*

(ESQUIRE, November 1994)

An *ampersand* is the sign &, used to represent *and*. The word dates back to the days when horn-books listed the letters of the alphabet and included &. as a twenty-seventh symbol after z. (For more information on the horn-book, see **criss-cross**.) Children obliged to recite the alphabet would chant *per se*, that is 'by itself', after letters that could stand alone as a complete word. Including & these numbered four: 'A per se, A ', 'O per se, O', 'I per se I' and '& per se, &'. It was not long before the drawling of '& per se, &' became *ampersey* and then *ampersand*.

Similarly, from the fifteenth to the seventeenth centuries, 'A per se, A' developed a life of its own. A Cambridge manuscript of around 1500 has *Thow schalt be an apersey, my sone, In mylys ij, or thre.* William Dunbar writes in his poem 'In Honour of the City of London' (1501): *London, thowe arte of townes A per se.* The sense is not far from that of the contemporary phrase *A 1 (at Lloyd's)*.

The literal character for *ampersand* is devised from the two letters of the Latin word *et*, meaning 'and'. Brewer points out that the 'e' and the cross of the 't' are more easily recognised in the italic ampersand *&*.

Words from classical mythology and literature

Classical mythology and literature have inspired many common English words. *Hector*, the hero of Homer's ILIAD, for instance, is the source of the modern verb *hector*. Champion of the Trojans in their war against the Greeks, and the embodiment of every virtue both on and off the battlefield, *Hector* was first used in Middle English to personify 'a valiant warrior'. His reputation remained intact until the second half of the seventeenth century when his name was uncharacteristically applied to well-off yobs who, for amusement, intimidated folk as they went about their business on the streets of London. How the Greek hero fell to these depths is a mystery, but his name lives on in English in the form of the verb *hector*, 'to behave in a blustering and intimidating fashion', which was coined at this time.

Panic finds its source in a divine bully. As the dangerous brooding god of forests and shepherds, *Pan* roamed the valleys and mountains. Travellers were terrified of him and believed him to be the cause of any eerie sound issuing from remote regions of the countryside. The Greeks accordingly described an attack of fear where there was no obvious reason for it as *panikos*, 'of Pan'. The adjective *panic* came into English at the beginning of the seventeenth century by way of French *panique*, and was used as a noun in the modern sense from the early eighteenth century.

Pan was also a fertility god who forced his attentions upon either sex. On one occasion the beautiful nymph *Syrinx* escaped his lustful advances when she was changed into a bed of reeds. It was from these reeds that the god made his pan-pipes, traditionally played by shepherds. The instrument was known as *surigx* in Greek, a word which also denoted 'tube'. This was borrowed into Latin as *syrinx* and the altered medieval Latin form *syringa* ultimately became English *syringe*. The nymph's name is also perpetuated in the Latin term for the lilac and mock orange bushes, *syringa*, since shepherds' pipes were once made from them.

In spite of Pan's high sexual libido, it was the Greek god *Eros* who was the personification of sexual love. Said to be the son of Ares, god of war, and Aphrodite, goddess of love, his nature reflected that of both parents. Early classical literature emphasises both his power over people and his cruelty towards them. In early visual art, his facial features and athletic physique are physical perfection. From *erōs*, 'sexual desire', the Greeks derived *erōtikos*, 'concerned with sexual love', and this adjective came into English in the mid-seventeenth century as *erotic*. The derivatives *erotica* and *eroticise* date from the mid-nineteenth and early twentieth centuries respectively.

Aphrodite was a faithless wife and bad example to her son. She had the power of making others as sexually irresistible as herself. From her name, Greek derived the adjective *aphrodisiakos*, 'lustful', from which English derived *aphrodisiac* in the early eighteenth century.

Eros was, of course, born of illegitimate passion, for Aphrodite was married to Hephaestos, the god of fire and smelting, whom the Romans knew as *Volcānus*, or *Vulcan*. Italian borrowed his Latin name as *volcano* to denote a 'mountain which discharges fire and molten matter' and this term was taken into English in the early seventeenth century.

See also **Otherworldly influences** (page 142), **amethyst, atlas, mint,** and **tantalise**.

anathema

something despised and abominated

He strode up the row of hives, striking with his gauntleted fist the trunk of one of the apple trees, then strode back to deliver upon me his verdict, his anathema.
(Graham Swift, EVER AFTER, 1992)

The British take comfort from the thought that the IRA may be split. What comfort? It is only split between those who think it worth conning the British Government a little longer and those who cannot see the point, those who agree with Mr Adams's desire for some rapprochement with the Protestant community and those to whom any ceasefire is anathema.
(THE TIMES, 2 February 1994)

The Labour Party for all its apparent new-found moderation continues to anathematise *what it calls 'the rich'. . . The Labour Party's spokesmen always enjoy the game of defining richness, so as to justify the restoration of a punitively high tax bracket. Mr Neil Kinnock's definition of the sort of people who should suffer such confiscation was as follows: 'You can talk about individual incomes in excess of £60,000 per year.'*

Mr Neil Kinnock will soon be taking up residence in Brussels on a salary of £120,000 per year as a European Commissioner. Mr Neil Kinnock will need to pay no tax on this. Mr Neil Kinnock, like most socialists, is remarkably generous with other people's money.
(DAILY TELEGRAPH, 8 October 1994)

Anathema derives from the Greek verb *anatithenai*, meaning 'to set up', 'to dedicate', 'to hold on high as an offering', and originally referred to a votive or sacrificial offering. There is an example of this use in the New Testament where St Luke makes reference to the riches and gifts (*anathemas*) to be found in the temple at Jerusalem (Luke 21:5), a statement verified by the Roman historian, Tacitus, who called the temple a 'shrine of immense wealth'.

But the word was often found in another, related, sense. It was used to translate the Hebrew *hērem*, 'a devoted thing' (from the verb *hāram*, meaning 'to cut off from social contact'). This was a dreadful and solemn ban which set an object, a person or even a nation apart for ultimate destruction. A *hērem* could never be redeemed by man. Such a *hērem* or *anathema* was placed upon Jericho after it fell to the Israelites. When one man, Achan, ignored it and carried booty away into his tent the whole of the Israelite camp suffered until the sin was uncovered and dealt with. Achan himself was contaminated by unlawful contact so that he, his household and belongings shared the fate of Jericho and were all destroyed. The story is in the book of Joshua, Chapter 7. There are similar warnings elsewhere, such as at the end of Deuteronomy, Chapter 7, which are rendered in various translations as *anathemas.*

In the New Testament *anathema* is used by St Paul to condemn and exclude from the Christian community those whose profession of faith was insincere: *If any man love not the Lord Jesus Christ, let him be* anathema, *Maranatha.* (AUTHORISED VERSION, 1611, 1 Corinthians 16:22) or who preached an erroneous gospel:

But though we, or an angel from heaven, should preach unto you any gospel other than that which are preached unto you, let him be anathema. *As we have said before, so say I now again, If any man preacheth unto you any gospel other than that which ye received, let him be* anathema.
(AMERICAN REVISED VERSION Galatians I:8–9)

The word was much used in the early church as a term of utter condemnation. When in AD 428, for instance, Nestorius was appointed bishop of Constantinople he began to expound his views on the duality of Christ as both God and man. These were disputed by Cyril of Alexandria who, empowered by the Pope, demanded that Nestorius accept no less than twelve *anathemas* denouncing his doctrine. Nestorius, not to be outdone, replied with twelve of his own. He was deposed in 431 and died in exile.

By the sixth century in the Roman Catholic church an *anathema* had become an extreme form of excommunication, a severing from the Christian community, in an extension of biblical usage. In a solemn ceremony ordained by the Roman Pontifical (a papal or episcopal court), a bell was rung, a book (the Bible) was closed and a candle was snuffed to signify the spiritual darkness of a person '*condemned to eternal fire with Satan and his angels and all the reprobate, so long as he will not burst the fetters of the demon, do penance, and satisfy the Church*'. And until the last century the dogmatic decrees of the Catholic church were prefaced by 'If *anyone say . . . let him be* anathema.'

By the end of the seventeenth century the word was no longer found exclusively in religious contexts but was being used in a general sense to apply to anything reviled and deserving of a curse. Sadly twentieth century usage has greatly devalued this powerful word, as the following fragment from a magazine interview shows:

Dawn [French] and Lenny [Henry] are extremely busy with their individual careers . . . But they have never wanted to be known as a show-business couple . . . They have no plans for cosy joint projects either: the idea of 'making a sitcom with a sofa and a strained marriage' is complete anathema.
(GOOD HOUSEKEEPING, March 1994)

May such trivialisation of a mighty word be *anathema.*

For other words concerning temple or sacrifices, see **fanatic**, **holocaust**, **mint** and **scapegoat**.

antimacassar

a chair back cover

The parlor at Green Gables was a rather severe and gloomy apartment, with rigid horsehair furniture, stiff lace curtains, and white antimacassars *that were always laid*

at a perfectly correct angle, except at such times as they clung to unfortunate people's buttons.
(Lucy Maud Montgomery, ANNE OF AVONLEA, 1925)

Fashionable and well-groomed nineteenth-century gentlemen would slick their hair into place with an application of Rowland's Macassar Oil, imported from Makasar, Indonesia. It was produced by Rowland and Son, and widely advertised. The younger Rowland, Alexander, in 1809 wrote an 'ESSAY ON . . . THE HUMAN HAIR, WITH REMARKS ON THE VIRTUES OF THE MACASSAR OIL.' The unguent made such an impact that it even made its way into Byron's DON JUAN of 1819:

In virtues nothing earthly could
surpass her,
Save thine 'incomparable oil', Macassar!

By the second half of the century there were complaints of an adulterated product far removed from the natural ingredients of the original oil. Perhaps that in part explains why the oil rubbed off on to the parlour upholstery leaving a greasy stain. In consequence practical Victorian housewives took to draping pieces of embroidered or lace-trimmed fabric known as *antimacassars* over the chair backs to protect them. Appropriately, the prefix *anti-* means 'against, to prevent the effects of'; it is found in other compounds such as *anticorrosion, antiattrition. Antimacassar* is first recorded in 1852 – where else but in the *Lady's Newspaper.*

The fall from favour of Macassar oil towards the turn of the century did not bring the demise of the antimacassar, however. The oil's successor in the 1880s was Brilliantine, which gave men hair as smooth and shiny as a billiard ball but was no kinder to the upholstery. Indeed, the antimacassar lingered on in sitting-rooms until the early 1960s when, for the first time, fashion dictated clean, natural-looking hair for men.

apricot

a fruit shaped like a plum, similar to a peach, yellow-orange in colour

To make cream ice. Peel, stone and scald twelve apricots, *beat them fine in a mortar, and put to them six ounces of sugar and a pint of scalding cream . . .*
(Elizabeth Raffald, THE EXPERIENCED ENGLISH HOUSEKEEPER, 1769)

The cultivation of fruit orchards began in the Near East around 3000 BC. The climate there was particularly favourable and over the centuries a large number of different crops flourished, including peaches and apricots, which originally came from China. Surprisingly, the cultivation of these delicacies had not progressed much further west by classical times, so that they were regarded as exotic fruits in the western Mediterranean (Brothwell, FOOD IN ANTIQUITY, 1969). The Greeks and Romans clearly thought the fruits originated from their source of supply. The peach was known to both as the 'Persian apple' (*Persicum mālum* in Latin) and the apricot as the 'Armenian plum' (*prūnum Armeniacum*) or the 'Armenian apple' (*mālum Armeniacum*). The Romans regarded the *apricot* as a kind of peach and, since supplies were available earlier in the year, they began to refer to the fruit as *praecoquum*, 'early-ripening', (from *praecox*, 'ripening before its time', from *praecoquere*, 'to ripen or cook before', from *prae-*, 'early' and *coquere*, 'to ripen, to cook'). This was taken into

Late Greek as *praikokion* and from there into Arabic in the form *al-birqūq* (*al-* being the definite article). Arab influence on the Iberian peninsula brought the word into Spanish, Portuguese and Catalan where it became *albaricoque*, *albricoque* and *abercoc* respectively. English probably picked the term up from Catalan in the sixteenth century as *abrecock*.

Within half a century this early English spelling was being subjected to two important changes. Firstly a final *t* was gradually being assimilated from French *abricot* – itself a product of Catalan influence – although the old *-ck* ending persisted until at least the mid-eighteenth century. Secondly a spelling with an initial *apr-* instead of *abr-* started to emerge. In Shakespeare's KING RICHARD II (1595), for instance, a gardener bids a servant '*Go, bind thou up yon dangling* apricocks' (Act III, scene iv). The answer to this puzzle is provided by the seventeenth-century language teacher and lexicographer John Minsheu. He explains the word as deriving from the Latin *in aprīco coctus*, 'ripened in a sunny place', an erroneous etymology which was obviously widely believed at the time.

By the time *apricot* made its appearance in English, *peach* had been long established. From Latin *Persicum mālum* came the elliptical form *persicum* which became *persica* in late Latin. This was taken into Old French as *pesche*, becoming *peche* before it was borrowed directly into Middle English in the fourteenth century. The modern spelling *peach* dates from the late sixteenth century.

• For another word from the same source see **precocious**. For more information about Arabic words see **Words from Arabic** (pages 10–11).

arena

1. a forum for combat or competition
2. a field of interest

I do not propose to turn this book into one of ordinary Christian apologetics; I should be glad to meet at any other time the enemies of Christianity in that more obvious arena. *Here I am only giving an account of my own growth in spiritual certainty.*
(G K Chesterton, ORTHODOXY, 1909)

Lysenko was so pre-eminent in this process that common English usage has accorded him an eponymous distinction: 'Lysenkoism' is now the accepted term for politically enforced manipulation of scientific truth. His arena *was agriculture, over which he presided as the USSR's scientific and administrative chief from the mid-1930s until Stalin's death in 1953. After that he rapidly faded.*
(NEW SCIENTIST, 1983)

The [market hall] entrance . . . led to a large, shallow square open to the sky. Step-like ledges rose up on all sides to a covered Roman gallery. The arena *in the middle was where the bigger sea-creatures were butchered.*
(Romesh Gunesekera, REEF, 1994)

Arena has a more gruesome history than might be imagined. Mankind has developed a number of ways of soaking up spilt blood: in previous centuries, when royalty and nobility were beheaded, straw was spread; in butchers' shops past and present, sawdust is strewn. Similarly with the Roman amphitheatre where a thick layer of sand would be scattered upon the ground in the *arena* to absorb the gore as the gladiators fought. *Arēna* is Latin for 'sand' and so the area of the amphitheatre where the combats took place became known by that name.

Today an *arena* is a place where a spectacle or contest takes place, especially where the spectators' seats surround the performance: a *sports arena*, for instance. Since the nineteenth century the word has also been applied metaphorically to areas of verbal or mental conflict or interest such as the *political arena*.

arrant

downright, out-and-out, utter

One morning, very early, before the sun was up,
I rose and found the shining dew on every buttercup;
But my lazy little shadow, like an arrant *sleepy-head,*
Had stayed at home behind me and was fast asleep in bed.
(Robert Louis Stevenson, A CHILD'S GARDEN OF VERSES, 1885)

The word was originally *errant*, from the Old French *errant* meaning 'wandering'. There is some uncertainty if the Latin origin is the vulgar form *iterāre*, 'to travel', or *errāre*, 'to wander, err'. Malory's LE MORTE D'ARTHUR (c1470) has familiarised us with the exploits of the knights errant of earlier centuries who travelled about the countryside seeking out opportunities to demonstrate the virtues of courage, loyalty, courtesy and charity. Knights were not the only ones to roam, however; others did so with evil intent. Chaucer describes a *theef erraunt* in his CANTERBURY TALES (1387) and, indeed, in its earliest uses *errant* was regularly coupled not with knights but with thieves. As a result, *errant* gradually lost its original meaning of 'wandering', because of its associations with society's wrongdoers. *Arrant*, a sixteenth-century variant, has been used since the middle of that century to emphasise just how unacceptable a person really is by intensifying the noun that follows it: *an arrant coward* (an unmitigated coward), *an arrant thug* (a notorious thug). This use was extended to include vices and undesirable qualities in the seventeenth century: *arrant hypocrisy* (out-and-out hypocrisy).

arrive

1. to reach a destination
2. to achieve success

. . . no nation in a state of foreign dependance, limited in its commerce, and cramped and fettered in its legislative powers, can ever arrive *at any material eminence.*
(Thomas Paine, COMMON SENSE, 1776)

To 'feel' our motion forward is impossible. Motion implies terminus; and how can terminus be felt before we have arrived*? The barest start and sally forwards, the barest tendency to leave the instant, involves the chasm and the leap.*
(William James, ESSAYS IN RADICAL EMPIRICISM, 1912)

This word has been current in English since at least the beginning of the thirteenth century, though with a rather more specific meaning than the one it has today. Ultimately it derives from the Latin *rīpa*, meaning 'shore' or 'bank'. Vulgar Latin had a nautical verb *arripāre*, meaning 'to come ashore, to land' (from Latin *ad-*, 'to' and *rīpa*, 'shore'), which passed in various forms into the Romance languages. It also developed the wider sense 'to reach a destination', wherever that might be. However, when it came into English by way of Old French *ariver*, it still meant 'to bring a ship to shore' or 'to come ashore', a use which persisted in nautical texts until the nineteenth century. Only gradually did the wider sense 'to come to a destination' take hold, from the time of Chaucer onwards.

The sense 'to achieve success' dates from the late nineteenth century and imitates a French use of *arriver*.

For a word from the same source, see **river**.

assassin

a murderer, usually of an important person for political or religious ends

Michael Portillo, blessed, a commentator once noted, with the lips of a tyrant and the eyes of an assassin . . .
(EVENING STANDARD, 19 July 1994)

. . . *if you are a company executive in danger of being kidnapped, or a politician threatened by* assassins, *you might want a leather jacket specifically designed to make you a less vulnerable target. Two young Colombian business graduates . . . have combined their interest in fashion and security to produce sweaters, coats and jackets that will stop .44 Magnum or 9mm Uzi bullets, yet look good on the wearer.*
(WEEKEND FINANCIAL TIMES, 14 January 1995)

In eleventh century Persia, Hassan ben Sabbah founded a fanatical sect of Islamic fundamentalists with the intention of controlling the Muslim world through acts of violence. His base was the fortress of Alamut in Persia (now Iran). He, and then his successors, became known as the Old Man of the Mountain. The sect opposed the Seljuk dynasties of central and western Asia and later also directed its efforts against the Crusaders in Northern Syria. During the next two hundred years the sect established a chain of hill forts in Syria as bases for brutal terrorist attacks. It is said that the members prepared themselves for their atrocities by eating hashish, hence the sect's name *hashshāshīn*, plural of *hashshāsh*, meaning 'hashish eater'. The English singular noun *assassin*, which appeared in the fourteenth century through French and, possibly, Late Latin, is therefore an Arabic plural.

Crusaders returning to Europe may have brought back reports of the sect's murderous exploits and historians like William of Tyre recorded details of their operations in Latin. However, Frank M. Chambers, a scholar of medieval French poetry, has advanced a theory that *assassin* entered the popular vocabulary of western Europe after a rumour was circulated by the French king, Philip Augustus, in 1192 to the effect that Richard the Lion-Heart had persuaded the Old Man of the Mountain to send some *Assassins* to France to murder him. Consequently Philip had increased his personal guard. The rumour was, apparently, widespread in France, and was the sort of gossip to bring the word into immediate popular use. Mr Chambers points out that, just after that date, Provençal troubadours became fascinated by the Old Man of the Mountains. They used him and the absolute allegiance borne by his followers to give expression to their theme of courtly love. Aimeric de Peguilhan, for instance, declared that his Lady had him more in her power '*than the Old Man of the Mountains his Assassins, who go to kill his mortal enemies*', and Bernart de Bondeilhs claimed: '*Just as the Assassins serve their master unfailingly, so I have served Love with unswerving loyalty.*'

◆ Leaves from the hemp plant, when dried, were discovered to have an intoxicating effect if smoked or chewed. The general Arabic word for grass plants, *hashish*, narrowed in its meaning to refer just to this intoxicant. The drug is still known to us today as *hashish* or *cannabis*. Interestingly, *marijuana* (an American Spanish word), also prepared from the hemp plant, is known too by the general terms *weed* and *grass*, both of which arose in America in the first half of the twentieth century.◆

atlas

a book of maps of the world

. . . Joseph sat in the drawing room listening with undivided attention as Winifred told him the story of the Holy Grail or showed him the coloured maps in an atlas *from her husband's study.*
(Roy Hattersley, THE MAKER'S MARK, 1990)

The Michelin road atlas *shows a tiny white road from the Pont Napoléon at Moissac, north-west of Toulouse, along the left bank to the exact place where the Tarn gives its water to the Garonne.*
(WEEKEND TELEGRAPH, 25 March 1995)

According to Greek mythology, when Atlas was defeated in his war against Zeus he was condemned to bear the weight of the heavens upon his shoulders. Representations of the demi-god in this posture were a common feature on the title-pages of sixteenth century map books, hence the term *atlas*. Credit for this inspiration is sometimes given to the respected Flemish cartographer Gerardus Mercator (1512–94) whose late sixteenth-century map book contains the earliest known written reference to the word. The volume was published in English in 1636 under the title *Atlas; or a Geographic Description of the World*. Later the term *atlas* was extended to cover other sizeable volumes of illustrative plates or charts.

◆ Another myth tells how Perseus asked Atlas for refuge. When Atlas refused, Perseus used the head of the Gorgon Medusa to turn him into *Mount Atlas* (in northwest Africa) upon which the heavens were then said to rest. The Greek stem of Atlas was *Atlant-* which gave the adjective *Atlantikos*, 'belonging to Atlas'. The Greeks called the ocean immediately beyond the Atlas Mountains *pelagos Atlantikos*, 'the sea of Atlas', and the Romans *mare Atlanticum*. Now, of course, the full expanse of the sea is known and bears the name *Atlantic Ocean*.◆

atone

make amends for

Catherine's swelling heart needed relief. In Eleanor's presence friendship and pride had equally restrained her tears, but no sooner was she gone than they burst forth in torrents. Turned from the house, and in such a way! Without any reason that could justify, any apology that could atone *for the abruptness, the rudeness, nay, the insolence of it. Henry at a distance – not able even to bid him farewell.*
(Jane Austen, NORTHANGER ABBEY, 1803)

While Germany wrestles with the problem, agonising about how far backwards it should bend over to atone *for the sins of a long-gone evil regime, Austria has been in a cold sweat all of its own.*
(THE EUROPEAN, 14 October 1994)

To get to hell you first travel through the many circles leading to the oddly menacing back roads around Wembley. Then you

drive round the carpark for several lifetimes, in the company of hundreds of other sinners trapped in their little private purgatories on wheels. Only after you begin to atone *for your sins, to beg forgiveness from the great and angry Ikea God, will you be allowed to find a space. Greater evils exist within the blue and yellow warehouse that should, by rights, stink of sulphur and brimstone. There you join the thousands of shoppers driven by some eerie compulsion to seek the fabric that answers to the name Sinna, or an eight-pack of mugs named Spurt.*
(THE SUNDAY TIMES, 23 October 1994)

Better to settle in with the week's new videos. Clint Eastwood's Unforgiven *is the deconstructed cowboy masterpiece that won its star-director a hatful of Oscars. . . And Victor Sjostrom's* The Phantom Carriage *(1920) and Benjamin Christenson's* Haxan *(1922) are two marvellous Scandinavian rarities – about ghosts and witches respectively – unearthed by the sex-and-horror video label* Redemption, *as if to* atone *for the tripe they usually turn out.*
(FINANCIAL TIMES, 24 October 1994)

Atone originated in the common Middle English phrasal verb 'to be, bring, set *at oon*' (sometimes written *at on* or *at one*) meaning 'to be as one', 'to be in one accord'. *At oon* was current in the twelfth century, along with the extended forms *at one accord* and *at one assent.* Increasingly the two words *at oon* were written as one. Thus, in Chaucer's CANTERBURY TALES (c. 1387), we find:

If gentil men, or othere of hir contree
Were wrothe, she wolde bringen
hem atoon.

and in Spenser's *Fairie Queene,* 1589:

So beene they both atone, *and doen*
upreare
Their bevers bright each other for to greet.

When the two words were permanently run together as one, the old pronunciation was preserved (just as it is in *alone* and *only*).

Middle English also had since the fourteenth century the noun *onemente* to mean 'reconciliation':

Bot onemente *thar hym nevyr wene,*
Or eyther other herte have sought.
(HARLEIAN MANUSCRIPT)

It was used thus independently and also in the phrase *set at onement*:

That sets such discord twixt agreeing
parts,
Which never can be set at onement
more.
(Bishop Joseph Hall, VIRGIDEMIARUM SEX LIBRI, 1597–98)

Everything was in place for the coining of a new word. *Atonement* as a noun (and concurrently the alternative spelling *at onement*) was first used in the early sixteenth century to describe the state of reconciliation. Thomas More writes of those '*hauyng more regarde to their olde variaunce then their newe* attonement' (HISTORY OF KING RICHARD III, 1513). The word also met a religious need. William Tyndale chose it for his translation of the Bible into English in 1526. In *atonement* he found a term that perfectly encapsulated the reconciliation of man to God through the sacrifice of Jesus Christ upon the cross: *God . . . hath geven unto us the office to preache the* atonement. (2 Corinthians 5:18)

Other translators followed Tyndale's lead using *atonement* in contexts where Wyclif had used *recouncilyng* or *accordyng,* and the term thus entered theological vocabulary.

Indeed Tyndale (1533) and then Coverdale (1548) even described Christ as an *atonemaker* between God and man. This particular term was not generally accepted but, in the middle of the sixteenth century, *atone* emerged as a verb, a back-formation from *atonement*. It helped that there had been in use since at least the fourteenth century a verb *to one*, 'to make into one, to unite'. It was superseded in time by the newcomer *atone*. The general sense was 'to reconcile':

> *The present need*
> *Speaks to* atone *you*
> (Shakespeare, ANTONY AND CLEOPATRA, Act 2 scene 2 1607)

> *Nay if he had been cool enough to tell us that, there had been some hope to* attone *you, but he seems so implacably enraged*
> (Ben Jonson, EPICENE, 1609).

This sense is now obsolete but in the seventeenth century *atone* was used with *for* to give the sense of 'to make amends', and *atonement* came to describe the steps that had to be taken if reconciliation was to be achieved, the meaning the two words retain in modern English. The narrower theological sense of 'to take away the penalty of sin, to expiate' is also still current.

bankrupt

insolvent and unable to continue trading

> *Juliet: O, break, my heart! poor* bankrout, *break at once!*
> *To prison, eyes; ne'er look on liberty!*
> *Vile earth, to earth resign; end motion here,*
> *And thou and Romeo press one heavy bier!*
> (Shakespeare, ROMEO AND JULIET, Act 3, Scene 2,1597)

> *The Elder's story became somewhat wearisome, and his audience grew gradually less, until it was reduced to twenty passengers. But this did not disconcert the enthusiast, who proceeded with the story of Joseph Smith's* bankruptcy *in 1837, and how his ruined creditors gave him a coat of tar and feathers.*
> (Jules Verne, AROUND THE WORLD IN EIGHTY DAYS, 1873)

> *When the king traveled for change of air, or made a progress, or visited a distant noble whom he wished to* bankrupt *with the cost of his keep, part of the administration moved with him.*
> (Mark Twain, A CONNECTICUT YANKEE IN KING ARTHUR'S COURT, 1889)

> *Don't panic - you will not be imprisoned for unpaid tax. Nor can you lose your home without being* bankrupted *first, and this is a lengthy process normally reserved for debts over £5,000.*
> (THE GUARDIAN, 14 January 1995)

Medieval Venice was a prosperous trading centre where a lot of money changed hands. Men in the business of lending money and exchanging currencies would set up simple counters in the main squares. The term for one of these tables was *banca* (from the Germanic root *bangk-*), the Italian word for 'bench' and the origin of our word *bank*. Many authorities, including Dr Johnson, have it that when one of these money-lenders was insolvent and could no longer trade he was legally obliged to break up his counter and was then declared *banca rotta*, literally 'broken bench' (from Italian *rompere*, from Latin *rumpere*,'to break').

There are two very significant authorities who suggest that the story is not only unfounded but also needless. Skeat in his ETYMOLOGICAL DICTIONARY (1879–82) points out that late Latin already had a figurative application of *ruptus* (from *rumpere*), 'broken', to mean 'a broken man, a bankrupt'. The

OED adds the further argument that Italian *rotto* (feminine *rotta*) could also mean 'wrecked' and therefore, figuratively, 'defeated, interrupted'. Probably, then, the sense of bankrupt is just a metaphorical development and does not imply the actual breaking of the bench.

As for the route of the word into sixteenth-century English, it came by way of French *banqueroute* but was soon modified along the lines of Latin *ruptus*, the spelling *bankrupt* occurring as early as the 1540s.

barbaric

1. uncivilised, coarse
2. cruel, brutal

I sailed and paddled together to the south, and got into the same creek from whence I set out in the morning, choosing rather to trust myself among these barbarians, *than live with European Yahoos.*
(Jonathan Swift, GULLIVER'S TRAVELS, 1726)

Depending on the concentrations, it is possible that a temporary youthful effect was noticed as cells multiplied rapidly to form a new layer of skin. The principle is the same as that behind modern dermabrasion, where the top layers of skin are removed mechanically, or by chemical peeling . . . Once again, this illustrates that while at first glance ancient wrinkle tactics can seem barbaric, *on closer inspection they are often the primitive precursors of more sophisticated, modern methods.*
(NEW ZEALAND WOMAN'S WEEKLY, 14 January 1991)

When confronted by something in a foreign language that he does not understand the stereotypical Englishman might well use that common idiom 'It's all Greek to me', accompanied by a dismissive shrug. Ironically, this is very much the attitude the ancient Greeks had towards the varied languages of the surrounding peoples. The Greek term for a foreigner was *barbaros*. It is thought that this word, with its overtones of 'not-Greek' and therefore 'not civilised', was originally intended to imitate the unintelligable babbling of foreign tongues and possibly originated in *barbaras*, a Sanskrit word meaning 'stammering'. When the word was adopted into Latin as *barbarus*, it became a derogatory term for 'brutal', 'rude', 'totally uncultured' and was particularly applied to the fierce northern tribes who eventually overthrew the Empire. Later it was used by Christians to denote any who were not of the faith and were therefore 'heathen'. *Barbaric* was borrowed into English from Latin towards the end of the fifteenth century. A word similar in origin, meaning and form, *barbarous*, also came into English just a few years later.

◆ Speech which is intelligible but nonsensical might be termed '*a load of old rhubarb*'. *Rhubarb* is a 'barbarous' plant native to China, where it was used as a purgative. At one time it was cultivated on the banks of the *Rha* (now the Volga) for export to Europe and the Levant. Consequently one of the two Greek terms for *rhubarb* was *rha*. From this Medieval Latin had the term *rha barbarum* (becoming *reubarb(ar)um*), literally 'foreign rha', which was borrowed directly into Middle English from Old French as *rubarbe* at the turn of the fifteenth century. The other Greek word for *rhubarb* was *rheon*, which became *rheum* in Latin and is now the botanical term for this family of plants. ◆

bastard

an illegitimate child

Dog Latin, a bastard *language composed of a mixture of Latin and modern words, came to be called macaronic Latin.*
(George Stimpson, INFORMATION ROUNDUP, 1948)

I came across . . . the story of a young postal worker who decided to have a baby without getting married; it was called Madame 60 bis. *The subject was . . . the suffering of her fatherless child; she told how there was always some imbecile to call him* 'bastard' *or 'love child' at school or anywhere he went.*
(Emilie Carles, tr Avriel H Goldberger, A WILD HERB SOUP, 1991)

[George IV's] brothers burdened the taxpayers with mistresses, bastards *and debts. Only one produced a legitimate offspring, the Princess Victoria.*
(Paul Johnson, WAKE UP, BRITAIN!, 1994)

From a plant label at R & R Saggers garden centre, Newport: '. . . flowering from June to July. That is when young children don't pull the heads off, and their parents conceal the fact. BASTARDS.*'*
(DAILY TELEGRAPH, 10 May 1994)

William the Conqueror, the illegitimate son of Robert, Duke of Normandy, was also known as William Bastard. The origin of the epithet that described him comes from France, as William did himself. *Bast* is an Old French word for 'a packsaddle', from the late Latin word *bastum* of the same meaning. An Old French phrase *fils de bast* ('packsaddle son'), was popularly used for a child born as a result of a passing liaison. Apparently, muleteers would use their saddles as beds, so it was not unknown for children to be conceived on the top of a packsaddle. Pierre Vidal was a muleteer in the early fourteenth century who transported grain and was based in the little mountain village of Montaillou. When an Inquisition questioned him on his morals he was of the opinion that it was not wrong to make love outside marriage if the man had paid for his pleasure or if the act had been mutually agreed and pleasing (Emmanuel Le Roy Ladurie, MONTAILLOU, 1978). With views like these and a cosy saddle, the results were inevitable – and not only for muleteers, as Robert, Duke of Normandy, proved.

The suffix *-ard* was used as an intensifier in Old French. Its use has passed into English in words such as *coward* and *drunkard.*

bedlam

a state of disorder and confusion

From then on it was bedlam. *We separated our mob into two groups, luggage and all. Distributing them into separate hotels took us over an hour. Two people had not arrived on the plane and we had hell's own job persuading the second hotel we hadn't sold them into slavery, or – worse – to another hotel.*
(Jonathan Gash, THE GONDOLA SCAM, 1984)

In 1247 Simon FitzMary founded a Priory at Bishopsgate, London. By 1330, if not earlier, the priory had a hospital attached to it; the Hospital of St Mary of Bethlehem, which was originally devoted to the medical needs of the poor. The admission of lunatics began around 1377 though their care probably amounted to nothing more than keeping them chained out of harm's way, and beating them or dousing them with water if they became too disturbed. In 1346 both the priory and hospital came under the protection of the Mayor and City of London who, in 1547 after the dissolution under Henry VIII, purchased the buildings to continue the work of the asylum.

Middle English already had *Bedleem* and *Bedlem*, reductions of Bethlehem, and in the sixteenth century both the hospital and its patients, or potential patients, were known by this name:

But his wife (as he had attired her) seemed indeede not to be well in her wittes, but, seeyng her housbandes maners, shewed herself in her conditions to bee a right bedlem.

(Barnaby Riche, FAREWELL TO MILITARIE PROFESSION, 1581)

Bedlam came to be used adjectivally to mean 'mad'. In a book on falconry (Turbery, 1575), restless falcons are described as being '*impatient and* bedlam' and Shakespeare speaks of '*a* bedlam *and ambitious humour*' (II HENRY VI, 1593).

In 1676 the hospital was rehoused on a new site. John Evelyn, who went to see it '*most sweetly placed in Moorfields*', was deeply impressed by the elegant new building which he compared to the Louvre in Paris. Magnificent architecture was not the only attraction, however. People were generally fascinated by the insane and this curiosity was tapped for revenue. Since the beginning of the seventeenth century, for a small entrance fee, visitors had been admitted to ogle and jeer at the inmates, chained in their cells in galleries. Such sport was disruptive and noisy bouts of disorder must have been commonly witnessed, so that *bedlam* came to be figuratively used to describe scenes of commotion and uproar, the sense it retains today.

At the beginning of the nineteenth century the building was declared unsafe and the hospital was moved to Lambeth. After the First World War it was in Addington, Surrey and at present is in Beckenham, Kent. Known as the Bethlehem Royal Hospital, its name has changed little, but patients now receive the highest standard of care.

For another word arising from a corrupting of a biblical name, see **maudlin**.

Mysteries

This dictionary gives the origins of several hundred words. There are many thousands more for which it is possible to give the likely sources. But there are still more for which it is impossible to give any certain information about the root. Here are just a few beginning with the letter B:

balderdash
beagle
bingo
blab
bleach
blight
blink
blouse
bludgeon
blunt
boar
bobbin
boffin
bonkers
booty
bore
bother
bounce
bribe
buffer
bug
buggy
bun
bunch
burr
burrow

beggar

a person living by asking for gifts of money, alms

A poor man begged *food at the Hall lately. The cook gave him some vermicelli soup. He ladled it about some time with the spoon, and then returned it to her, saying, 'I am a poor man, it is true, and I am very hungry, but yet I cannot eat broth with maggots in it.'*

(William Cowper, LETTER TO LADY HESKETH, 27 November 1787)

As we came up the White Moss, we met an old man, who I saw was a beggar *by his two bags hanging over his shoulder; but, from a half laziness, half indifference, and a wanting to try him, if he would speak, I let him pass. He said nothing, and my heart smote me. I turned back, and said, 'You are* begging*?' 'Ay,' says he. I gave him a halfpenny.*

(Dorothy Wordsworth, JOURNAL, 22 December 1801)

They [pilgrims] also come because, many followers say, Padre Cicero will return. Jose Augusto looks after the house where the padre spent much of his life and which is now a shrine and hostel for beggars.

(WEEKEND FINANCIAL TIMES, 14 January 1995)

The origin of the word probably lies within the surname or nickname of a priest Lambert Le Bègue (Lambert the Stammerer) who, in twelfth-century Liège, founded a religious order for women which flourished in the Low Countries and the neighbouring lands of continental Europe. The *Béguines*, as they were known, lived a communal life in houses called *Béguinages*. The sisterhood took no vows and were free to leave the communities whenever they pleased, to own property and even to marry. Any gifts they received were totally devoted to works of charity; these included caring for the elderly, nursing and teaching. In the early thirteenth century a similar lay order was established for men who became known as the *Beghards* (their name deriving from *Béguine* with the masculine suffix *-ard*). Sadly the brotherhood was brought into disrepute by idle outsiders who claimed to be *Beghards* in order to receive alms. They were denounced by the Pope and persecuted by the Inquisition. It is from the name of this devalued brotherhood that Old French derived the word *begard*, 'hypocrite, mendicant', which gave the Middle English *beggare*. (The verb to *beg* may be a derivative of the noun; an alternative account suggests an Old English root *bedecian*.) Although the modern form *beggar* occurred in the fourteenth century it did not become standard until the eighteenth. Until that period the regular form was *begger*.

biscuit

a dry, crisp cake or pastry

On the Continent the household bread is usually unwholesome and nasty, and captain's biscuits *are never to be obtained. It is prudent to carry a store of them to use when the staff of life is found especially abominable.*

(Dr T K Chambers, A MANUAL OF DIET IN HEALTH AND DISEASE, 1875)

'We met 16 years ago and I remember not particularly liking Dawn. I was such a snob then. She'd had a year in America and said cookie instead of biscuit. *I thought that was just the end . . .'*

(GOOD HOUSEKEEPING, March 1994)

. . . my taste in biscuits *is for plain rather than fancy. No iced wafers, no sandwich*

creams, no chocolate encrustations for me – though I admit to having inherited a family weakness for petit beurre or small rich tea biscuits eaten in tandem with a bar of best bitter chocolate.
(Philippa Davenport, WEEKEND FINANCIAL TIMES, 14 January 1995)

Middle English had *besquite* which became *bisket*, or *bisket bread* in the sixteenth and seventeenth centuries. Its source is the Old French *pain bescuit*, 'twice-cooked bread' (from *pain*, 'bread', *bes-*, 'twice', *cuit*, past participle of *cuire*, 'cooked'), although some authorities suggest that the French may have come from a Medieval Latin term with the same meaning, *biscoctus panis*. Originally *biscuits* were thin, flat discs made of unleavened bread dough which were baked twice until they were hard and dry. In this form they kept well and were useful for lengthy journeys; *ship's biscuit*, for instance, was a staple ration for sailors on a long voyage.

Gradually, however, creative cooks experimented with different ingredients and made a variety of twice-cooked sweetmeats that could be offered on social occasions:

1644, August 2nd. It is this day ordered, by reason of theise troublesome times, that there shall not be this yeare as formerly hath bine any eleccon dinner, at the choise of the Mr and Wardens, but oneley wine and Naples bisketts. (ACCOUNTS OF THE CARPENTERS' COMPANY IN LONDON)

And in the ACCOMPLISH'D FEMALE INSTRUCTOR of 1719, we find the following recipe for biscuits with full instructions for the important second cooking:

To make Queen's Bisket, *Genoua* Bisket, *etc. – Take as much fine flower, a loaf-sugar finely beaten, nine yolks and twelve whites of eggs, to a pound of flower, and a pound of sugar, corriander-seeds, and anni-seeds, of each three quarters of an ounce finely beaten and sifted; rose-water and ale-yest very new, of each two or three spoonfuls; then boil up as much fair water as will make it into a convenient thin past something like batter; take it up with a spoon or ladle, and drop it on fine paper on which fine sugar is strewed, or put it into tin coffins four or five inches long, and an inch and a half broad, and put them into an oven not too hot; and when sufficiently baked, take them out and lay them on a paper to cool; after that, harden them in a stove or warm oven, to keep long: and thus you may make Genoua-*bisket.

There has been a remarkable variety of spellings over the centuries, from *bysqwyte* to the contemporary *biscuit*. The latter is a rather precious borrowing of the French form. It supplanted *bisket*, which had been the regular spelling for three hundred years up to the eighteenth century, and had reflected the common pronunciation.

bistro

a restaurant in French style

They first tried (and failed) to buy a bistro *in Worcester. Sarah worked as a souschef there and started a course in wines and spirits at a local college.*
(GOOD HOUSEKEEPING, March 1994)

Scorn is a deadly weapon: despite two decades of non-stop gentrification, there are still many suburbs which no amount of social engineering, bistro *culture or tampering with post codes will turn into socially acceptable addresses.*
(GUARDIAN, 14 April 1994)

Some authorities suggest that the word came into popular use in France after the fall of Napoleon in 1815 when Russian troops entered Paris. Details of the story differ. Some say that impatient soldiers chivvied harassed restaurant owners with cries of '*bistro*' ('quick' in Russian): others maintain that it was the owners themselves who shouted '*bistro*' from the doors of their establishments to advertise the fact that a good, cheap meal was instantly available – a nineteenth-century fast-food gimmick.

Other authorities claim that this explanation is both imaginative and erroneous. Pointing out that the word did not appear in print until sixty years or so after the invasion, they suggest that *bistro* derives from the word *bistouille*, the cheap wine sold in these modest cafes. Emilie Carles, describing her childhood in the Alps of south-eastern France, has this to say about the hard drinking that took place in village bistros:

The bistro *was all there was, the only entertainment around, and those peasants certainly did not deny themselves. Bored and worn out . . .they believed that their hard labor gave them the right to drink wine . . . 'A liter in the morning, one at noon, and another at night,' they'd say, 'that doesn't make me drunk, and I can still drink a glass or two in the bar.'*
(Emilie Carles, tr Avriel H Goldberger, A WILD HERB SOUP, 1991)

The term was borrowed into English in the first quarter of the twentieth century when, as in France, it was used of a small wine-shop or restaurant. In the 1960s and 1970s, however, it became a vogue word for an intimate little restaurant with a French flavour. Suddenly there was a bistro in every town, with prices far removed from the original humble French roots.

In French, the spelling can be *bistro* or *bistrot*. Both forms could be found in English, although the former has prevailed in more recent years.

blackguard

a rogue, a scoundrel

. . . the fog lifted a little and showed him a dingy street, a gin palace, a low French eating house, a shop for the retail of penny numbers and twopenny salads, many ragged children huddled in the doorways, and many women of many different nationalities passing out, key in hand, to have a morning glass; and the next moment the fog settled down again upon that part, as brown as umber, and cut him off from his blackguardly *surroundings.*
(Robert Louis Stevenson, THE STRANGE CASE OF DR JEKYLL AND MR HYDE, 1886)

'Did you go to Blackheath?'

'Yes, Watson, I went there, and I found very quickly that the late lamented Oldacre was a pretty considerable blackguard. *The father was away in search of his son. The mother was at home. . . "He was more like a malignant and cunning ape than a human being," said she, "and he always was, ever since he was a young man."'*
(Sir Arthur Conan Doyle, THE RETURN OF SHERLOCK HOLMES, 1905)

In the sixteenth century, *blackguards* were menial kitchen servants who had care of pots, pans and utensils blackened by the flames and who turned the spits over the fires. It was grimy and back-breaking work. When a wealthy family travelled with full retinue or a royal progress was underway, these drudges travelled with the greasy pots and pans, their filthy condition exposed to full view. In his play THE WHITE DEVIL (c.1608), John Webster speaks of '*a lousy slave, that within these twenty years rode with the* black guard *in the Duke's carriage, 'mongst spits and dripping pans*'.

It is also possible that there was a Black Guard of soldiers in medieval times – many of the early sixteenth century references relate to a military context. If true, this is probably a complementary explanation to the well-attested etymology given above.

Exactly how the word became pejorative is unclear, though one can conjecture. Possibly it was because such servants were rough and untrustworthy, or were generally despised, or even because of the overtones of evil associated with the word black. In any event, the *black guard* came to denote the vagrant delinquent class, as this proclamation on the Lord Steward's office of 1683 shows: *Whereas . . . a sort of vicious, idle and masterless boyes and rogues, commonly called the* Black guard, *with divers other lewd and loose fellows . . . do usually haunt and follow the Court.* Some of these were out and out villains, others were boys who lived on the street and earned their living by blacking shoes – or picking pockets. By the 1730s the reputation of such characters was so low that the term was applied to any individual who was regarded as a downright rogue and to be called a *blackguard* became a deep insult.

For other words for scoundrel, see **cad** and **villain**.

blackmail

money or favours obtained by extortion

When the harvest was at last gathered, then came the procession of robbers to levy their blackmail *upon it: first the Church carted off its fat tenth, then the king's commissioner took his twentieth, then my lord's people made a mighty inroad upon the remainder; after which, the skinned freeman had liberty to bestow the remnant in his barn, in case it was worth the trouble.*
(Mark Twain, A CONNECTICUT YANKEE IN KING ARTHUR'S COURT, 1887)

LICKSPITTLE, n. A useful functionary, not infrequently found editing a newspaper. In his character of editor he is closely allied to the blackmailer *by the tie of occasional identity; for in truth the lickspittle is only the* blackmailer *under another aspect, although the latter is frequently found as an independent species.*
(Ambrose Bierce, THE DEVIL'S DICTIONARY, 1911)

His friendship is highly conditional and possessive: sooner or later payment for it will be asked. A specialist in emotional blackmail, he can become hysterical when slighted or – as inevitably happens – rejected.
(Peter Shaffer, BLACK COMEDY, 1967)

The word has nothing to do with the exploits of the Black Prince or with knights in armour who have behaved dishonourably. *Mail* was a Scottish word for 'rent' or 'tax' (from Old English *mal*, meaning 'agreement'). W Bell's DICTIONARY OF THE LAW OF SCOTLAND of 1861 has the following entry: Maills *and Duties are the rents of an estate, whether in money or grain; hence, an action for the rents of an estate . . . is termed an action of maills and duties.*

Burrow-mails, for instance, were the dues payable within boroughs during the reign of James 1 (1394–1437). Such tributes were usually paid in silver coin, or 'white money'.

During the sixteenth and seventeenth centuries, marauders plagued farmers in the border country between England and Scotland by demanding protection payments. If a farmer refused to comply, the bandits would lay his property waste. Black has always carried overtones of evil and so this demand by extortion, usually made for cattle, was known as *blackmail*, in contrast with 'white' money payments, which were in coin and were lawful. Protection rackets are obviously no new thing.

It's all in a name

Some pursue immortality, others have a kind of linguistic immortality thrust upon them. There are many dictionaries of eponyms, which list entries such as *bloomer, guillotine, sandwich, wellington,* all of which are mentioned in this book. The common theme of these and hundreds of other words is that they all began as someone's name. Rudolf Diesel (1858–1913), for example was a German engineer who invented a type of internal combustion engine. Both the engine and the fuel required to drive it bear his name.

The popular etymology for the entry *blanket* in this dictionary is that a Mr Blanket gave his name to the woollen bed covering in medieval times. Unfortunately there is no evidence of this. If a Mr Blanket is listed in this year's phonebook, then his antecedents got their name from another common linguistic process which named people for the work they did. One category of surnames concerns trades and manufacturing: *Cooper, Crocker, Sawyer, Smith, Shepherd, Taylor,* etc. Makers of blankets might well, then, be named after the product of their labours.

As surnames go, Blanket could be a lot worse. In the medieval period people bore some quite extraordinary surnames and nicknames – Jan Jönsjö's STUDIES ON MEDIEVAL NICKNAMES lists *Beltgut, Cheese and bread, Doglet, Foulmouth, Illwilly, Liebythefire* and many others. With family names such as these, who would want linguistic immortality!

See also **Who was who?** (page 124) for trade names that have become ordinary words in the language.

Both *blackmailer* and the verb *to blackmail* arose in the nineteenth century. *Blackmail* itself is now used in wide metaphorical senses, such as *moral blackmail* and *emotional blackmail.*

blanket

1. a warm woollen covering for the bed
2. all-inclusive, indiscriminate

I had never shivered before. Nor had I slept under blankets, *their weight making me dream of lying in a grave with earth piled on top.*
(Alexander Frater, CHASING THE MONSOON, 1990)

MPs' postbags can be leaving them in little doubt that the general public would welcome controls of some kind. Anxiety about screen violence is now being rightly distinguished from the blanket *censoriousness of earlier campaigns which condemned the depiction of sex as vehemently as that of torture.*
(THE TIMES, 22 January 1994)

Mulching should take place when the soil is warm, so late autumn is a good time . . . The mulch will act as a blanket, *stabilising the temperature and water retention of the soil.*
(SUNDAY TIMES, 6 November 1994)

A favoured etymology claims that the blanket is named after one Thomas

Blanket who was the first to manufacture them in the fourteenth century. This story apparently originates in a fanciful invention in a book by Thomas Costain (1885–1965), a prolific Canadian author of historical novels, who humorously suggested that a man named Blanket wove fine wool bed covers, which in time came to be described by his name. Others took Costain's fancy for fact and a new etymology was born.

Although there are many words coined from a person's name (see **It's All in a Name, page 37**), blanket is not one of them. The word's origin lies not in the apocryphal Mr Thomas Blanket but in the whitish colour of the raw wool from which the articles were first made. *Blanket* comes from the Old French word *blanquet* or *blanchet*, a diminutive of *blanc*, meaning 'white'.

blindfold

to place a bandage over someone's eyes so that he cannot see

Scrooge . . . begged the Ghost to lead him where he would.

'You recollect the way?' inquired the Spirit.

'Remember it.' cried Scrooge with fervour; 'I could walk it blindfold.*'*

(Charles Dickens, A CHRISTMAS CAROL, 1843)

Andrew Wyke: I took a leaf out of the book of certain 18th century secret societies. They knew to a nicety how to determine whether someone was worthy to be included amongst their number and also how to humiliate him in the process. I refer of course to the initiation ceremony . . . When Count Cagliastro, the noted magician, sought admission to one such society, he was asked whether he was prepared to die for it, if need be. He said he was. He was then sentenced to death, blindfolded *and a pistol containing powder but no shot placed against his temple and discharged.*

(Anthony Shaffer, SLEUTH, 1970)

Old English had *blindfyllan* where *fyllan* meant 'to fell', 'to strike down', as one would a tree. This verb, therefore, meant 'to strike blind'. It became *blindfellen* in Middle English with the past participle *blindfelde*. By the fifteenth century the letter '*d*' had become part of the infinitive stem of the verb; by the sixteenth century this form was frequently corrupted to *blindfolden* – the folding of the cloth to make the bandage for the eyes obviously triggering the change, since the common meaning by then was not 'to strike blind' but 'to make blind by covering the eyes'.

For another example of a word influenced by an etymologically unrelated one, see **uproar**.

blitz

1. an intensive air bombardment
2. an energetic, concentrated effort

Despite long hours in the garden from the age of eight onwards, I have no memory of anyone ever planting anything. The whole business was a process of reduction, grass and hedges being cut, weeds weeded and wherever possible more cultivated yardage grassed over. The only creative area was the kitchen garden, which . . . had to be run within the rhythm of the kitchen rather than the garden. In this role it escaped the full tyranny of her horticultural blitzkrieg.

(Life, THE OBSERVER MAGAZINE, 27 November 1994)

Once the Blitz *started, London's nightlife survived only fitfully. Most theatres closed in*

the first two or three days of the Blitz *because managers did not believe that audiences would venture out . . . One by one the familiar icons of London life were assailed. Madame Tussaud's was in ruins after only two nights of* Blitz*; its cinema demolished and the rows of tip up seats blown over the top of nearby Baker Street station.*
(DAILY MAIL, 20 February 1995)

When Hitler launched Germany into open conflict in 1939, he did so with confidence, believing that he held superiority both on land and in the air. His key strategy, which proved very effective in Poland, was the *Blitzkrieg* or 'lightning war' (from *Blitz*, 'lightning' and *Krieg*, 'war'), a sudden, sharp attack that would swiftly overwhelm the enemy. The short form *Blitz* entered English vocabulary early in the war when major British cities were subject to sudden, heavy air-raids. Referring to this period, the word is now written with an initial capital letter: *Blitz*. Since the war, *blitz* has been used figuratively to describe a sudden, energetic endeavour to complete a task.

bloomers

voluminous knee-length knickers

Stagg's wife, Stella, who caught his eye 'playing men's basketball in her bloomers*' as a Chicago coed, lives alone now in the modest, cream-colored frame house on West Euclid Ave.*
(SPORTS ILLUSTRATED, 29 August 1994)

Bloomers are the type of knickers one imagines one's maiden aunt to be wearing under her tweed skirt. They may be out of vogue today but at one time they were ahead of fashion and caused no small upset in polite society.The word derives from the name of Amelia Jenks *Bloomer* – not because she invented the garment but because she associated herself with it.

Mrs Bloomer ran a paper, THE LILY, for which she wrote articles on temperance, social reform and women's rights. In 1850 she wrote in support of a group of women who turned up in her home town of Seneca Falls, New York State, wearing practical knee-length skirts over baggy trousers that were gathered at the ankle. This costume was favoured by members of the Women's Rights Movement, who argued that the fashionable crinoline, which skimmed the ground, was both cumbersome and unhygienic. The new outfit was very decent by modern standards but mid-nineteenth century society reacted unfavourably to women in trousers. Mrs Bloomer, however, was persuaded that it was a practical way to dress and said so in THE LILY. She also took to wearing the costume herself. Her spirited defence was noted by the national press and brought instant notoriety. Before long those plunging into the controversy were referring to the outfit as the *Bloomer*. Mrs Bloomer had plenty of opportunity to publicise her way of dress, for she was soon in demand as a speaker. In 1852 she toured the northern cities as a lecturer, doubtless hoping that her audiences were there to inform themselves of her many worthy convictions rather than simply to gawp at her attire.

In fact, Mrs Bloomer was not too happy with this particular type of celebrity – she would have preferred to be known for her work for women's suffrage. So at one stage she suggested that, as the idea for the apparel originally came from Elizabeth Smith Miller, the garments should really be called *millers*. However, her protestations got

Garments

What has a saint to do with underwear? *San Pantaleone* or *Pantalone* was a much-loved Venetian saint in whose honour boys of the city were frequently baptised. Amongst Italians, therefore, the name often denoted a Venetian and was accordingly given to a Venetian character in the *commedia dell'arte.* He appeared as a scrawny, bespectacled dotard wearing slippers and tight trousers. The word *pantaloon* came into English via French *pantalon* to describe a kind of tight trouser-cum-hose, similar to that worn by *Pantalone,* which was fashionable during the reign of Charles II. Over the years the word was applied to other styles of fashionable trouser. French retains *pantalon* to mean 'trousers' to this day and American English did the same with *pantaloon,* shortening it to *pants* in the nineteenth century. In British English, however, *pants* are strictly underwear.

Like San Pantaleone and the character Pantalone, a number of figures who were once well-known are now remembered chiefly by the garments named after them. Amelia *Bloomer,* whose story is told in detail elsewhere in this book, is one of them (see **bloomers**). Another is Jules *Léotard,* a famous nineteenth-century French acrobat and inventor of the flying trapeze. He was also the designer of the *leotard,* the figure-hugging one-piece garment that was adopted by others of his profession and subsequently by dancers and gymnasts.

A more substantial garment bears the name of Charles *Mackintosh* (1766–1843) who layered cloth with rubber to form an impermeable material from which heavy-weather cloaks and coats were then made. Later the word *mackintosh* was used to denote any type of raincoat and, at the beginning of the nineteenth century, was subject to the inevitable abbreviation, *mack* or *mac.*

The dress of military commanders seems to have been much noted and copied in the nineteenth century. Arthur, first Duke of *Wellington,* was such a prominent and popular figure through his decisive military triumphs in the Peninsular War and his victory over Napoleon at Waterloo (1815) that coats, hats, trousers and boots were named in his honour. Today he is remembered only for *wellington boots,* which were originally long and loose topped, the fronts coming above the knee. The unglamorous rubber variety were an invention of the first quarter of the twentieth century. According to the OED the affectionate abbreviation *welly* dates back to the early 1960s.

But military success was not a prerequisite of sartorial prominence. Two figures responsible for the ill-fated Charge of the Light Brigade, where British troops sustained heavy losses at Balaclava during the Crimean War (1854–6), are also remembered for their style. Lord *Raglan* was responsible for the ambiguous order which initiated the Charge. He wore a sensible overcoat without shoulder seams, which was named after him. Later his name was given to the *raglan sleeve*, which continues seamless up to the neck. His name is often found in knitting patterns, as is that of his fellow officer James Thomas Brudenell, seventh Earl of *Cardigan*, who is remembered in name for his woolly button-through jackets and for leading the disastrous Charge. Indeed the Crimean campaigns did much foı knitting. *Balaclava caps* or *helmets* were named after the town of *Balaclava*, site of the British base, where soldiers wore them to weather the freezing temperatures. After the war the cosy winter headgear was worn by the civilian population also.

The adoption by civilians of garments issued to soldiers was nothing new. During the Thirty Years' War (1618–48) Croatian mercenaries pressed into service for France wore linen scarves round their necks. French men and women of fashion copied the garment in fine fabrics trimmed with lace, bestowing on it the name *cravate*, 'cravat' (from *Cravate*, 'a Croatian', from German *Krabate*, from Serbo-Croatian *Hrvat*).

Balaclava was not the only place to lend its name to an article of clothing. *Jodhpurs*, the breeches commonly worn for riding, come from the city by that name in Rajasthan, India, and were brought to England in the nineteenth century. Also from India come *dungarees*. *Dungrī* is a district of Bombay where a rough kind of calico known as *dungrī* was manufactured in the seventeenth century. Stout trousers made of the fabric have been known as *dungarees* since the nineteenth century.

Closer to home *duffel* (or *duffle*) *coats* take their name from the heavy woollen fabric from which they have been made since the seventeenth century. Of course the fabric is named for its place of manufacture, the Belgian town of *Duffel*. Knitted goods have been produced on the island of *Jersey* since at least the sixteenth century. In the nineteenth century the knitted fisherman's *jersey* tunic became fashionable and the same century saw the emergence of the *sporting jersey*, originally made of close-knit woollen cloth.

For various fabrics that are called after their place of origin, see **Fabrics** (page 235).

her nowhere. Over a century later, she is remembered, if at all, as a clothes designer rather than a feminist.

Towards the end of the century improved bicycles made cycling a pleasure and many cycling clubs were formed. Women were as eager to participate as men and so naturally more practical women's clothing was required. The historian Christopher Hibbert (THE ENGLISH, 1987) quotes an account of those days by the daughter of the Plumian Professor of Astronomy at Cambridge, who says:

> *And soon after that everyone had bicycles . . . and [they] became the smart thing in society . . . We were then permitted to wear baggy knickerbockers, horridly improper, but rather grand . . . I only once saw a woman (not, of course, a lady) in real* bloomers.

Even as the century closed, it seems, bloomers were not quite the thing in polite circles.

For more articles of clothing named after their wearers see **Garments** on pages 40–41.

bonanza

a tremendous opportunity for gain, a source of sudden great wealth

> *Gerry Adams scored a resounding propaganda coup on his first visit to the United States yesterday, subjecting the American people to a one-sided tutorial on the conflict in Northern Ireland.*
>
> *His huge exposure angered Unionists and dismayed British officials, while even members of the Clinton Administration were taken aback by the publicity* bonanza *enjoyed by the Sinn Fein president.*
>
> (THE TIMES, 2 February 1994)

> *Magic Eye – and its successor in the bestseller lists, Magic Eye II – consist of what psychologists call autostereograms. Superficially, these are a meaningless jumble of whirls and dots, no worse than plenty of abstract expressionist masterpieces but no better, either. . .*
>
> *Nor are these two books the only places where such illusions can be entertained. A huge international* bonanza *is building, with postcards, posters, T-shirts, calendars, puzzles, phone cards, grocery bags, comic strips, and even Pepsi cans sporting the images.*
>
> (THE TIMES, 7 May 1994)

> *To the British bourgeoisie, the rising house market has proved a* bonanza *for a generation; but now it has fallen it has left a million new buyers with negative equity.*
>
> (THE SUNDAY TIMES, 19 March 1995)

A high street estate agent advertising in the free press proclaims:

> *PROMOTIONAL EASTER* BONANZA
> *For three months until the end of May 1994 we are offering an excellent promotional opportunity to anyone who is serious about selling their home.*

YOUR GARDEN magazine for April 1994 has: *SPRING* BONANZA *over £3,000 worth of prizes* splashed on its cover, and a leisure centre tempts customers with an *EASTER* BONANZA *of activities.*

Bonanza is an Americanism which hits British advertising and promotions from time to time, usually when a competition carrying a great deal of prize money is announced or a sale is advertised. There is no such razzmatazz in the word's origins, however. *Bonanza* is a Spanish word and simply means 'good sailing weather'. It derives from the Latin *bonus*, 'good', via the unattested Vulgar Latin *bonacia*. (This word was modelled on Latin *malacia* which meant 'calm at sea'. Calm conditions are unfavourable to sailing and so the word was erroneously supposed to derive from *malus*, 'bad'.)

Formerly *bonanza* was used as a salutation to convey good wishes for a safe journey or to wish a person prosperity. Spanish adventurers in colonial times would pray to the *Virgen de la Bonanza* on their departure for the New World. *Bonanza* was, therefore, a particularly appropriate word to apply to the riches of the Americas, especially to the abundant mining deposits found there. Mines were named *Bonanza* by the Spanish as early as the mid-sixteenth century. It became a familiar mining term in Mexico, meaning 'a rich seam of ore', and, when the western states of America were probed for gold in the nineteenth century, was borrowed into the vocabulary of American prospectors. To this day there are many towns, mountains and rivers called *Bonanza* throughout the North American continent.

The Gold Fever of nineteenth-century America gave the word unfavourable connotations. So often, apparent great riches failed to materialise or the bubble of Stock Market speculation led to ruin. *The Big Bonanza*, for example, near Virginia City fuelled wild investment in the late 1870s that rapidly came to nothing. There is no hint of ruin in the British 'bonanza' advertising campaigns, however. You can't lose; everyone is a winner.

For another word originating in fair weather, see **opportunity**.

bonfire

a large fire, often for the public

> *. . . and yet Pope Paul the Third . . . pitifully complains of the cruelty of King Henry VIII for causing all the bones of Becket to be burnt, and the ashes scattered in the winds; . . . and how his arms should escape that* bone-fire *is very strange.*
> (W Stanley, THE ROMISH HORSELEECH, 1674)

> *But she did believe in a good* bonfire. *It was the only time she was really happy in the garden. She had the knack of keeping one smouldering away for days, even weeks.* Bonfires *are environmentally incorrect now, but a quarter of a century ago we burnt everything - long grass, cabbage stalks, leaves, twigs, anything that could be cajoled into burning. In our household it was mainly couch grass. This made ideal fuel for my mother's* bonfires, *being present in limitless supply and burning satisfyingly slowly.*
> (THE OBSERVER MAGAZINE, 27 November 1994)

> *The beacon at Harting Hill, West Sussex . . . is part of a chain that has long been used for sending messages from the South Coast to London.* Bonfires *were used to signal the coming of the Spanish Armada in 1588, and there is evidence that they were used 1,000 years earlier for a similar purpose . . . Since the war, there have been* bonfires *here for the Coronation, the Silver Jubilee and, indeed the anniversary marking the Armada.*
> (DAILY TELEGRAPH, 8 March 1995)

Large *bonfires*, not the garden-rubbish variety, are usually lit for public celebration. This has led some etymologists to seek out a happy origin for the word. They attempt to derive it from the French *bon feu*, or 'good fire,' but do not take into consideration that this term does not exist in French and that the expression for a celebration bonfire in that language is, in fact, *feu de joie*. Rather the word is English, its true origins being a little grisly but still celebratory.

In past times great piles of clean cattle bones were burnt to commemorate certain anniversaries, a practice which probably had pagan origins. In England, for instance, the midsummer feast of St John (June 24) was traditionally marked by the pagan practice of kindling a chain of bonfires. In pre-Christian times the sun was recognised as the source of life, and people sought to prevent the gradual diminishing of its intensity after midsummer's day. Dr Brewer quotes from the FESTYVALL of 1493 (printed in 1515):

In the worship of St. John the people . . . made three manner of fires: one was of clean bones and no wood, and that is called a bone fire*; another of clean wood and no bones, and that is called a wood-fire . . . and the third is made of wood and bones, and is called St. John's fire.*

Festivities apart, *bone fires* were a regular feature of agricultural life in medieval times. A thirteenth-century verse which celebrates the fact that *'Of the sheep is cast away nothing'* goes on to say '*to ashes goeth his bones*'. In WATER IN ENGLAND (1964), Dorothy Hartley discusses the value to the medieval community of the huge annual medieval markets; all the by-products of the fair, ranging from the animal dung to the waste from the butchers' stalls benefited the land. *Bone fires* burned continually, with the additional benefit that the smoke from them acted as a medieval insect-repellent.

In the fifteenth century the word was written as *bone-fire* and reflected its origins, but over time the stressed syllable was contracted, first in speech and then in written form. By the sixteenth century *bonfire*, though still sometimes written as *bone-fire*, was more generally applied to a large prepared blaze of any sort. Still, some of these were fuelled with bones – the burning of saints' relics during the dissolution of the monasteries, for instance, or of heretics at the stake.

boom

1. a loud, resonant noise
2. a surge of growth and activity, often economic

The dew fell from the trees till there was no more left to fall, and the booming *went on, and the ground rocked and shivered, and Little Toomai put his hands up to his ears to shut out the sound.*
(Rudyard Kipling, THE JUNGLE BOOK, 1894)

Legislation could be introduced to control the booming *industry in pre-paid funerals, the head of the Office of Fair Trading warned yesterday . . . Under the schemes, customers buy a funeral at today's prices; the money is invested and pays for the arrangements when the customer dies.*

The growth in the industry and the large sums involved led to an OFT [Office of Fair Trading] investigation.
(INDEPENDENT, 7 March 1994)

Warm, milky drinks are sexy. Forget pyjamas and slippers; we're talking negligees. Recently, a report was published which showed that rising demand for alternatives to tea and coffee have meant something of a boom *for hot chocolate and malted drinks such as Ovaltine, sales of which grew by 35% between 1989 and 1993. The market is now worth £119m annually, and is expected to grow at a rate of 8% a year.*
(SUNDAY TIMES, 6 November 1994)

Boom is an onomatopoeic word to describe a deep, sonorous sound which disturbs the air. Possibly this imitation of natural sounds was originally English; maybe it was a borrowing from German or Dutch, which both have similar words. In any event, *boom* was used, as noun and verb, from the fifteenth century on to describe anything from the buzzing of a bee to cannon fire, crashing billows or any other loud, resonant noise. Moreover, the word also encapsulates a sense of the rushing motion required to generate the sound: a ship sailing at full speed, for instance, was said to be *booming*. It is probably with this in mind that *boom* was given a new twist of meaning in nineteenth-century America when it was applied to a rush of political activity during Ulysses Simpson Grant's bid for a third term as Republican president.

The St Louis GLOBE DEMOCRAT first used the word in this context in 1879; other newspapers were more cautious because of its 'slangy' nature. Nevertheless, before long it had been unreservedly adopted and was soon on everyone's lips. For a month or two *boom* circulated in the political sphere until the press recognised its potential as a punchy term to describe a spurt of economic growth. THE INDIANAPOLIS JOURNAL of October 1879 quoted a frustrated businessman who remarked, '*Nearly everything has had a* boom *except soap, and I'm looking for a soap* boom *every day.*'

Since then *boom* has been applied to many areas of business and investment and, in more recent times, to population figures when the large number of babies born after the Second World War was termed the *baby boom*. But the word's popularity was almost stillborn. Towards the end of 1879, in a mood of sour grapes, some of the Democratic press condemned the term and tried to suppress it, but to no avail:

Since the Ohio election one or two Democratic papers have suggested that the word has an unpleasant sound, and ought to be done away with, but it is evident this suggestion springs from base partisan motives. It is a good word, and answers a great many purposes. Let it boom.
(INDIANAPOLIS JOURNAL, October 1879)

bridal

connected to the bride or wedding

Juliet: Is there no pity sitting in the clouds
That sees into the bottom of my grief?
O sweet my mother, cast me not away!
Delay this marriage for a month, a week;
Or if you do not, make the bridal *bed*
In that dim monument where Tybalt lies.
(Shakespeare, ROMEO AND JULIET, Act 3, Scene 5, 1597)

There was something of delicacy in my husband's bridal *attentions; but now his tainted breath, pimpled face, and blood-shot eyes, were not more repugnant to my senses, than his gross manners, and loveless familiarity to my taste.*
(Mary Wollstonecraft, MARIA OR THE WRONGS OF WOMAN, 1798)

The sun suddenly burst through the gray and poured a flood of radiance on the happy bride. Instantly the garden was alive with dancing shadows and flickering lights.

'What a lovely omen,' thought Anne, as she ran to kiss the bride. Then the three girls left the rest of the guests laughing around the bridal *pair while they flew into the house to see that all was in readiness for the feast.*
(Lucy Maud Montgomery, ANNE OF AVONLEA, 1925)

There are often exquisite lace bridal *fans, parasols and even old lace handkerchiefs, which would provide brides wearing a new dress with the 'something old' required by the rhyme.*
(WEEKEND TELEGRAPH, 25 February 1995)

In Old English *bridal* was originally a compound noun *brydealu*, literally 'bride-ale' (more recognisable in its Middle English form *bridale*), and denoted a 'wedding feast'.

The *bridale* was a rowdy affair, obviously helped along by the consumption of copious amounts of ale. This was especially brewed for the festivities and was sold to the guests for the benefit of the couple. Nevertheless participation was wholehearted and generous. Christopher Hibbert (THE ENGLISH, 1987) quotes Bishop Richard Poore of Salisbury who, in the first quarter of the thirteenth century, felt moved to remind his flock that marriages should be *'celebrated reverently and with honour, not with laughter or sport or at public potations or feasts'*. The Bishop's plea had little effect, however, for not until the last quarter of the sixteenth century does the learned clergyman William Harrison report a reduction in '*the heathenish rioting at bride-ales*' (DESCRIPTION OF ENGLAND, 1587). Indeed a sermon delivered some twenty-two years later suggests more sober ingredients as a recipe for a joyful celebration and subsequent wedded bliss:

How happy are those in whom faith and love, and godlinesse are maried together, before they marry themselves? For none of these martiall, and cloudy, and whining mariages can say, that godlines was invited to their bride-ale*; and therefore the blessings which are promised to godlinesse, doe flie from them.*
(Smith, SERMONS, 1609).

These sentiments would have gladdened Bishop Poore's heart. Edmund Spenser, it seems, got it right. He narrates his wooing of his bride, Elizabeth Boyle, in AMORETTI, and lyrically celebrates their marriage in EPITHALAMION (1595):

And let them make great store of bridale *poses,*
And let them eeke bring store of other flowers,
To deck the bridale *bowers.*
And let the ground whereas her foot shall tread,
For feare the stones her tender foot should wrong,
Be strewed with fragrant flowers all along.

The spelling *bridale* to denote the celebrations occurs as early as 1200, though the less recognisable forms *bredeale, brydale* and *brydeale* are found in the fifteenth and sixteenth centuries. From the second half of the fourteenth century the word was sometimes used in the plural and applied not just to the feast but to the ceremony as well. By the seventeenth century *bridal* was being used attributively, the word being erroneously influenced by adjectives of Latin origin such as *cordial, circumstantial, natal* and *mortal*. This gave rise to couplings such as *bridal bed, bridal cake, bridal house, bridal knot* and *bridal lace*. By the eighteenth century *bridal* was understood to be an adjective, surviving as a noun only in the form *bride-ale* where the writer was intent upon historical effect.

For further discussion of **ale** as a feast, see that entry. See also **bridegroom**.

bridegroom

a man about to be married

Mrs Pring was married to James Fogers last Thursday as quietly as possible . . . It was with great difficulty that she was prevailed upon to go to Brecon for the night and to let her husband accompany her. Her own wish was that the bridegroom *should return to his own house while she slept at the Vicarage as usual. She said she did not want any of that fuss and nonsense. She looked upon marriage as a religious thing. But Mrs Venables represented to her what a talk*

would be caused by such a proceeding, so she consented to go as a bride to Brecon for one night and to let the bridegroom *go too.*
(Francis Kilvert, DIARY, 6 August 1872)

[In Karachi] the next day, a group of nervous off-duty policeman blindly pointed their guns towards a side street and fired in response to celebratory shots fired in the air by people in a marriage party. The bridegroom *and best man died.*
(FINANCIAL TIMES, 28 December 1994)

The blushing Anglo-Saxon bride did not take a *bridegroom* for her husband but a *brȳdguma*. *Guma* was a rather poetic word for 'man'. It was akin to *homō*, a Latin term with the same meaning. In Middle English *guma* became *gome* but poetic words do not have much staying power and, by the time William Tyndale was undertaking his translation of the Bible in 1526, *brydegrome* had become current – *gome* having been replaced with the more common *grome*, which in those days also meant 'man'.

Grome is of mysterious origin. Middle English *grome* (our contemporary spelling *groom* dates from around 1580) was originally used of a young boy but the sense was widened to 'man' in the fourteenth century. However, references from the end of the thirteenth century show that *grome* was also a general term for a man-servant, one who may or may not have had charge of horses. Not until the seventeenth century was the term restricted to one performing this particular service.

◆ The Old English word *bryd*, 'bride' goes back to the hypothetical Germanic form *bruthiz*, 'bride'. See **bridal**.◆

brogues

strong leather shoe

He sometimes wondered if she even saw Cosmo, quite literally; whether, when her eyes rested upon her youngest son – a triumph, born when she was forty-two – she saw, not the reality of his macabre sooty hair and clothes, but a fantasy of tweed jacket and corduroys and well-polished brogues.
(JOANNA TROLLOPE, The Choir, 1988)

Danny retained a depraved sartorial look in immaculate jacket, brogues *and scruffy jeans. He always looked divine.*
(EVENING STANDARD, 6 May 1994)

Modern day *brogues* are stout leather shoes, embellished by perforated patterning, for country wear. They have even become stylish fashion items but this is only a twentieth century development. *Brogues* were originally crude heavy footwear made of untanned leather which were worn in Scotland and Ireland. Sometimes they were strengthened with clouts or nails, as this reference from Shakespeare's CYMBELINE (c. 1610) shows:

I thought he slept, and put
My clouted brogues *from off my feet, whose rudeness*
Answer'd my steps too loud.
(Act 4 scene 2)

The word is from the Old Irish *brōce*, meaning 'shoe' (probably from the Old Norse *brok*, 'trousers'). The connection of covering for foot and leg is hardly surprising since shoe and leggings might be made of just one piece of material. This link is further reflected in *brogue* being used not only for 'shoe' but also for 'trousers' in the English of the seventeenth to nineteenth centuries. The English *breeches* is probably related to the same Old Norse root.

brusque

rough-mannered, rude, sharp

Where Charles was brusque, *abusive and volcanic, the baby-faced Maurice was thoughtful and ameliorative.*
(THE INDEPENDENT, 14 January 1995)

The source of *brusque* is thought to be the unattested Vulgar Latin word *bruscum,* the name commonly given to the very spiky plant, *butcher's broom.* This became *brusco* in Italian, which then used the name of the disagreeable shrub as an adjective to describe unpleasantly sharp-tasting wine or tart fruit. The word was borrowed into other Romance languages in the sixteenth century with the figurative sense of 'harsh, lively, fierce, abrupt'. It came into English by way of the French *brusque* in the seventeenth century. Initially it was spelt *brusk* but the French spelling was adopted in the mid-eighteenth century.

◆ It is probable that *brisk* was an earlier sixteenth-century borrowing of French *brusque.* Throughout the late sixteenth and the seventeenth centuries *brisk* is often used in contexts where *brusque* would serve just as well.◆

buccaneer

pirate, adventurer

The buccaneer *on the wave might relinquish his calling and become at once if he chose, a man of probity and piety on land; nor, even in the full career of his reckless life, was he regarded as a personage with whom it was disreputable to traffic or casually associate. Thus the Puritan elders in their black cloaks, starched bands, and steeple-crowned hats, smiled not unbenignantly at the clamour and rude deportment of these jolly seafaring men; and it excited neither surprise nor animadversion when so reputable a citizen as old Roger Chillingworth, the physician, was seen to enter the market-place in close and familiar talk with the commander of the questionable vessel.*
(Nathaniel Hawthorne, THE SCARLET LETTER, 1850)

'You have heard of this Flint, I suppose?' 'Heard of him!' cried the squire. 'Heard of him, you say! He was the bloodthirstiest buccaneer *that sailed. Blackbeard was a child to Flint. The Spaniards were so prodigiously afraid of him that, I tell you, sir, I was sometimes proud he was an Englishman' . . . 'Come away, Hawkins,' he would say; 'come and have a yarn with John. Nobody more welcome than yourself, my son. Sit you down and hear the news. Here's Cap'n Flint – I calls my parrot Cap'n Flint, after the famous* buccaneer *– here's Cap'n Flint predicting success to our v'yage. Wasn't you, cap'n?'*
(Robert Louis Stevenson, TREASURE ISLAND, 1883)

In the seventeenth century many Europeans who had fallen foul of the law in their own countries ended up in the New World colonies. Some were contracted there as indentured servants to supply much needed labour on the plantations, others simply fled and ended up living wild. The word *buccaneer* originated amongst French outlaws who settled in the West Indies. These men lived by hunting and adopted the Indian custom of drying or smoking meat by laying it upon a raised framework of sticks placed over a fire. The South American Tupi word for the wooden frame was *mukem,* which the French hunters corrupted to *boucan* (borrowed as *buccan* in seventeenth-century English). From this was derived the verb *boucaner* which meant 'to dry meat on a *buccan*', and also the word *boucanier*, 'buccaneer', which originally referred to one of these woodsmen.

The outlaws soon found a more profitable means of existence, however. The islands and coves in the Caribbean provided excellent cover for surprise attacks on Spanish shipping and settlements, so that the term *buccaneer* soon became synonymous with 'pirate' and was then applied to a sea-rover who attacked Spanish American interests irrespective of nationality. One of the most notorious buccaneers was a Welshman, Henry Morgan, a former indentured servant.

Far from frowning upon these dishonest dealings, from the middle to the end of the seventeenth century the French and English governments sanctioned them, so that the buccaneers ended up recognised by the authorities of which they had fallen foul.

In Haiti a similar wooden framework for curing meat, or even for use as a sleeping platform, was called a *barbacoa*, which was originally derived from a Taino word. The Spanish borrowed the term which passed into English in the late seventeenth century as *barbecue*.

For a word with a similar meaning see **pirate**.

budget

1. an allocated sum of money
2. a plan for spending money, personally, corporately or in a statement to Parliament

In April the new company car income tax regulations, introduced in Mr Lamont's budget, *come into effect. The new rules are based on a brain-numbing combined calculation of car age, mileage and original price.*
(GUARDIAN, 2 February 1994)

When I ran the Crucible in Sheffield, I had a budget *of over £5 million and made sure the theatre was in the black, but my own bank account was a complete nightmare.*
(GOOD HOUSEKEEPING, March 1994)

Government economic policy even before the crash was to reduce or remove subsidies on food, which is the main item in the budget *of the poor. Now food prices are set to rise again.*
(GUARDIAN, 14 January 1995)

Although the mention of *budget* brings the thorny question of finance to most minds, the word had a very long history before such considerations became part of it. The Romans had the word *bulga* for a little pouch made of animal skin which, according to the Latin lexicographer Festus, was derived from a Gallic source. Old French made *bouge* from the word and the diminutive *bougette*. Both words were borrowed into English with roughly the same sense of 'bag, leather bottle'; the former in the late fourteenth century as *bouge*, the latter a few decades later as *bowget*, a spelling that was still found in Shakespeare's day, although the variant *budget* was preferred in later editions:

If tinkers may have leave to live,
And bear the sow-skin bowget,
Then my account I well may give
And in the stocks avouch it.
(WINTER'S TALE, Act 4, scene 3)

Towards the end of the sixteenth century *budget* referred not only to the pouch, as Shakespeare's lines show, but also to its contents, whatever they might be.

In an extension of this use, *budget* was later applied to the package of papers containing the annual financial statement presented to the British parliament by the Chancellor of the Exchequer – and presumably carried there in a leather wallet. The first recorded use was in a satirical pamphlet of 1733 entitled THE BUDGET OPENED. Its next appearance, in an issue of THE GENTLEMEN'S MAGAZINE of 1764, shows that *budget* had since become established as a political term. In this financial sense the word remained linked to government until the mid-nineteenth century when it began to be applied to more modest domestic accounts.

The verb *to budget* has come to mean 'to plan one's expenditure' or 'to build the cost of something into one's financial plan' and dates from the 1880s. In recent times the word has also become an adjective meaning 'inexpensive', 'within the financial reach of most people', so that *budget car-hire*, *budget holidays* and *budget ranges* of various goods are now on offer.

◆ When a political opponent derisively calls the Chancellor's *budget* 'bilge', he is being more accurate than he realises. Surprising though it may seem, the Chancellor's *budget* and the *bilge* of a ship are etymologically one and the same. The swollen shape of a leather bag or bottle suggested the curve of a ship's hull and so *bulge* (from the Old French *bouge*, like *budget*) was used for this part of the vessel, as well as originally for a bag. The term persisted for some centuries before it was finally superseded by the variant *bilge*. Of course, *bulge* still means 'a protuberance, a hump' in contemporary English. Thus *budget*, *bilge* and *bulge* all owe their origin to the one source.◆

bugbear

1. a cause of irritation
2. an object of irrational dread

TAM DALYELL DEFENDS A FRIEND AND ATTACKS A BUGBEAR
I am deeply interested in the row that has been brewing for some time in the heat of the nuclear arms debate, and not only because the key figure is a friend of mine. Now the row has burst into the open round the broad shoulders of Monsignor Bruce Kent, threatening to blast the career of that redoubtable cleric by forcing him into an invidious choice between his cloth and his commitment to the Campaign for Nuclear Disarmament (CND). (NEW SCIENTIST, 1983)

The Conservative party, the right in particular, is desperate for strong leadership. It adores natural authority . . . Ted Heath, bugbear *of monetarist and Monday Clubber alike, exuded authority in his heyday. Mrs Thatcher and Sir Keith Joseph cowered at the other end of the Cabinet table to escape his attention.*
(THE TIMES, 1 October 1993)

Despite Chechnya, inflation remains Russians' main bugbear*: 30% tell pollsters that Chechnya is one main concern, but nearly 90% say they worry most about inflation, which was running at 17.8% a month in January.*
(THE ECONOMIST, 25 February 1995)

The *bugbear* was a Tudor English invention, a terrifying ghost, presumably in the shape of a great bear, invented to terrify the young into good behaviour. In his Italian dictionary A WORLDE OF WORDES (1598) John Florio teams him with two more endearing spectres common to Tudor children: *Imagined spirits that nurces fraie their babes withall to make them leave crying, as we say* bug-beare, *or else rawe head and bloodie bone.*

There were probably a good number of unlearned and credulous Tudor adults who had a dread of the bugbear themselves, however, for imaginations in those days were stimulated by a rich folklore of fairies, goblins and spectres, which blended easily with Christian superstitions. In the more matter-of-fact eighteenth century, Pope used *bugbear* figuratively for a 'haunting desire':

> *To the world no* bugbear *is so great*
> *As want of figure and a small estate.*
> (IMITATIONS OF HORACE, EPISTLES, 1733)

Already at the end of the sixteenth century *bugbear* was used as an evocative description of an 'irrational dread or fear' which casts its shadow over life. Essayist and critic William Hazlitt wrote that '*it is the test of reason and refinement to be able to exist without* bugbears' (EMANCIPATION OF THE JEWS, 1819). This sense is still current today although later nineteenth-century use also lent the word its present popular weakened sense of 'burden, persistent annoyance', applicable to problems or people.

Bug, the first element of *bugbear*, was *bugge*, 'hobgoblin', in Middle English and remained current until the early eighteenth century. '*Tush, tush, fear boys with* bugs', says Petruchio, making light of Katerina's fearsome reputation (Shakespeare, THE TAMING OF THE SHREW, c. 1594). Its origins are probably Welsh from *bwg*, meaning 'ghost'. This is also present in *bugaboo* (the ending *boo* from the Welsh *bw*, intended as an exclamation to frighten children) and possibly in the nineteenth century *bogy* or *bogey*, ancestor of the present day *bogeyman*.

Skeat is amongst those who suggest that the ghostly *bug* may have influenced an Old English word *budd*, meaning 'beetle', to lend it an overtone of unpleasantness that *budd* alone did not have. The result is *bug* as a term for 'creepy-crawly' which arose in the seventeenth century. Certainly, the bedbugs to which the word was often applied were distasteful enough. Nevertheless there is no real proof of the theory. The use of *bug* as a device for secretly listening in on people developed from the sense 'insect' in the twentieth century.

bureau

a desk or office

> *MEN WANTED. Free passage on cattle-boats to Liverpool feeding cattle. Low fee. Easy work. Fast boats. Apply International and Atlantic Employment* Bureau, *– Greenwich Street.*
> (Sinclair Lewis, OUR MR. WRENN, THE ROMANTIC ADVENTURES OF A GENTLE MAN, 1914)

> *This* bureau *is very special. We know where it was made, when it was made and, most significant of all, who made it. It is one of those lovely pieces of furniture made rare by the presence of the maker's name, in this case written in ink on the base of a drawer: 'Wm Palleday at ye Crown in Aldermanbury, London, Cabinit Maker' (sic). It is now known as a William Palleday* bureau . . . *There are a number of walnut and oak* bureaux *by William Palleday, all with features such as this one's two short and two long drawers, a high waist moulding and well-figured walnut veneers. So while this* bureau *is a fine example, its type is not unique.*
> (John Bly, SMALL AND DECORATIVE FURNITURE, 1995)

Burel was a type of rough-textured cloth of a dark reddish-brown colour that was woven in medieval France. Written references to it date back to the first half of the twelfth century. The term is thought to be a diminutive of *bure*, or else derives from an old adjective *buire* which means 'reddish-brown'. All of these words can be traced back to a Latin adjective *burrus*, meaning 'bright red', and further still to the Greek *purros*, meaning 'red'. (This adjective in turn is a derivative of *pur*, 'fire', which also gave the English *pyre* and *pyrotechnic*.)

Burel was also known as *borel* in the medieval England of 1300 when the word is first recorded. It continued in use into the eighteenth century. Sometimes the fabric was used for coarse clothing. Chaucer speaks of men roughly clad in *borel*. An adjective *borrel* which meant 'unlearned, rough-mannered' derived from this particular use:

> *How be I am but rude and* borrel'
> *Yet nearer ways I know.*
> (Spenser, SHEPHEARDS CALENDAR, 1579)

In France from the thirteenth century onwards, however, there are records of *burel* being spread over writing tables in courts and offices to provide firm surface that yielded under the pressure of the soft quill nib. Gradually this application of the word was transformed into *bureau* and, according to Randal Cotgrave's FRENCH AND ENGLISH DICTIONARY (1660), was variously applied to the cloth, the desk beneath it and even, on occasion, to the office where the desk was situated. While all the original connection with the cloth was gradually forgotten, the two new applications of the word remained and by the first half of the eighteenth century they had been borrowed into English and were firmly established in the vocabulary. In time the sense of 'office' became stronger and eventually emerged as an abstract term referring to the administration of a large organisation.

Nowadays a *bureau* can be an up-market desk or antique (with a substantial price tag to match), a *travel bureau* or a *ticket bureau*, or a government department (the *employment bureau*). This last sense is particularly common in America. As *bureaux* (usually British English) or *bureaus* (usually American English) have proliferated, so have the *bureaucrats* that staff them and the *bureaucracy* associated with them. It's a long way from a piece of common, rough cloth on the back of a medieval Frenchman.

butterfly

an insect with a long body and with large, usually brightly coloured, wings

> *Now he wasn't hungry any more – and he wasn't a little caterpillar any more. He was a big, fat caterpillar. He built a small house, called a cocoon, around himself. He stayed inside for more than two weeks. Then he nibbled a hole in the cocoon, pushed his way out and . . . he was a beautiful* butterfly*!*
> (Eric Carle, THE VERY HUNGRY CATERPILLAR, 1970)

> *INVASION OF THE* BUTTERFLY *SNATCHERS*
> *A night patrol has been set up to try to stop frogs wiping out hundreds of rare* butterflies. *Four volunteers armed with torches, nets and jam jars spend hours scouring one of Britain's biggest* butterfly *parks in the hope of catching the deadly frogs. So far more than 250 rare* butterflies *worth up to £7 each have been gobbled up by the 'invaders' at the* Butterflies *Pleasure Park near Mansfield, Nottinghamshire. Owners Tony and Vicky Slack are having to import 150 replacements a week from South America and the Philippines to stock up the park's*

tropical house. They suspect someone is planting the frogs there.
(DAILY MAIL, 17 April 1994)

Anyone watching these graceful creatures flitter around the garden buddleia or nettle bed would be convinced by the theory that the insect was not originally called a *butterfly* but a *flutterby* – an understandable confusion since fluttering is what butterflies do best, while the insect in them certainly suggests some types of fly. Sadly this can be nothing more than a charming folk etymology since the word goes back a thousand years and no evidence of *flutterby* has ever been recorded. Old English had *buttorflēoge*, which became *butterflie* in Middle English, so what can the connection with butter be? One theory derives the word from an old belief that butterflies stole milk and cream; Skeat cites the German *Molkendieb*, 'milk-thief', as an alternative to *butterfliege*, 'butterfly', though this really only serves to confirm that the belief was once prevalent. Another, less appealing, suggestion rests on the Dutch word *boterschijte*, literally 'buttershit', and points out that the butterfly's excrement is both creamy and yellow like butter. This last offering is probably the more likely of the two.

See **caterpillar**.

buttonhole

to seize someone physically or metaphorically in order to speak to him

We also met a short stout gentleman with a double chin and large umbrella, a kindly face and a merry eye, who buttonholed *Mayhew and began to inveigh in an aggrieved tone against the folly, perversity and bad taste of the University residents and visitors rushing in crowds of 1200 to hear the Bishop of Derry (Alexander) give an ornamental rhetorical flourish by way of a Bampton Lecture in the morning and leaving himself (Professor Pritchard, Professor of Astronomy and Select Preacher) to hold forth to empty benches in the afternoon. He thought it was a sin and a shame.*
(Francis Kilvert, DIARY, 22 May 1876)

In the eighteenth century, when a gentleman wished to detain someone in conversation, it was common practice for him to seize a button of his jacket and hold it thereby forcibly keeping his undivided attention. In Oliver Goldsmith's play THE GOOD-NATURED MAN (1768), for instance, the line '*I take my friend by the button*' meant 'I detain him in conversation'. The habit was so common that, by the early nineteenth-century, the term *buttonholder* had been coined to be followed some thirty years later by the verb to *buttonhold*.

The custom was something of a nuisance for to *buttonhold* implied that the person was being detained very much against his will. Sometimes drastic action was called for; the American periodical HOME JOURNAL (21 January, 1880) reported that *Charles Lamb, being* button-held *one day by Coleridge . . . cut off the button.* Nor was this annoying habit uniquely British, for the French had an equivalent phrase, *serrer le bouton à quelqu'un.*

Folk etymology has it that in the 1860s, when jackets that could be buttoned to the neck were finally abandoned in the interests of fashion, tailors still made a top buttonhole in the lapel which was just large enough to hook a finger through, so that the verb to *buttonhold* gradually changed to *buttonhole.* It is more likely, however, to be a simple matter of confusion between two very similar words, *buttonhole* being the more common as well as possibly easier to pronounce.

buxom

well-rounded, full-bosomed

And, this once known, shall soon return,
And bring ye to the place where thou and Death
Shall dwell at ease, and up and down unseen
Wing silently the buxom *air, embalmed*
With odours.
(JOHN MILTON, Paradise Lost, 1667)

'Christians! ay, marry are we, and have divinity among us to boot,' answered the Outlaw. 'Let our buxom *chaplain stand forth, and expound to this reverend father the texts which concern this matter.' The Friar, half-drunk, half-sober, had huddled a friar's frock over his green cassock, and now summoning together whatever scraps of learning he had acquired by rote in former days, 'Holy father,' said he, 'Deus faciat salvam benignitatem vestram — You are welcome to the greenwood.' The Outlaw accordingly led the way, followed by the* buxom *Monarch, more happy, probably, in this chance meeting with Robin Hood and his foresters, than he would have been in again assuming his royal state, and presiding over a splendid circle of peers and nobles.*
(Sir Walter Scot, IVANHOE, 1819)

'For my part' said the younger and prettier of the two daughters, a fair, buxom, *smiling wench, 'I hate Black Michael!'*
(Sir Anthony Hope, THE PRISONER OF ZENDA, 1894)

The Feb. 19 wedding of Baywatch babe Pamela Anderson and Motley Crue drummer Tommy Las makes it official: There are six degrees of separation between the buxom *blond and Michael Jackson. In her brief history of time in Hollywood, Anderson 27 has emerged as the unifying center of the celebrity-dating universe.*
(ENTERTAINMENT WEEKLY, 17 March, 1995)

This adjective has undergone startling changes in meaning over the centuries. The word has its roots in an Old English verb *būgan*, 'to bend'. Early Middle English (perhaps via an unattested Old English form) derived the adjective *buhsom* from it with the sense of 'pliant' and hence 'yielding, humble and obedient'. By the end of the fourteenth century *boxam* and *buxam* were current, though still meaning 'compliant'.

By the late sixteenth century, however, *buxom* had evolved to mean 'lively and spirited'. Shakespeare used the word in this way in his play HENRY V (1599) where Pistol says:

Bardolph a soldier, firm and sound of heart,
Of buxom *valour.*
(Act 3, scene 6)

Liveliness suggests physical wellbeing and so the next slight shift of meaning was towards 'healthy, vigorous'. To be in *buxom health* was a blessing in an age of primitive medical care, and men and women were alike described as *buxom*. It was only in the nineteenth century that the word was restricted increasingly to women, with the emphasis on general plumpness (considered a sign of good health), and then on having full breasts.

◆ It might be conjectured, given the similar ending and relatedness of sense, that *bosom* is etymologically connected to *buxom*. In fact this is not so. *Bosom* comes from Old English *bōsm*, which itself goes back to a Germanic stem.

The ultimate source might be in an Old Aryan word meaning 'arm'. This would fit quite nicely with one sense of *bosom*, meaning the space surrounded by the two arms and the breast, as in phrases such as *in Abraham's bosom*.

Although not very obvious at first sight, *buxom* contains the same suffix *–some*, meaning 'tending to be', as a number of other English words. Some of these go back to Old English (*lovesome, winsome*), others to Middle English (*cumbersome, handsome, loathsome, wholesome, twosome*) and quite a list to the succeeding centuries: *awesome, quarrelsome, foursome* (sixteenth-century); *venturesome, lonesome* (seventeenth-century); *adventuresome, fearsome* (eighteenth-century); *bothersome* (nineteenth-century).

The stem of *buxom*, Old English *būgan*, 'bend', is also the precursor of modern-day *bow*.◆

For other words that have undergone a complete change in meaning, see **nice** and **silly**.

cad

a scoundrel, a rogue

'You won't go back to your wife?' I said at last.

'Never.'

'She's willing to forget everything that's happened and start afresh. She'll never make you a single reproach.'

'She can go to hell.'

'You don't care if people think you an utter blackguard? You don't care if she and your children have to beg their bread?'

'Not a damn.'

I was silent for a moment in order to give greater force to my next remark. I spoke as deliberately as I could. 'You are a most unmitigated cad.*'*

'Now that you've got that off your chest, let's go and have dinner.'

(W Somerset Maugham, THE MOON AND SIXPENCE, 1919)

For 11 years [Chesterton] also wrote a column in the teetotal George Cadbury's Daily News, *but this association was abruptly terminated when GKC rashly but innocently published 'A Song of Strange Drinks', which contained the line 'Cocoa is a* cad *and a coward'.*

(THE TIMES, 29 December 1994)

Nigel, who went to the gallows for his sins as Ralph Gorse in the Thirties adventure The Charmer *seven years ago, says: 'Edmund is an absolute* cad *– a rogue. Next to him even Ralph had his good points.'*

(TODAY, 30 December 1994)

The origins of this word lie in *cadet* and *caddie*. (For the full story of their history, see **cadet**.)

In the seventeenth century *caddie*, the Scottish term derived from *cadet*, was the word for a porter or someone who made a living by doing odd jobs. By the 1820s the word had been taken up and shortened to *cad* by the English upper classes. At public schools such as Eton and at Oxford University in particular, a *cad* was an ill-bred, low-class townsman who hung about the college precincts waiting to be hired to fetch and carry for the students. A quotation in the OED from Arthur Hughes Clough's DIPSYCHUS of 1850 captures the superior, dismissive tone:

If I should chance to run over a cad,
I can pay for the damage if ever so bad.

Cad survived into the twentieth century as a slang word of the higher social classes with a similar meaning to 'bounder' and 'rotter'.

For other words for scroundrel, see **blackguard** and **villain**.

Words from Malay

Expanding European trade in the Malay Archipelago in the sixteenth and seventeenth centuries brought a number of Malay words into European languages, often through the Dutch or Portuguese, who had extensive colonial interests in the East. Amongst those which came into English are:

bamboo (16th cent): probably from a Malay term represented by the Portuguese as *mambu*. Its use in English was soon supplanted by *bambos*, apparently influenced by the Dutch form *bamboes* (the initial *b* and final *s* are a mystery). This was misunderstood to be a plural, so the s was dropped in English to give *bamboo* in the eighteenth century.

batik (19th cent): this method of producing a pattern in fabric by waxing the areas not to be penetrated by the dye was originally a Javanese term meaning 'painted'. It came into English through Malay.

cockatoo (17th cent): from Malay *kakatua* through Dutch *kaketoe*. Several authorities assume the word is imitative of the bird's cry. The English spelling is undoubtedly influenced by *cock*.

compound (17th cent): from Malay *kampong*, 'enclosure, village, cluster of buildings'. Borrowed into English by way of either Dutch *kampoeng* or Portuguese *campon*. A term used by the English of factory sites in the Malay Archipelago and spread to similar enterprises in India, China, Africa, etc.

gecko (18th cent): from Malay *ge'kok*, representing the noise the lizard utters.

gong (17th cent): from Malay *gōng*, representing the sound of the instrument.

kapok (18th cent): Malay *kāpok*, the name of the fibre surrounding the seeds inside the fruit of the silk cotton tree.

orang-utan (late 17th cent): Malay *ōrang ūtan* meant 'man of the woods', therefore, 'wild man'. The term was probably originally used to refer to the wild uncivilised tribesmen who inhabited the dense forests, but was mistakenly applied to the apes by European explorers. The form *orang-utang* is a rhyming corruption found in other European languages such as Dutch, Swedish and French.

sago (16th cent): from Malay *sāgū*. English originally had *sagu* from Portuguese. The form *sago* evolved in the seventeenth and eighteenth centuries, influenced by Dutch.

(See also **caddy** and **From all points of the compass**, page 5.)

caddy, tea-caddy

a container for storing tea

In spite of a hectic career as a management consultant, Andy Moretti, 22, has found a way of sustaining contact with the homeless. Every Monday night a small group of friends meets on the Strand, London, with a tea caddy *and sandwiches. The practice was started by two Etonians seven years ago; it has evolved into a small, efficient organisation run by an evolving group of friends, supported by The London Run charity.*
(DAILY TELEGRAPH, 23 December 1994)

Whenever he made forecasts of this sort, the folksy Harold Wilson used to urge his listeners to tuck his prediction behind the tea-caddy *on the kitchen* mantelpiece *for future reference. I hope no one does anything so sternly practical with my offering. But rest assured, you will be reminded of it if it turns up trumps.*
(GUARDIAN, 31 December 1994)

Rather disappointingly, this cosy little word associated with everything that is warm and comforting about a nice cup of tea is nothing more than a measurement of weight commonly used in China and Southeast Asia. The *kati*, a word of Malay origin, is roughly equivalent to 1⅓ lb (or 625 grammes). The term was taken into English for commercial purposes as *catty* in the sixteenth century. *Caddy*, found from the end of the eighteenth century, is a corruption of this and originally referred to 'a small box containing one *caddy* of tea'. Later it simply denoted 'a box for storing tea'. Such boxes, however, were decorative and lined with lead foil and, since good quality tea was very expensive, could be locked with a key. Walsh quotes '*an affecting advertisement from a London newspaper copied by Horace Smith in "Tin Trumpet"*':

If this should meet the eye of Emma D-, who absented herself last Wednesday from her father's house, she is implored to return, when she will be received with undiminished affection by her almost heart-broken parents. If nothing can persuade her to listen to their joint appeal, – should she be determined to bring their grey hairs with sorrow to the grave, — should she never mean to revisit a home where she had passed so many happy years, – it is at least expected, if she be not totally lost to all sense of propriety, that she will, without a moment's further delay, send back the key of the tea-caddy.

In recent years *caddy* has been applied to any storage container for small items, particularly the box that protects CDs and floppy disks.

For a quite different meaning of *caddy*, see **cadet**. See also **tea**. And for other words from the same geographical source, see **Words from Malay** (page 56).

cadet

1. a young recruit in the armed services, police, etc
2. a younger son

There's also a fascinating mock-up of the wireless operator's cubby-hole in a Lancaster bomber. Ex-schoolboy army cadets *will feel a twinge of nostalgia on sight of an old 38 walkie-talkie set, which worked, in a loose manner of speaking, on batteries in the 7.3-8.9 MHz band. After the war, the army dumped thousands of these sets on* cadet *forces, where they were treated far harder than in any battle zone.*
(NEW SCIENTIST, 1983)

Hers is the heaviest golf bag I have ever encountered. Caddies *flee at her approach.*

Carrying her bag for 18 holes is quite beyond the capability of any one man.
(DAILY TELEGRAPH, 3 April 1995)

In noble medieval Gascon families, the older son was known as the *caput*, the 'head' (from Latin *caput*, 'head') and the younger brother as *capdet*, 'little head' (from Late Latin *capitellum*, 'little head', diminutive of *caput*). Many of these younger sons served at the French court amongst others of their kind from all over France. They used their dialect word *capdet* when referring to themselves and eventually it was taken up by the entire court as a general term for 'younger son', and also more specifically for a younger son of noble birth who was embarking upon a military career without a commission. This was a common practice for gentlemen up to the French Revolution. The hero of Edmond Rostand's famous play CYRANO DE BERGERAC (written in 1897 but set in the seventeenth century) was a leader of a company of Gascon cadets. The word with both French senses was borrowed into English in the early seventeenth century; nowadays it refers mainly to a young trainee in the armed forces or police force.

Cadet met with a different fate across the border in Scotland where the alternative English forms *cadee* and *caddie* were used. Initially they were synonymous with the French but, by the mid-eighteenth century, *caddie* also referred to a man or boy who waited about in the street to be hired for porterage, errands and other odd jobs. In one of his LETTERS FROM THE NORTH OF SCOTLAND (c.1754) Edward Burt describes to a friend in London the customs and manners of Inverness, remarking how the caddies organised themselves into bands, rather like an army:

The Cawdys, *a very useful Black-Guard, who attend . . . publick Places to go of Errands; and though they are Wretches, that in Rags lye upon the Stairs, and in the Streets at Night, yet are they often considerably trusted . . . This Corps has a kind of Captain . . . presiding over them, whom they call the Constable of the* Cawdys.

By the mid-nineteenth century *caddie* also referred to the lad who carried a golfer's clubs around the links in the Scottish sport of golf. Surprisingly, this use gave rise to an upper class slang term for a scoundrel — see **cad**.

◆ The Latin *caput* is found in many English words, amongst which are: *biceps* (a muscle with two 'heads' or tendons), *cape, capital, capitation, captain, chieftain, decapitate, precipitous* (from *praeceps*, 'headlong': *prae*, 'in front' and *caput*).◆

For a superficially similar, but very different, word to *caddie*, see **caddy.** For other words for scoundrel, see **villain** and **blackguard**.

cadge

to beg, to scrounge

Of course, apocryphal stories only proliferate about someone widely held in great affection; and in Runcorn's case the reason for the affection is not hard to find. I first met the Southport wizard 20 years ago in a remote Welsh outpost; and within minutes we were immersed in a fascinating discussion about rises in sea level and the expanding Earth. It is true that, characteristically, he was about to cadge *a lift; but lift or no lift, most elevated academics of those (and these) days when accosted by some unknown student would look at him as if he were something deposited on the pavement in contravention of the local by laws. The lack of even a hint of that attitude in Runcorn, combined with his remarkable equability, endeared him to me from the start.* (NEW SCIENTIST, 1983)

In the fifteenth century, a *cadger* was a travelling dealer who would buy dairy produce in the country to sell in the town and manufactured merchandise in the town to take to the country. It is thought that the word comes from the Middle English *caggen*, 'to tie', 'to carry a pack', although there is some uncertainty about the etymology. Possibly the *cadger* turned from honest dealer into a rogue who made extra money for himself wherever possible by coaxing and begging from his customers, for in the first half of the nineteenth century the meaning of the word shifted from 'hawker' to 'one who made a livelihood from begging'.

The verb to *cadge* actually precedes the noun *cadger* by more than a century, but the early senses are obscure; it is only in the seventeenth century that it is used of the itinerant hawker, and only in the nineteenth of a beggar.

Cadger, meaning 'a scrounger', is still found in modern English, but less so than the verb *to cadge*, which remains common – attempting to get something for nothing seems not to have changed down the centuries.

cajole

to persuade by attentiveness and flattery

From that moment on, the ladies' gallery began to empty. One mother after another was lured away to her kitchen by overpowering thoughts of roast chicken, chopped herring, luscious desserts and all the ritual preparations for breaking the fast. Food always tasted marvellous on that night. It was amazing how much you could put away, once your tummy had been cajoled *into coping with the onslaught by a glass of milk and soda water. What would it be tonight?*
(Michele Guinness, CHILD OF THE COVENANT, 1985)

For all these reasons, he [John Golding] is a true model within his chosen calling, and it is to be hoped that young art historians – and indeed artists— will eagerly devour the contents of this book. It might even convert members of the 'a child of four could have done that' or 'taxi driver' school of criticism to the notion that at least the best modern art is perfectly serious, in the unlikely event that they could be cajoled *into giving it the time of day.*
(THE TIMES, 3 March 1994)

Like making pop-star scrapbooks and playing jacks, wanting a hamster is a rite of passage which can be as bright and painful as first love. As caring parents we understood that, so when she [my 11-year-old daughter] first raised the issue, moon-faced and cajoling, *we said forget it.*
(WEEKEND TELEGRAPH, 6 August 1994)

This is a direct borrowing of *cajoler*, a French verb meaning 'to get one's way by means of attentions and flattery'. The Middle French verb was *cageoler* which meant 'to prattle and chatter like a pet jay in a cage'. (The Larousse Dictionary lists 'to call, with reference to the jay' under *cajoler*.) The word has been used in English since the mid-seventeenth century. It was still new to the language when Pepys used it in his diary to describe how Sir Richard Ford won over the somewhat stubborn Lord Mayor who was 'a talking, bragging Buffhead'.

Here we staid talking till eleven at night, Sir R. Ford breaking to my Lord our business of

our patent to be Justices of the Peace in the City, which he stuck at mightily; but however, Sir R. Ford knows him to be a fool, and so in his discourse he made him appear, and cajoled *him into a consent to it: but so as I believe when he comes to his right mind to-morrow he will be of another opinion.'*
(17 March, 1663)

For another word deriving from bird call, see **jargon**.

calculate

to work out, to reckon

The U.S. Department of Defense has estimated there were approximately 210,000 atomic test servicemen. Most other sources say the number was higher. The National Association of Atomic Veterans has calculated *the figure at between 250,000 and 400,000. These estimates do not include the many thousands of civilians who participated in the testing at close range.*
(Harvey Wasserman and Norman Solomon, KILLING OUR OWN, 1982)

In Latin a *calculus* was 'a small pebble', the word being a diminutive form of *calx*, 'limestone'. It was also the term for a counter in a game or on an abacus since small pebbles were used for this purpose. The Latin verb *calculāre*, therefore, meant 'to reckon, to compute'. *Calculate* came into English from the past participle stem *calculāt-* in the sixteenth century.

◆ The stem of *calx* (which ultimately derives from Greek *khalix*, 'pebble') is *calc-*, from which the New Latin word *calcium* was derived by the British chemist Sir Humphry Davy in 1808.

In the seventeenth century Latin *calculus* was also borrowed directly into English in two very different contexts. As it meant 'small stone' in Latin, it was not surprising that it should be applied in medicine to the 'stones' or hard masses which form in organs such as the kidneys or gall bladder. Given the connection with *calculate*, developing types of mathematics, such as integral and differential *calculus*, were appropriately so called.◆

calendar

1. a system for dividing the year up into periods of time
2. a table of the months, weeks and days in a year

'Dorothea, dear, if you don't mind—if you are not very busy—suppose we looked at mamma's jewels to-day, and divided them? It is exactly six months today since uncle gave them to you, and you have not looked at them yet.'...

'What a wonderful little almanac you are, Celia! Is it six calendar *or six lunar months?'*
(George Eliot, MIDDLEMARCH, 1872)

. . . Christmas dinner is the only meal we eat that is still attached to a season. All the rest of our meals have been cut free from the reality of seed time and harvest. Our food in unconnected to a time or place. Without a thought, we eat Cypriot wedding lunch (doner kebab) after the pub, and asparagus in November. We expect to consume around the world, around the calendar, *every day, in our own kitchens. Except at Christmas, when we eat a special dinner that we would never dream of eating at any other time.*
(THE SUNDAY TIMES, 18 December 1994)

Moneylenders in ancient Rome each kept a *calendārium*, an account-book which detailed the interest they would collect on the *calends* (from Latin *calendae*), that is the first day of the month. Modern practice is usually to settle accounts by the last day of the month, but the Romans calculated the date by counting backwards from the *calends*. Thus the date of a particular day in August would be so many days before the *calends* of September. It is uncertain why the *calends* were so called, but authorities have identified their origin in the verb *calāre*, 'to call out, to announce' (from the root *kal-*, 'to shout'), perhaps indicating that the start of each new month was proclaimed.

The word entered English at the turn of the thirteenth century when it was spelt *calender* following the Anglo-Norman *calender* and Old French *calendier*, from which it had immediately come. *Calendar* as a spelling first appears soon after 1400, but does not become the universal standard form until the nineteenth century.

◆ Other words also go back to the root *calāre*. In ancient Rome a man canvassing for election would be accompanied by his *nōmenclātor*, a slave who reminded him of the names and offices of those he met (from *nōmen*, 'name' and *clātor*, 'caller', from *calāre*). From this English derived *nomenclature* in the seventeenth century.

Council first denoted an 'ecclesiastical assembly' when it came into English in the twelfth century through Old French. It derives from Latin *concilium*, 'meeting', from *con-* (for *cum-*), 'together', and *calāre*, 'to summon'.

The *calendula*, the orange or gold coloured pot marigold, obviously takes its name from the *calends*, though authorities differ in their suggestions as to why. Some say that the flower came into bloom at the first of the month. This seems rather vague. A more satisfying explanation is that the medicinal qualities of the plant were helpful during monthly menstruation.◆

Another shift from *-er* to *-ar* in the spelling of a final syllable is catalogued in the entry for **caterpillar**.

canard

a fabricated report or news item, an exaggerated story

Whitman pleased conservatives in Tuesday's rebuttal by repeating the canard *that Clinton was responsible for the biggest tax hike in history. (Right answer: Ronald Reagan in 1982.)*
(TIME, 6 February 1995)

Canard is the French for 'duck' but it has also come to mean 'an unfounded piece of news, a tall story' in both French and English. Indeed there is a satirical newspaper in France called LE CANARD ENCHAÎNÉ, literally 'The Chained Duck'.

The word in this particular sense has been current in English since the first half of the nineteenth century. In his DICTIONNAIRE DE LA LANGUE FRANÇAISE (1877), the French lexicographer Littré, traces it to an old French idiom. *Vendre un canard à moitié* literally means 'to half-sell a duck'. Anyone trying to do this, of course, has clearly no intention of selling at all and is merely trying to fool a gullible customer.

Although this is undoubtedly the source of the word, some authorities have attributed it to a Frenchman, Norbert Cornelissen, who is said to have carried out a hoax on the French press. As the story he told was all about ducks, *canard* came to mean 'tall story'. Cornelissen claimed that he had twenty ducks. He killed one of them and threw it to the other nineteen who snapped it up. He then killed a second duck and threw that to its remaining fellows. Similarly he killed a third and a fourth and so on until only one was left. The remaining duck had thus feasted upon all its companions. It is reported that Cornelissen's story, which was widely circulated, was also widely believed. And if you believe that, you have just been half-sold a duck.

canary

1. a songbird of the finch family, kept domestically in a cage
2. a light sweet wine

Little Clotilda,
Well and hearty,
Thought she'd like to give a party.
But as her friends were shy and wary,
Nobody came
But her own canary.
(ANON)

Mary had a pretty bird,
Feathers bright and yellow,
Slender legs – upon my word
He was a pretty fellow.

The sweetest notes he'd always sing,
Which much delighted Mary;
And near the cage she'd ever sit
To hear her own canary.
(ANON)

The next [shock of discovery] came in the sudden appearance of a person called 'Milly' . . . whom I found in his room one evening . . . sharing a flagon of an amazingly cheap and self-assertive grocer's wine Ewart affected, called 'Canary sack.'
(H G Wells, TONO-BUNGAY, 1909)

This small greenish yellow songbird is native to the *Canary Islands.* It did not lend its name to the islands, however, but took its name from them. Curiously these volcanic islands, situated off the northern coast of Africa, were named after a different creature altogether. King Juba II (c. 50 BC–AD24), of the ancient north African country of Numidia (modern Algeria) sent a company of men on a voyage of exploration to the islands. The men returned with tales of a breed of large dog which lived on one of them. This fact, which was spread abroad through the king's written account of the voyage, led the Romans to call the islands *Canariae Insulae,* that is 'dog islands' (*canarius* is an adjective from Latin *canis,* 'dog'). Although King Juba's account is long lost, some of its contents are available to us through the writings of the elder Pliny (AD 23–79).

In 1476 the islands became the property of Ferdinand and Isabella of Aragon-Castille and in 1479 totally Spanish. Following colonisation the islands lent their name to various European exports: the popular, sweet *canary wine* much loved by Shakespeare's Falstaff; a spirited sixteenth-century court dance often mentioned by Shakespeare, Nash and others; and, of course, the little songbirds, known as *canary birds,* which arrived in England in the sixteenth century. The plumage of the captive cagebirds is now the *canary yellow* of the paintbox, a result of interbreeding over the centuries.

◆ *Kennel* is from *canis* with a suffix: *canile* was where dogs spent the night, *ovile* was a sheepfold where a sheep, *ovis,* was kept.

Canaille is *canis* with a collective suffix, 'pack of dogs'. It is a rather self-conscious French borrowing today, meaning 'the rabble, the common herd'. From a group of dogs to 'a little dog' – Latin *canicula* has given us today *chenille*, with a hairy surface that must have been reminiscent to its eighteenth century inventor of the hair of a little dog (see also **caterpillar**).

One word that is not connected with *canis*, though many have made the link, is *cannibal*. In fact it comes from *Canibales*, a fierce people in the West Indies (see under that entry).◆

See **gorilla.**

cancel

to withdraw, to nullify

... no one could have made head or tail of the queer gibberish murmured in front of the statue of Francis, Duke of Bedford, save that the name of Ralph occurred frequently in very strange connexions, as if, having spoken it, she wished, superstitiously, to cancel *it by adding some other word that robbed the sentence with his name in it of any meaning.*
(Virginia Woolf, NIGHT AND DAY, 1919)

... if you fail her, by which I mean cancelling *the account at Harrod's, or short-changing her on winter in Jamaica, she'll be back to me in a jiffy mewing for support – and guilty wife or no, she may be entitled to get it.*
(Anthony Shaffer, SLEUTH, 1970)

John Kennedy complained he was 'reading more but enjoying it less,' and canceled *the White House subscription to an unfriendly daily.*
('Clinton's hot kitchen', THE PROGRESSIVE, January, 1994)

For a moment, she thought of cancelling *the migraine.*
(Leslie Wilson, Market Choice in GOOD HOUSEKEEPING, November 1994)

The verb to *cancel* has the same root as *chancellor*. In Roman times, when a deed, a legal document or contract was nullified it was done by crossing it through horizontally and vertically, the result being a lattice pattern. This gave the verb *cancellāre*, 'to score out in a lattice form', from *cancellī*, 'latticework'. Medieval legal practices followed the Roman pattern and so Old French had *canceller* from which Middle English borrowed *cancellen*. This original sense of *cancel*, 'to cross out', is still current though today a simple line serves the purpose, without need for the original strict criss-cross scoring pattern.

Towards the end of the fifteenth century the verb was applied figuratively to mean 'to annul, to invalidate', with regard to debts, promises, appointments, etc. This remains very much the principal use today.

◆ The east end of a church has been known as the *chancel* since about 1300 and similarly takes its name from the Latin *cancellī*. Formerly this area, which contains the altar and the choir stalls, was separated off from the main body of the building by a latticed screen.◆

See **chancellor**.

cancer

a malignant tumour, a diseased growth

Even the most uxorious of men would prefer their wives to have a lover rather than an interior designer. Like cancer, *the first outbreak of interior designeritis may be small – a charmingly re-upholstered chair in the drawing-room – and then, before you*

can say £20,000, he has spread through the whole house.
(THE TELEGRAPH MAGAZINE, 14 January 1995)

The name of this much-feared disease originates in the Greek *karkinos*, meaning 'a crab' (from Sanskrit *karkata*, 'a crab', possibly from *karkara*, 'hard'). According to the second-century Greek physician Galen, the malignant tumour was so named because the swollen and distorted veins in the surrounding tissue looked something like the legs of a crab.

Karkinos was taken into Latin as *cancer*, where it meant both 'crab' and 'tumour', and from there was borrowed into Old English as a medical term, *cancor* or *cancer*, the medial *c* having a hard *k* pronunciation, after the Latin. To reflect this, and also influenced by the pronunciation of the Norman French *cancre*, the common spelling from the Middle English period onwards became *canker*.

Over time, however, *canker* came to be widely applied to ulcerations in general and the need was felt for a more specific medical term. Around the turn of the seventeenth-century *cancer* was reintroduced from Latin, but this time pronounced with a soft medial *c*. For the next century, *canker* and *cancer* overlapped in meaning; nowadays, *cancer* continues to refer to the malignant tumour, whereas *canker* is restricted to various rotting diseases that afflict plants and to sores on animals.

Cancer in its astrological senses was borrowed direct from Latin in the fourteenth century.

◆ The Greek noun *karkinōma* derives from *karkinos* and was borrowed into English as *carcinoma* by way of Latin in the eighteenth century.◆

candidate

someone who seeks nomination for a job or position

Julian Critchley's Parting Shots *included a poignant snapshot of our beleaguered Prime Minister as a 16-year-old lad. He had applied for a job as a bus conductor. There were three* candidates. *Young Mr Major lost out to a more limber West Indian woman applicant and then had to walk all the way home from the south London bus depot. The story was told with rueful affection.*
(DAILY TELEGRAPH, 10 May 1994)

While it is difficult to believe now, Kennedy was not a particularly popular presidential candidate *– he beat Richard Nixon by the narrowest of margins – but as soon as he became president he immediately gained stature because of the authority of his office.*
(INDEPENDENT, 26 May 1994)

One day when I was seven my mother drove me and Thomas to Birmingham, where she was a prospective Labour candidate, *and we spent the day at a local elementary school. Of course, she had never been anywhere near a state school in her life. She had no idea that we required lunch money, so we sat there like a pair of bewildered prats and had no lunch.*
(Lady Antonia Fraser about her mother, Lady Elizabeth Longford, in THE SUNDAY TIMES MAGAZINE, 18 December 1994)

In Shakespeare's play of that name (1584), Titus Andronicus is begged to stand for election as emperor of Rome by the people's Tribune, Marcus Andronicus:

Titus Andronicus, the people of Rome,
Whose friend in justice thou hast ever been,
Send thee by me, their Tribune and their trust,
This palliament of white and spotless hue;

And name thee in election for the empire
With these our late-deceased Emperor's
sons:
Be candidatus *then, and put it on,*
And help to set a head on headless Rome.
(Act 1, scene 1)

The allusion is to a practice of ancient Rome, where anyone who put himself forward for election to an office would appear in public dressed in a white toga, a symbolic statement that his character was spotless and that he was therefore upright and trustworthy. Such a man was described as *candidatus*, that is 'wearing a white robe' (from *candidus*, 'brilliant white'). The word, if not the customary white toga, entered English in the first half of the seventeenth century. Applied originally to someone seeking an appointment to public office or position of honour, its use was extended in the mid-eighteenth century when it acquired the sense of 'aspirant' – Johnson, for example, describes someone as '*a* canditate *for literary fame*'. At the same period, the term could foretell a less positive outcome, just as it can today. Goldsmith writes in THE VICAR OF WAKEFIELD (1766): *If ever there was a* candidate *for Tyburn, this is one.* Tyburn, lest we forget, was the place for public executions in the heart of London until 1783.

◆ The adjective *candid*, meaning 'frank, straightforward and honest' shares the same root as *candidate*. Latin *candidus*, 'gleaming white', itelf derived from *candēre*, 'to be white, to glow'. Quite a number of other words come from the same source: *(in)candescent, candour, candle, candelabra, chandelier, incendiary, incense.*◆

For another word whose etymology lies with Roman politics, see **ambition**.

cannibal

a man-eating savage

I knew I had seen eyes like that before and then, all at once, I remembered the cannibals *– half a dozen dissolute-looking, furtive-mannered men shackled outside the Vila court house years ago. My father had said, 'See their eyes? That's how you spot a* cannibal, *Sandy, and it's worth bearing in mind in case chaps like that ever ask you to lunch.'*
(Alexander Frater, CHASING THE MONSOON, 1990)

The most northerly regions of South America and the islands of the Lesser Antilles were once occupied by people called *Galibi*. Also current was a related form *Carib* and a dialectal variant *Caniba*. The name signified 'valiant men' and this was borne out by their legendary ferocity. When Christopher Columbus stumbled across some of these people on 18 October 1492, he heard the name *Caniba* and called them *Canibales*. Imagining himself to be on mainland China he easily confused the name with that of the Grand Khan and rejoiced. He was, in fact, on Cuba.

Over time the Spaniards became convinced that the natives in those parts ate human flesh so that, eventually, Columbus's term *Canibal* became synonymous with 'man-eater'. The word excited the European imagination with dark tales of the New World and was also user-friendly – until the sixteenth-century European languages had been stuck with the ponderous classical term *anthropophagus*. The acceptance of the new word was probably helped by an etymology – popular but false – that attempted to derive the term from Spanish *can* and Latin *canis*, both meaning 'dog'.

The word was used in English from the mid-sixteenth century onwards, though the spelling with a double *n* dates only from the second half of the seventeenth century. Shakespeare mentions *cannibals* in his plays and appears to have enjoyed manipulating the various forms from which the word originally derived to coin the name *Caliban* for the semi-human island savage in THE TEMPEST (1611).

After Columbus's landfall in Cuba, further exploration of the region in the succeeding weeks lead him to Haiti where, to his confusion, he heard the form *Carib. Caribbean,* an adjective applied to some of the West Indian islands and the surrounding sea, derives from *Carib,* which is still used as an adjective in its own right to describe the language and culture of areas once occupied by these people.

carnival

fair or festival

Gooch shut out the sights and sounds of a rowdy Australian carnival *to make a measured, deadly earnest 129 and to give England a seven-wicket victory in their first semi-serious contest of the tour.*
(DAILY MAIL, 26 October 1994)

. . . for three days in February Binche [in Belgium] is transported back to the Midddle Ages, as townsfolk metamorphose into dancers or 'Gilles', to take part in what is undoubtedly the most authentic Mardi Gras carnival *left in Europe.*
(WEEKEND TELEGRAPH, 21 January 1995)

Scholars have identified *carnival* as a continuation of pagan springtime feasts in the ancient world which revolved around the concept of death and renewal. More particularly they say that *carnival* evolved from the Roman feast of *Saturnalia* which celebrated the sowing of the year's harvest and was marked by a period of excessive revelry. Saturnalia was such a popular festival that it continued to be celebrated in Christian Rome. The church could not approve of its pagan character but was reluctant to deny the people their festivities. It sought, therefore, to lend them a new significance. Thus, Saturnalia became *carnival.*

The word comes from the Old Italian *carnelevare* and the subsequent *carnelevale,* ultimately contracting to *carnevale.* It is associated with the medieval Latin *carnelevāmen.* The basic sense is 'the putting away of meat' (from *carō,* 'flesh' and *levāre,* 'to remove, to put aside') and reflects the fact that the Roman Catholic church required its members to abstain from eating meat during Lent.

This meaning and the ultimate form of the word strengthened a persistent but erroneous supposition that the word derived from *carne,* 'flesh' and *vale,* 'farewell' and thus meant 'Farewell, O flesh', a statement of self-denial. This folk etymology has had wide circulation since at least the time of John Florio, an influential linguist and translator, in the late sixteenth century and was perpetuated by Byron in these lines from BEPPO (1818):

This feast is named the Carnival, *which being*
Interpreted, implies 'farewell to flesh' –
So called, because the name and thing agreeing,
Through Lent they live on fish both salt and fresh.

Certainly the *carnival* season was seen as a last fling, a chance to enjoy and indulge oneself in revelry and feasting before the sombre and reflective season of Lent. As such it received the blessing and even the patronage of the papacy. Pope Paul II (1464–71), for instance, was a vain man who loved spectacle and show. During his papacy masked balls were organised and races of different kinds took place in Rome. Some of the expense fell on the Jews, who were forced to contribute to the merrymaking. The *carnival* season varied in length. In general, it stretched from Epiphany (6 January) to Mardi gras (literally 'fat Tuesday') or Shrove Tuesday. More specifically, however, it was confined to the last few days before Lent or, possibly the original use, to just the eve of Lent.

Carnival customs first spread throughout Italy and then through Catholic Europe. From there settlers in Catholic colonies in the New World introduced the festivities to the American continent. Today *Carnival* is still celebrated widely, most spectacularly throughout Brazil and in New Orleans in North America.

The word *carnival* entered English in the mid-sixteenth century to describe the pre-Lenten revelries in Europe, but rarely those in England. By the end of the century the word was being applied loosely to refer to any kind of riotous celebration or festival not connected with any particular season. In modern English a *carnival* is also a procession with floats followed by sideshows.

For words on a related theme see also **Lent** and **Shrovetide**.

carol

a song of joy, particularly on a religious theme at Christmas

In the fore-court, lit by the dim rays of a horn lantern, some eight or ten little field-mice stood in a semi-circle . . . As the door opened, one of the elder ones that carried the lantern was just saying, 'Now then, one, two, three!' and forthwith their shrill little voices uprose on the air, singing one of the old-time carols *that their forefathers composed in fields that were fallow and held by frost, or when snow-bound in chimney corners, and handed down to be sung in the miry street to lamp-lit windows at Yule-time.*

(Kenneth Grahame, THE WIND IN THE WILLOWS, 1908)

. . . he was in no shape to deny anyone anything. I really believe that if at this point in the proceedings I had tried to touch him for a fiver, he would have parted without a cry.

'Of course, of course, of course, of course,' he said, carolling *like one of Jeeves's larks on the wing. 'I am sure that Pinker will make an excellent vicar.'*

(P G Wodehouse, STIFF UPPER LIP, JEEVES, 1963)

At about this time of year, Malcolm Stacey will be putting up his traditional Christmas decorations. Nothing showy, you understand, just an artificial tree, a few cards, and a sign on his front door that says 'Danger: Subsiding Porch'. 'It's a much better way of keeping carol *singers away than turning all the lights off and pretending to be out,' he says. Just to make sure, though, he ties his gate with wire to make it difficut to open.*

(THE SUNDAY TIMES, 18 December 1994)

Although the exact etymology of this word is disputed, authorities agree that it has a classical origin. In medieval Europe a *carole* was a ring-dance where men and women joined hands to form a circle and then sang and danced to a musical accompaniment. *Carole* was borrowed directly into Middle English from Old French around the turn of the fourteenth century. However literary references in Old French are much older and date back to the middle of the twelfth century. The Swiss Romance and Old Provençal forms (*coraula* and *corola* respectively) are just some of the indications that originally the word began with *co-*. Some authorities consider that the meaning of the word was 'circle' and attempt to link it to Latin *corolla*, 'coronet'. However, most etymologists consider that *carole* evolved from Late Latin *choraula*, 'choral song'. In earlier Latin this same term referred to the instrumentalist who piped the accompaniment for the *chorus*, the word coming from Greek *khoraulēs* which was a compound of *khoros*, 'chorus' and *aulos*, 'reed instrument'.

Carols were sung in Latin, English or, frequently, a mixture of the two, as in the *Boar's Head Carol* below. The subject matter was not prescribed except that *carols* were songs of joy whose main feature was the repetition of a burden or refrain. Christmas was a festival that was celebrated with much enthusiasm and songs with similar repetitions were composed in honour of the season. These also became known as *carols*, whether they were ring-dances or not, by virtue of their refrains. This jolly carol was written to accompany the bringing in of the boar's head at the feast:

Caput apri defero,
Reddens laudes Domino.
The bore's heed in hande bring I,
With garlands gay and rosemary.
I pray you all synge merelye
Qui estis in convivio.

The bore's heed, I understande,
Is the chief service in this lande,
Look wherever it be fande,
Servite cun cantico.
Be gladde lordes both more and ladde,
For this hath ordeyned our stewarde,
To cheere you all this Christmasse,
The bore's heed with mustarde.
Caput apri defero,
Reddens laudes Domino.
(Published by Wynkyn de Worde, 1521)

Others, such as this fifteenth century carol, celebrated the religious significance of the season:

I sing of a maiden
That is makeles;
King of all kings
To her son she ches.

He came al so still
There his mother was,
As dew in April
That falleth on the grass.
He came al so still
To his mother's bour,
As dew in April
That falleth on the flour.

He came al so still
There his mother lay,
As dew in April
That falleth on the spray.
Mother and maiden
Was never none but she;
Well may such a lady
Goddes mother be.

The once popular ring-dances have long since passed away but the celebration of Christmas has gathered up traditions over the centuries that defy change and are still with us today.

◆ Greek *khoros*, 'chorus', besides being ultimately responsible for English *chorus* by way of Latin *chorus*, is also the source of *choir* (from *quire*, from Middle English *quere*, borrowed from Old

French *cuer*, from medieval Latin *chorus*, 'church choir', from Latin *chorus*, 'dance, chorus', from Greek *khoros*).◆

carouse

to indulge in a drinking bout

Monarchs reflected the spirit of the times. During World War 1, King George V had his court give up drink as a measure of austerity and commitment, a sharp contrast to the carousing *of his father as Prince of Wales at the end of the previous century.*
(Jancis Robinson, THE DEMON DRINK, 1988)

The word has its origins in medieval German drinking bouts. When drinking someone's health or celebrating a great event or victory, the assembled company would fill their glasses brim full and encourage one another to down the contents to the last drop, *garaus* (*gar*, 'completely', *aus*, 'out'). First the French (Old French *carous*), then the English and even the Spanish (*caraos*) followed suit. In the sixteenth century, therefore, *to quaff carouse* meant 'to drain one's cup', and *a carouse* was 'a toast', 'a generous measure drunk to the dregs':

Then in his cups you shall not see him shrink,
To the grand devil a carouze *to drink.*
(Michael Drayton [1563-1631], MOONCALF)

By the late seventeenth century a *carouse* had come to mean 'a drinking bout'. *Carousal* was an eighteenth century coinage for the same thing.

Today, the verb *to carouse* (which also dates back to the sixteenth century) is more commonly used.

For another word originating in a drinking refrain, see **lampoon**.

cartoon

a humorous or satirical drawing

Even the daily papers woke up to the disturbances at last, and popular notes appeared here, there, and everywhere concerning the volcanoes upon Mars. The serio-comic periodical PUNCH, I remember, made a happy use of it in the political cartoon.
(H G Wells, THE WAR OF THE WORLDS, 1898)

Part of the chapter on motivation deals with obesity, and the discussion of theories of why we stuff ourselves is capped by a cartoon *in which a chef tells a fat blimp 'As far as I know there's no such thing as a cream puff diet.' Such touches make one go on reading. . .*
(NEW SCIENTIST, 1983)

Cartoon derives from the Italian *cartone* which denoted 'thick paper, pasteboard' and was itself an augmentative of *carta*, 'paper'. When preparing their work – a fresco, tapestry or oil painting, for instance – artists made preliminary full-size drawings on pasteboard. In time, *cartone* was transferred from the material used for the drawing to the sketch itself, a transference which was complete by the time the word was borrowed into English in the seventeenth century, possibly by way of French *carton*. This specialised use of the word is still current but a more familiar modern meaning emerged in the 1840s when satirical papers such as PUNCH published full-page comic sketches which they termed *cartoons*. These were the forerunners of the outline drawings in present-day newspapers and periodicals which make a humorous or satirical statement on daily life or current affairs. Animated cartoons date from around 1915.

◆ *Papyrus* is an aquatic reedlike plant, indigenous to Egypt. From it was made the material on which the ancients used to write. The Greeks used the word *khartēs* to describe 'a leaf of papyrus', which was borrowed into Latin as *charta* (or *carta*). In turn the Latin was the origin of a number of English words. Several of these, like *cartoon*, came through Italian.

card (15th cent): from Old French *carte* and Italian *carta*, ' card'

cartel (16th cent): from French *cartel*, from early Italian *cartello*, diminutive of *carta*, 'paper'. The early sense of the word was 'a written letter of challenge'. In the late seventeenth century it was used in times of war to denote 'a formal written agreement for the exchange of prisoners'. Only in the twentieth century, under the influence of German *kartell*, did it acquire its more familiar present-day meaning of 'an agreement between independent businesses to regulate marketing, output and prices'.

carton (19th cent): from French *carton*, a borrowing of Italian *cartone* , 'pasteboard'

cartridge (16th cent): corruption of French *cartage*, 'a charge of powder for a pistol'. This was a variant of *cartouche*, a borrowing of Italian *cartoccio*, 'cornet of paper', augmentative of *carta*. The term arose from the practice of wrapping shot in a folded, cornet-shaped piece of paper, ready measured for easy use. From here military science applied the term to the tubular cases of propellent and primer of the *cartridge* proper.

chart (late 16th cent): from Old French *charte*, 'card, map', from Latin *charta*, which later developed the sense 'map' besides that of 'paper'. *Chart* was introduced to replace *carte* and *card* , both of which were used to mean 'map' from the fifteenth to the seventeenth centuries. *Carte* is now obsolete, but may have influenced the development of *cartographer* in the nineteenth century.

charter (13th cent): Middle English *chartre*, from Old French *chartre*, from Latin *chartula*, 'a small leaf of paper, a deed', diminutive of *charta*.◆

---

cataract

---

1. a very large cascade, a waterfall
2. rapids on a river
3. an opacity of the lens of the eye, causing impaired vision

The photograph was certainly very off-coloured. An unkind critic might easily have misinterpreted that dim surface. It was a dull grey landscape, and as I gradually deciphered the details of it I realized that it represented a long and enormously high line of cliffs exactly like an immense cataract *seen in the distance, with a sloping, tree-clad plain in the foreground.*
(Sir Arthur Conan Doyle, THE LOST WORLD, 1912)

The survey also came up with 10 reported cases of cataracts, *which can also be caused by radiation exposure. The condition is, however, almost unknown among healthy men of the same age as those in the survey. This is a 'strong indication that some of those involved (in the sample of 330) had received radiation greatly in excess of a safe dose,' according to a letter in* The Lancet *from a group of doctors who support the call for an independent inquiry into the atom bomb tests. Meanwhile, the MoD has yet to decide.*
(NEW SCIENTIST, 1983)

The Greek word *kataraktēs*, meaning 'a rushing or swooping down' (from *katarassein,* 'to dash down', from *kata-*, 'down' and *rassein,* 'to strike'), was used figuratively to denote a plunging thing: this might be a swooping bird, for instance, or a waterfall rushing headlong, or a plummeting portcullis. The word became *cataracta* in Latin where it meant 'waterfall', 'floodgate', 'portcullis', senses which Old French retained when it borrowed the term as *cataracte.*

Its use in Middle English was restricted to 'floodgate', as in the expression *cataracts of heaven,* ('the floodgates of heaven' – from the French *cataractes du ciel*), which supposedly controlled the rainfall. Late sixteenth-century English then used the word to denote 'a mighty waterfall tumbling over a sheer drop', a sense that had been common in Latin and Old French.

In French and then in English from the mid-sixteenth century onwards, the ancient application to a 'portcullis' became an important medical term when *cataract* was figuratively applied to the 'opacity of the eye lens' which impairs vision. The apparent reasoning was that the cataract obscures vision in the same way that a portcullis obstructs a gateway. It gradually replaced *web in the eye,* an earlier term for the condition dating back to the fourteenth century. A fifteenth century manuscript prescribed '*succle [honeysuckle], a good medycyne for ye web in ye eye*' – later equally efficacious against cataracts.

caterpillar

the larva of a butterfly or moth

Ah, what's a butterfly? At best
He's but a caterpillar *drest.*
(John Gay, FABLES, 1727)

In the light of the moon a little egg lay on a leaf. One Sunday morning the warm sun came up and – pop! – out of the egg came a tiny and very hungry caterpillar.
(Eric Carle, THE VERY HUNGRY CATERPILLAR, 1970)

If the climate in this country truly becomes warmer, the Summer Fruit Tortrix Moth will tell us. Its caterpillars *can ruin orchards by feeding on apples, eating away the surface and making the fruit unsaleable.*
(GUARDIAN, 14 April 1994)

A vivid visual imagination is required to appreciate the origin of this strange word. To the medieval French eye, the hairy varieties of *caterpillar* resembled cats, giving rise to the Old French *chatepelose* and its northern dialect variant *catepelose,* 'hairy cat' (from *cate,* 'female cat' and *pelose,* the feminine form of the adjective *pelous* 'hairy'). This was a not uncommon association – the Lombards referred to a *caterpillar* as a 'cat or kitten' and the Swiss as a 'devil's cat'. Even today, we refer to the soft, downy, caterpillar-like flowers of willows and hazels as *catkins.*

Middle English borrowed *catyrpel* from the French. The later addition of the suffix *-er* to the English word, to give *caterpiller,* was probably influenced by *pilour* and *piller,* 'a pillager or plunderer', because caterpillars were destructive to crops. These two words were common in the sixteenth and seventeenth centuries. Indeed, in this period *caterpiller* itself (as it was then regularly spelt) was used synonymously with *piller.* It also had the secondary figurative meaning of 'an extortioner'.

The modern spelling with a final *-ar* is owed to Dr Johnson (1709–84). This was, some claim, possibly under the influence of the separate word *pillar* ('column'), although the evidence is less than clear.

Incidentally, the humble caterpillar provides more evidence of a faculty of vivid imagination in the French. Their modern term for caterpillar is *chenille* which comes from *canicula*, a Latin word meaning 'little dog'. But perhaps they are surpassed in invention by the Scots, who had *hairy woubit*, meaning 'woolly bear'.

See **butterfly**.

catgut

a tough cord, originally made from twisted, dried intestines

Their music had a dismal sound, for half were out of time and a few among their fellows sometimes allowed an untutored bow to scrape across the gut.
(Eric Linklater, JUAN IN AMERICA, 1931)

'This is the oldest stringed bass in the world,' says Gnawa rocker Hassan Hakmoun, taking out his sintir. Pointing to the instrument's resonating area, the Moroccan-born Brooklyn resident explains, 'This is skin from a camel's neck. The body is from a nut wood tree. The string is catgut. *I added the tuning pegs when I moved to America seven years ago.' The sintir's neck resembles a three-foot length of one-inch doweling with two tuning pegs at the head.*
(Hank Bordowitz, GUITAR PLAYER, July 1994)

Musical instruments and tennis rackets never were strung with the intestines of a cat, neither were wounds stitched together with them in surgery. The dried, twisted guts used are those of a sheep or, occasionally, a horse. Three theories are advanced for the appearance of *cat* in this sixteenth century word. Some authorities suggest it originates with *kit*, both a word for a small violin and a kitten. Others note that *catling* was the word for the string of an instrument and, in the plural, for stringed instruments in general. Thus the fiddler in Shakespeare's ROMEO AND JULIET (1597) is called Simon *Catling* (Act 4, scene 5) and in TROILUS AND CRESSIDA (1602) we find:

What music will be in him when Hector has knocked out his brains, I know not: but I am sure none; unless the fidler Apollo get his sinews to make catlings *on.*
(Act 3, scene 3)

Finally comes the suggestion that the word is a humorous coinage, the sound drawn from the strings as the bow glides over them being reminiscent of that made by a courting cat.

Any might be the correct source but, equally, all three may be wrong.

cemetery

a burial ground

Far from famous sepulchres, toward a lonely cemetery, *my heart, like a muffled drum, goes beating a funeral march.*
(Charles Baudelaire, LE GUIGNON, 1861)

The fence around a cemetery *is foolish, for those inside can't get out and those outside don't want to get in.*
(Arthur Brisbane, THE BOOK OF TODAY, 1923)

'Due to industrial action, the cemetery *will be run by a skeleton staff.'*
(Peter Gammons, ALL PREACHERS GREAT AND SMALL, 1989)

Here lapped in hallowed slumber Saon lies,
Asleep, not dead; a good man never dies.
(Callimachus, c. 260–240 BC)

Many common words and expressions connected with death are euphemisms. When Saon of Acanthus 'fell asleep', as the epitaph for him by

Callimachus suggests, he was naturally 'laid to rest' in a 'dormitory'. *Cemetery* comes from the Greek word *koimētērion*, which strictly meant 'a sleeping-room, a dormitory'. It was subsequently used to denote a 'burial chamber' by early Christian writers. During the first eight centuries or so the Late Latin borrowing *coemētērium* was used to refer to the Roman catacombs and it is in this particular sense that the word first came into Middle English in the fourteenth century. The word was not applied to a churchyard until the 1480s and first denoted a burial-ground in general in the early seventeenth century.

The theme of the grave and the cemetery is so universal that it has made its way into many international sayings:

Six feet of earth make all men equal
(George Herbert, JACULA PRUDENTUM, 1640)

The grave is the general meeting place
He who seeks equality should go to a cemetery
(German Proverb)

For more words on a funereal theme, see **coffin**, **hearse**, and **sarcophagus**.

cesspool, cesspit

a drainage pit for effluent

'What about the goldfish, mummy? Will they eat the eggies?' asked my daughter. 'Yes,' said the frog expert on the Herpetofauna Conservation helpline, 'you bet your life they will. And any tadpoles that hatch.'

Hence the arrival of an expensive three-foot glass tank, shoehorned on to a kitchen work-surface and filled with spawn, a fiddly pump, and little bags of gravel and amphibian feed . . . The tank made the house smell like a cesspit. *It defied all brands of freshener. My daughter held her nose when she got home from school. Fortunately, juvenile tea-time visitors seemed able to ignore the odour, but my parents made excuses when asked to dinner.*
(WEEKEND TELEGRAPH, 14 May 1994)

Since the *pool* element of this word is self-evident, then it must follow that *cess* is an old term for 'muck and mire', 'nightsoil and sewage'. This is the line that a number of commentators on this word have taken. As a result the origins of *cess* have been sought from sources as varied as *cess*, 'bog', Italian *cesso*, 'privy' (from Latin *secessus*, 'privy, drain') or dialect words such as *suss*, 'hogwash' or *soss* 'muck' (proposed from the form *suspool*).

Sadly all of these ingenious suggestions are inconclusive. More probable is a theory which treats the word as a whole rather than as a compound and therefore makes no etymological connection with *pool* at all.

THE ANNALLS OF IPSWICHE (1583) contain a reference to the form *cesperalle*, used to denote a 'cesspool'. It appears to be a variant of *suspiral*, which in the fifteenth century denoted a water-pipe or air-vent but which, in the sixteenth century, was also sometimes applied to a cesspool. *Suspiral* was a borrowing from Old French *souspirail* which ultimately derived from Latin *suspirare*, 'to breathe' or 'to sigh' (a verb applicable as much to deep breathing as to the sighs of a love-sick maiden, and source of the now practically defunct poetical verb *suspire*).

If this is the correct origin, then the *pool* element of the modern word is merely a folk etymology inspired by visions of collected waste and effluent. *Cesspit* then would be a logical nineteenth-century variant.

chancellor

a high-ranking official

A lot of people aren't sure of the difference between the Chancellor *and the President in Austria, but it's quite simple. The* Chancellor *decides national policy and runs the country, while the President rounds up the Jews.*
(Bill Bryson, NEITHER HERE NOR THERE, 1991)

On the day waste in the public sector was in the spotlight the Chancellor *of the Exchequer was attending a meeting of the World Economic Forum in the Swiss ski resort of Davos. He left on Thursday, made a six-minute speech and returned on Sunday.*
(THE TIMES, 2 February 1994)

The Lord Chancellor may not be flattered to know that the office in which he takes such pride began with a humble lattice-fence. In the Roman Empire a *chancellor* was a low-ranking officer, an usher, who stood at the lattice screen or fence which separated off the judgement seat in a law court, and announced those persons who were permitted to enter. He took the title of his job from the lattice screen (*cancelli*, 'lattice-work' from *cancellus* 'a grating'). Later, in the Eastern Empire, the *chancellor* discharged the duties of a secretary. In time, he was also given certain additional judicial responsibilities and, eventually, the duties of overseer. Gradually, therefore, the role of *chancellor* became more prestigious.

Edward the Confessor was probably responsible for creating the office of chancellor in England. The title was given to the king's secretary who was accountable for all documents of state and keeper of the king's seal. Under the Norman kings the office developed an increasingly important judicial role because of the large number of appeals submitted to the king's justice. In early times the position was usually occupied by a churchman who was also the king's confessor, the 'keeper of the king's conscience' and so he must, even today, be a member of the Established Church in England. The chancellor's power gradually increased until it was second in state only to that of the sovereign. The present-day Lord Chancellor in England is not only the head of the judiciary but also the speaker of the House of Lords and, usually, a senior cabinet minister.

The title chancellor is also held by the Chancellor of the Exchequer, an appointment that originated in the reign of Henry III, and the Chancellor of the Duchy of Lancaster. It is an ancient administrative title in the church and the name given to the head of a university. Some countries – Germany, for instance – have chosen the title for their chief minister of state.

◆ The office pertaining to *chancellor* was first written *chancellery*, subsequently becoming *chancelry* and *chancery*.◆

See **cancel** and **exchequer**.

chapel

1. a private place for prayer and worship
2. a non-conformist meeting house
3. a separate area of an Anglican or Catholic church or cathedral
4. a local group of a Trades' Union or club

The chapel *is carved from the grotto where the half-legendary St Marina lived – a virgin clothed as a monk, who saved*

a dying child with her miraculous milk;
and women whose milk has run dry come
to her altar and tend her candles.
(Colin Thubron, THE HILLS OF ADONIS, 1968)

The whole history of this word is contained in a holy relic; the cape of St Martin of Tours. Martin's father was an officer in the Roman army and Martin, too, began a military career. One day in about the year AD 337, he came across a shivering beggar. Moved with compassion, Martin tore his cloak in two so that he could share it. That night, in a dream, he saw Christ wrapped in the piece of cloak that he had given away. Martin became a Christian and, because he would no longer fight, left the army. After years of preaching and conflict with church authorities, followed by a period as a recluse, Martin became a follower of St Hilary, Bishop of Poitiers and eventually, in 372, was made Bishop of Tours. During his twenty-five-year episcopate, Martin was zealous in his efforts to reach the heathen. Upon his death his following spread rapidly and his shrine at Tours became one of the foremost objects of pilgrimage in France. Artistic representations show Martin sharing his cloak with the beggar.

This cloak was treasured by the Frankish kings who used to carry it into battle. It was kept in a sanctuary called the *cappella* (Medieval Latin 'little cloak', diminutive of the Latin *cappa*, 'cloak'). Later the same word was applied to other sanctuaries containing holy relics and later still extended to buildings designated for Christian worship. *Chapel* was borrowed into Middle English from Old French *chapele* in the thirteenth century.

Ironically, in England during the second half of the seventeenth century, despite its Catholic origins *chapel* was often applied to the places of worship used by the growing numbers of nonconformist groups. The term conveniently set these simple meeting-places and their congregations apart from those of the established Church of England.

This same idea of the separation of a group of like-minded individuals is probably the motivation for a chapel of Trades' Union members, or the local branch of a club or association. Both are contexts in which the word is also found today.

◆ English *chaplain* comes from Medieval Latin *cappellānus*, which originally denoted 'one who had the charge of St Martin's cloak'. This same term was then applied to guardians of other sanctuaries. It became *chapelain* in Old French and was borrowed into Middle English as *chapeleyn* in the fourteenth century.◆

chauvinism

extreme, insensitive promotion of a cause or country

. . . schoolteachers are all at fault for what goes on in class; they are the ones who have a chance to change the youngsters' mentality . . . I did what I could; I never had them sing the 'Marseillaise,' the words are so bellicose, so chauvinistic *that for me it was out of the question to make them learn and recite it.*
(Emilie Carles, tr Avriel H Goldberger,
A WILD HERB SOUP, 1991)

The word derives from the name of Nicolas *Chauvin*, soldier and patriot, of Rochefort in France. During his service in the French army, Chauvin gained a reputation for tireless devotion to Napoleon and to his country. Admiration turned to ridicule, however, when Chauvin's behaviour was deemed fanatical. Although he was wounded many times he retired only when he was physically incapable of fighting on. His reward was a medal, a ceremonial sabre and a meagre pension of 200 francs a year, but still his patriotism and loyalty to his Emperor were undiminished. His reputation came to the notice of the playwrights Charles and Jean Cogniard, who exploited it in a musical comedy, LA COCARDE TRICOLORE (1831), where the character of the young Chauvin, idolator of Napoleon, sings the refrain '*Je suis francais, je suis* Chauvin'. The character became a favourite with other comedy writers and the word *chauvinisme,* 'excessive and bellicose patriotism', was born. The term, publicised by the plays, was first used in England around 1870. By the mid-twentieth century *chauvinism* was no longer exclusively linked to patriotism but was also applied to blind and intolerant belief in the pre-eminence of any cause or set of people, the most obvious example in recent times being that of *male chauvinism.*

See **jingoism.**

cheat

a swindler

Money did not come in quickly, for Ellen cheated *him by keeping it back, and dealing improperly with the goods he bought.*
(Samuel Butler, THE WAY OF ALL FLESH, 1903)

Cheat derives from the Middle English word *chete,* meaning 'an escheat'. In feudal times this was a forfeiture of a fief to the lord when the holder died without immediate legal heirs. (The word was from Old French *eschete,* 'that which falls as one's due', from the verb *escheoir,* 'to befall' from unattested Vulgar Latin *excadēre,* 'to fall out'.) The Crown, as a major landowner, was one of the main beneficiaries of this law. The officers appointed by the Exchequer both to manage these affairs and to collect rents and taxes were known as *escheators,* or sometimes as *cheaters.* Shakespeare uses *cheater* in this sense in THE MERRY WIVES OF WINDSOR (1602) when Falstaff says: *I will be a* cheater *to them both, and they shall be exchequers to me.* (Act 1, scene 3)

No tax-collector is ever a popular figure, but the fact that many escheators took advantage of their position to exploit people gave them a reputation of deviousness and dishonesty. From the early seventeenth century, then, *cheater* was used to denote 'one who practises fraud, a swindler'. Although this form persisted well into the nineteenth century and beyond, it has been superseded by the briefer *cheat,* which arose in the 1660s.

chemist

1. a scientist concerned with the properties of matter
2. a pharmacist, a druggist

Like all houses, Dr. Skinner's had its peculiar smell. In this case the prevailing odour was one of Russia leather, but along with it there was a subordinate savour as of a chemist's *shop. This came from a small laboratory in one corner of the room – the possession of which, together with the free chattery and smattery use of such words as 'carbonate,' 'hyposulphite,' 'phosphate,' and 'affinity,' were enough to convince even the most sceptical that Dr. Skinner had a profound knowledge of* chemistry.
(Samuel Butler, THE WAY OF ALL FLESH, 1903)

The history of *chemist* is fairly straightforward. The English word was borrowed from the French *chimiste* in the mid-sixteenth century. From it, by the end of that century, came *chemic, chemical* and *chemistry*. In those days the spelling varied (*chymist, chimist*), only settling to the contemporary form by the end of the eighteenth century.

What is not so obvious at first sight is the link between *chemist* and *alchemist*. The latter had been in English since the fourteenth century; it denoted both 'a scientist concerned with the properties of matter' (in other words, very much what we understand by *chemist* today) and, more narrowly, 'a transmuter of base metals into gold'. It was only from about 1600 onwards that *alchemist* took on its more magical, dark connotations. Similarly *chemist* had the same dual sense, so that, in its early uses and up into the eighteenth century, it sometimes meant what we understand by *alchemist* today. In other words, it took over a century for the divergent strands of meaning to differentiate themselves and become attached to separate forms.

The original Arabic form of the two words was *al-kīmiyā*, a borrowing from Greek *khēmeia*, 'the science of transmutation'. The probable source is *khyma*, 'fluid' and *khein*, 'to pour' – it is suggested that Greek *khēmeia* was concerned with extracting substances from plants. A more exotic but less likely theory is that since *alchemy* was assumed to have been first practised in Egypt and, since *Khemīa* is an ancient Greek word for 'Egypt', the art was named for its place of origin. In any event, the art attracted the Arabs, who took it to Spain in the Middle Ages. From there, it spread to the rest of Europe. Medieval Latin had both *alchymia* and the new Latin term *chimista* (having realised that *al-* was simply the definite article). From these there arose in medieval French *alquemie* and *chimiste* respectively, the precursors of the English terms.

See **Words from Arabic**, (pages 10–11).

chess

a game for two people, each attempting to capture the other's king with 16 pieces, on a chequered board

Poe, for instance, really was morbid; not because he was poetical, but because he was specially analytical. Even chess *was too poetical for him; he disliked* chess *because it was full of knights and castles, like a poem. He avowedly preferred the black discs of draughts, because they were more like the mere black dots on a diagram.*
(G K Chesterton, ORTHODOXY, 1909)

Out here it seemed as though the people of England must be shaped in the body like the kings and queens, knights and pawns of the chessboard*, so strange were their differences, so marked and so implicitly believed in.*
(Virginia Woolf, THE VOYAGE OUT, 1915)

Another death for coherence was indicated early when Heseltine referred to the Russians as 'the most cold, calculating, chess*-playing people on Earth'. This made me lose track of his subsequent drift as I struggled to imagine how* chess*-playing came to have such a pejorative connotation for him. Had he been a dunce at it or did his present situation, despite the opportunity it affords for the histrionics he so loves, make him feel like a pawn?*
(NEW SCIENTIST, 1983)

The ancient game of *chess* was known in India as early as AD 500 where it was *chaturanga*, 'the four angas'; these were the four components of an army – horses, elephants, chariots and foot-soldiers. The game was adopted and adapted by the Persians and from there it caught the interest of the Arabs who were responsible for introducing it to Europe through Spain during the Moorish conquest. The game was brought to England at the time of the Norman conquest when it was popular at court. A mark of the game's popularity in the Middle Ages is that the second book published by Caxton in 1474 was THE GAME AND PLAYE OF CHESSE.

The arabic term *shāh* (itself from an earlier Persian form) gave a stem *scāc-* that became widespread in medieval Latin, Italian and French. The plural form of the stem, *scāci*, became in Old French *eschecs* and *eschès*, from which the Middle English *chess* was derived. It was in use before 1300.

The singular *scacus* was the base some centuries earlier for the meaning 'check' (a move that threatens the opponent's king), which spread into several north European languages in this sense. The immediate precursor of the English *check* is the Old French *echec*. It was in use by the early fourteenth century. From these earliest times the word has developed a range of figurative and metaphorical senses: a restaurant bill, a token (both especially in American English), a banker's draft (*cheque* in British English, a spelling perhaps influence by *exchequer*), a confirmation that everything is in order, a restraint or control, a sudden stop, and quite a number of others.

Checkmate is also associated with the root *shāh*, from the phrase *shāh māt*, literally 'the king is dead'. It reached English through Old French *eschec mat*.

See **exchequer**.

chocolate

1. a drink produced from processed cacao seeds
2. a sweet produced from processed cacao seeds

She happily volunteers her love, lust, need – whatever – for chocolate *by opening her fridge door to reveal a shelf full of* chocolate *bars. 'It is in my contract, I have to have* chocolate *available at all times . . .' I have no idea if she is joking.*
(GOOD HOUSEKEEPING, March 1994)

While the Swiss may claim to make the best chocolate, *our national love of this confection has spawned a host of specialist* chocolate *shops, a* chocolate *club with mail-order service and a* chocolate *society that holds* chocolate *weekends and* chocolate *tastings.*
(WEEKEND TELEGRAPH, 11 February 1995)

When Cortes entered the Aztec capital, Tenochtitlan, in 1519, the importance of the cocoa bean in the Aztec economy was immediately obvious since it was used for religious ritual, currency and trade. Besides this, the rulers and nobility enjoyed a drink made by roasting cocoa beans and crushing them to a paste which was mixed with water, chilli, honey, vanilla and powdered aromatic flowers. This was known as *xocolatl* in the Nahuatl language, a compound of *xococ*, 'bitter' and *atl*, 'water'. Bernal Diaz reported how the foaming drink was served to the Emperor Moctezuma in a golden cup before he visited his wives.

Naturally, when Cortes returned to Spain in 1528 he took the recipe for *xocolatl* and a supply of cocoa beans with him. *Chocolate*, as the Spaniards called it, immediately became a popular drink at court, although the recipe was modified somewhat: the chilli was omitted in favour of nutmeg, cinnamon and sugar. *Chocolate* was exported to Spain in paste form. However, since supplies of cocoa beans were limited, the Spaniards kept their discovery a close secret, to the extent that, when a Spanish ship laden with chocolate paste was seized by English and Dutch pirates, the cargo was not recognised and was thrown overboard with cries of 'cacura de carneros' ('sheep shit').

For about a hundred years Spain enjoyed her cocoa monopoly, but gradually the secret leaked out, possibly through the comings and goings of missionary activity and certainly through the marriage of Philip II of Spain's daughter to Louis XIII of France, which took the beverage to the French court. Chocolate was probably introduced into England from France in the 1650s. It was available in coffee houses for a price. Samuel Pepys records a visit *'to a Coffee-house, to drink* jocolatte' in his diary for 24 November 1664, adding that it was 'very good'. Before long chocolate could be had at specialist *chocolate houses* such as the Cocoa Tree (see **sandwich**) and widespread cultivation of the cocoa bean made it more affordable. The English love-affair with chocolate had begun.

For the etymology of chocolate-drink ingredients, see **cocoa** and **vanilla**. For other beverages new to seventeenth-century tastebuds, see **coffee** and **tea**.

chore

a piece of boring, repetitive, menial work

The mushers who survive this arduous trail have . . .exhausted themselves with examining their teams' pads and claws each day, making and mending bootees for the footsore, rubbing Vick's ointment on the affected part when a bitch goes into heat, and attending to all the other chores *inseparable from running dogs.*
(DAILY TELEGRAPH, 4 March 1995)

Records of the Old English noun *cerr* go back to the writings of King Alfred in the ninth century. The word derived from the verb *cierran*, 'to turn', and meant 'a turn of work, a deed'. It is, perhaps, more recognisable in its Middle English form *char(re)*, 'a piece of work', a term which, from the fifteenth century, was particularly applied to menial, repetitive household tasks. Women called in to lend a hand with these on a daily basis have been called *charewomen*, *chairwomen* and finally *charwomen* since the end of the sixteenth century.

Chore was originally a dialectal variant of *char*. It also became the dominant form in American English. In 1789 Noah Webster, compiler of AN AMERICAN DICTIONARY OF THE ENGLISH LANGUAGE, had this to say about the word:

Chore . . . *is an English word . . . but in America, it is perhaps confined to New England. It signifies small domestic jobs of work, and its place cannot be supplied by any other single word in the language.*

The American influence doubtless helped chore to supercede *char*. The latter now only remains in *charwoman*.

◆ It is possible that *charcoal* also owes its origin to *char(e)*, in which case the sense would be 'turned into coal', for *coal* itself originally meant 'charcoal'. An alternative etymology, however, suggests that the term derives from Old French *charbon*, 'charcoal'◆

cigar

tightly-rolled tobacco leaves for smoking

And a woman is only a woman, but a good cigar *is a smoke.*
(Rudyard Kipling, THE BETROTHED, 1885)

There is a demon in him, for all the easy gaiety: it is as certain that this man will consume and destroy himself as that he will erect monuments to his undying memory. I have grasped the meaning of I.K.B.'s perpetual cigars*: he must have them, as furnaces must have chimneys – they are lit from within.*
(Graham Swift, EVER AFTER, 1992)

It might be supposed that the Spanish *cigarro*, from which English borrowed *cigar* in the eighteenth century, is derived from a West Indian language, since it was from this part of the New World that the Spaniards first brought tobacco and the native custom of rolling the leaves together to smoke them. This does not appear to be the case, however. There are a number of theories to account for the word; one is that it comes from a Mayan word *sicar*, meaning 'smoke'. Other etymologists have remarked upon the word's similarity to the Spanish *cigarra*, meaning 'grasshopper' – they see a resemblance between the creature's cylindrical body and tapering apex and the shape of a *cigar*. Others look to the word *cigarral* for an explanation. *Cigarrales* were country houses built for recreation and surrounded by orchards and gardens, in which tobacco could be grown; it is possibly a Cuban term for a tobacco nursery. All the suggestions are unproven speculations.

See **tobacco**.

coach

1. a horse-drawn vehicle, usually for carrying passengers, a carriage
2. a bus, comfortably equipped for longer journeys
3. a tutor, trainer

The coach *was swerving. The man on the motorbike was hovering nearer the front end of it. . . The* coach *went faster; the bike slipped back.*
(Jeremy Vine, THE WHOLE WORLD IN MY HANDS, 1994)

There are ways and ways of enjoying a holiday in North Africa. The first is to stay in the best hotels...You mix only with fellow tourists , make the obligatory coach *trips, buy a stuffed camel and send postcards.*
(INDEPENDENT WEEKEND, 28 January 1995)

. . . the King [George III] commissioned that incredible gilded concoction the state coach*, without which no coronation procession would be complete.*
(DAILY TELEGRAPH, 25 March 1995)

The coach takes its name from the Hungarian village of *Kocs* (pronounced 'kotch'). Here, in the second half of the fifteenth century a large horse-drawn carriage was produced known as the *kocsi szeker*, literally 'cart from Kocs'. The vehicle was apparently unsprung and uncovered and does not appear to have been in any way out of the ordinary. Nevertheless during the first half of the sixteenth century demand for it spread throughout Europe. In Germany it was known as the *cotschy wagen*, which was soon reduced to *kotsche*. This shortened German form was borrowed as *coche* into Spanish (where it remains as the modern word for 'car'), Portuguese and French. English borrowed *coche* from French in the mid-sixteenth century. The spelling *coach* dates from the beginning of the seventeenth century. The term has been used for a vehicle or carriage in horse-drawn, rail (nineteenth century) and motorised (twentieth century) transport ever since.

In the nineteenth century, there was a less obvious extension of the term. *Coach* as both 'private tutor' and 'sports trainer' originated in the latter half of that period, the idea being that they carried the trainees through to the goal on the back of their experience and expertise.

cocoa

a powder made from roasted and ground cocoa beans, used in a drink

Once, you might have boiled up a pan of milk because you knew you had trouble sleeping; now, apparently, you are more likely to drink a mug of cocoa *mid-afternoon because work is particularly stressful.*
(SUNDAY TIMES, 6 November 1994)

The *cocoa* tree is believed to be native to the Amazon rain forests. It was the Mayas who first discovered the properties of the beans and then began to cultivate them in the humid tropics of Central America. Cocoa beans were highly prized. They often featured in religious ceremonies. Roasted, ground and mixed with various spices and flavourings, they were made into a bitter 'chocolate' drink (see **chocolate**). They were also used for currency and were a trading commodity. One of the peoples who traded for beans was the Aztecs, who learnt to value them as much as the Mayas. The Aztecs lived in a dry arid area unsuitable for the cultivation of cocoa trees and so they became dependent upon the Mayas for their supplies. As they became more powerful, the Aztecs demanded beans as a tribute from their conquered neighbours.

The delights of the cocoa bean were revealed to Europeans in the sixteenth century, following Cortes's expedition to Mexico in 1517. In Nahuatl, the Aztec language, the beans were known as *cacahuatl* and this was borrowed into Spanish as *cacao.* Since supplies of beans were limited, the Spaniards kept the discovery of cocoa to themselves. For this reason references in sixteenth-century English texts are scant, but when they do occur the Spanish borrowing and three-syllable pronunciation, *cacao,* is used. By 1615 the closely guarded secret of cocoa and chocolate had been revealed and demand for the commodity grew, first in France and then in England, so that, after the mid-seventeenth century, references in English texts are more plentiful.

The Spanish borrowing *cacao* is still currently applied to the bean in English. In the early eighteenth-century, however, this was corrupted to *cocoa* which, since the 1780s, has been used to denote the powder obtained from the beans once they have been roasted and ground. This corruption was also originally pronounced with three syllables, but confusion over the spelling of this word and that of *coco* (as in *coconut*) helped to produce a two-syllable term (see **coconut**).

For further information on *cocoa,* see **chocolate**.

coconut

the seed of a type of palm, with a hard shell, and white flesh and milky fluid inside

We chatted about the rains. When I mentioned Trivandrum's great fiery prayer

meeting the physician smiled. 'Yes, yes, but there is really no need to go to all that trouble. If you break tender young coconuts *on a statue of Shiva as the priest chants certain mantras you will get rain. Within twenty-four hours. Absolutely guaranteed.'*
(Alexander Frater, CHASING THE MONSOON, 1990)

It's an odd sensation, settling down to write a piece which I know in advance will be read mainly by people with savage hangovers. I feel as if this column should be employing a specially subdued, reassuring typeface and non-rustle paper. I strongly recommend that you don't under any circumstances attempt to make a prairie oyster – in fact, don't even read the recipe. I mean, who wants to imagine eating raw eggs and Worcestershire sauce when they're feeling like this? And the other important advice I'd like to give any readers who are feeling at all queasy is: don't think about pink fairy cakes, especially not the kind with icky coconut *icing on top.*
(OBSERVER, 1 January 1995)

The *coconut* palm is native to the East Indies and consequently, since at least the sixth century, its fruit had been known as the *Indian nut*. In the late fifteenth century, however, the Portuguese began to use the term *coquo* for the fruit, becoming *coco* in the sixteenth century. The word meant 'grimace' and also 'goblin', and was apparently applied to the nut because the three dark indentations at its base suggested a horribly grinning face. English borrowed the term in the mid-sixteenth century, initially in the rather pedantic Latinised form *cocus*, but by the close of the century the Portuguese forms *coquo* and, more especially, *coco* were being used. The word was made into a compound with the addition of *nut* around 1613 and this gradually replaced *coco* altogether.

The publication of Dr Johnson's DICTIONARY (1755) brought long-lasting confusion to the spelling of the word. Johnson himself used the standard spelling *coco* in his writings, but in the dictionary this entry appears to have been confused with that for *cocoa*:

CO'COA. n.s. [coca, or coco, *Span. and Port.*] *A species of palm-tree, cultivated in the East amd West Indies. Miller.*

The result was that even careful writers were misled and misspelt the word. The poet William Cowper was one of these and, in her BOOK OF HOUSEHOLD MANAGEMENT (1861), Mrs Beeton instructs her readers, *'Whisk the eggs until they are very light; add the sugar gradually; then stir in the* cocoa-nut.' The confusion continues to this day, so that some modern dictionaries have *cocoanut* as an alternative spelling.

For more information on the confusion between *coconut* and *cocoa*, see **cocoa**.

coffee

a mildly stimulating drink made from coffee berries

English coffee *tastes like water that has been squeezed out of a wet sleeve.*
(Fred Allen, TREADMILL TO OBLIVION, 1954)

We prefer our coffee *as strong as love, as black as sin, and as hot as Hades.*
(Hale Boggs, House of Representatives, US Congress, 1960)

There was once an astute Arab goatherd who observed that his flock became skittish when allowed to browse upon a certain bush. Curious, he sampled a few of the berries himself and found them invigorating. This, at any rate, is the legend and indeed it is thought that *coffee* was originally made into a paste and eaten for its stimulating qualities. It was the Muslims who experimented with making a drink out of the beans while endeavouring to find a substitute for the wine they were forbidden to touch. *Coffee* was drunk in Cairo in the early sixteenth century but the stimulant was censured by strict Muslims. And then in 1524 the beverage was finally approved and was soon after enjoyed in other parts of the Muslim world and Europe (Brothwell, FOOD IN ANTIQUITY, 1969).

Coffee derives from the Arabic word *qahwah*. The significance of the term remains a mystery, however. Some Arab authorities, with an eye to its history, say it originally referred to a kind of wine, others hazard the theory that it derives in some way from *Kaffa*, the region of the former Abyssinia where the bush is indigenous. The Arabic word was borrowed as *kahweh* by the Turks and from there passed into all the European languages around 1600. Throughout the first half of the seventeenth century English writers attempted anglicised spellings of *kahweh*: *cahve*, *caffa*, *capha* and *cauphe* are amongst them. *Coffee* became a more frequent spelling, possibly under the influence of Italian *caffè*, in the second half of the century.

The beverage became popular in England when enterprising businessmen began to open *coffee houses* in the cities. These soon became the haunts of the professional classes who met there to discuss business and exchange news. Some say the first such establishment was opened in Oxford in 1649, others that it was in London in 1652 but, by the mid-1660s, London alone boasted over eighty of them. Nor did they serve only coffee. Tea and chocolate were also novelties in the seventeenth century and were often offered as well.

◆ Words we associate with light refreshment derive from foreign terms for *coffee*.

Café is a French word for both 'coffee' and ' coffee house' and was borrowed directly into English in the nineteenth century

Cafeteria (19th century) originated in American English and is from American-Spanish *cafetería*, 'coffee shop', from *cafetero*, 'coffee seller or maker', from *café*, 'coffee'

Caffeine, the stimulant chemical in coffee, tea and chocolate, is thought by some to derive from German *Kaffein* (from *Kaffee*, 'coffee', from French *café*, 'coffee'). Others, however, find the derivation direct from the French *caféine*.◆

For the etymologies of other beverages that became popular in the seventeenth century, see **chocolate** and **tea**.

coffin

a box to contain a body for disposal

So the clergy and choir came to meet us at the door, then turned and moved up the Cathedral nave chanting in solemn procession, 'I am the Resurrection and the Life saith the Lord'. But meanwhile there was a dreadful struggle at the steps leading up from the Cloisters to the door. The bearers were quite unequal to the task and the coffin *seemed crushingly heavy. There was a stamping and a scuffling, a mass of struggling men swaying to and fro, pushing and writhing and wrestling while the* coffin *sank and rose and sank again. Once or twice I thought the whole mass of men must have been down together with the*

coffin atop of them and some one killed or maimed at least. But now came the time of the fat chief mourner. Seizing his opportunity he rushed into the strife by an opening large and the rescued coffin *rose. At last by a wild effort and tremendous heave the ponderous* coffin *was borne up the steps and through the door into the Cathedral where the choristers, quite unconscious of the scene and the fearful struggle going on behind, were singing up the nave like a company of angels. In the Choir there was another dreadful struggle to let the* coffin *down. The bearers were completely overweighted, they bowed and bent and nearly fell and threw the* coffin *down on the floor. When it was safely deposited we all retired to seats right and left and a verger or beadle, in a black gown and holding a mace, took up his postition at the head of the* coffin, *standing.*
(Francis Kilvert, DIARIES, Friday, 2 December 1870)

Two decks of playing-cards lay next to each other: one pack backed with a picture of a jaded princess on a Mogul bed, decorated in gold leaf, and the other with her gazing at a blue peacock while her attendants whispered among themselves. Red, blue and white chips were stacked in a small mahogany coffin.
(Romesh Gunesekera, REEF, 1994)

Today the word *coffin* has a melancholy, funereal ring to it, so much so that a study of some of the uses to which the word was applied in past centuries makes strange reading. In the fifteenth century a *coffin* was a raised pie-crust and later denoted the pie-dish itself. Shakespeare's Titus Andronicus (1594) seeks this gory revenge:

Hark, villains! I will grind your bones to dust,
And with your blood and it I'll make a paste;
And of the paste a coffin *I will rear,*
And make two pasties of your shameful heads;
(Act 5, scene 2)

In THE TAMING OF THE SHREW (1594) Petruchio teases Katerina over the purchase of a cap with these words:

Why, thou say'st true; it is a paltry cap,
*A custard-*coffin, *a bauble, a silken pie;*
(Act 4 scene iii)

And in Ben Jonson's THE STAPLE OF NEWS (1625) we read:

Therefore if you spend
The red-deer pies i' your house, or sell them forth, sir,
Cast so that I may have their coffins *all*
Return'd here, and pil'd up.
(Act 2, scene 3).

In the sixteenth century, a *coffin* was a conical screw of paper into which a grocer might weigh out goods such as spices, for instance. Around the mid-seventeenth century the term was applied both to the carriage of a printing machine and a container in which objects were fired in a furnace. And in the first half of the nineteenth century *coffin* or *coffin-ship* was a colloquial term given to an unseaworthy vessel likely to be the burial container of all on board. This last lugubrious sense obviously evolved from the present meaning of the word, 'a box to contain a corpse for burial', which has been current since the first quarter of the sixteenth century.

All these very varied applications share a common characteristic; they are all containers of one sort or another. In the fourteenth century *coffin* was first and foremost a general term for 'a basket, box or chest'. It was a direct borrowing of *cofin*, an Old French word of the same meaning.

This, in turn, came from Latin *cophinus* and Greek *kophinus*, 'a basket'.

Modern society is rather squeamish about death and cloaks the inevitable, unthinkable truth in euphemism. American English has abandoned the stark *coffin* for the more comforting *casket*. But when it comes down to it, since *casket* comes from the Old French *cassette*, a diminutive form of *casse*, meaning 'box', there really is very little to choose between them.

◆ Also from *cophinus* comes Old French *coffre*, meaning 'a strong box, a chest'. This was borrowed into Middle English at the turn of the fourteenth century, eventually becoming *coffer*.◆

Other funereal words discussed in this book are **cemetery**, **hearse** and **sarcophagus**.

companion

someone who accompanies another, and is of like mind

I feel that I-write-books-therefore-I-am is a sad and limiting motto for any culture. More personally, I have found writers spurned by publishers make gloomy companions, *since they frequently feel they, not simply their books, have been rejected by an uncaring world.*
(DAILY TELEGRAPH, 21 January 1995)

Whippet people think their canine companions *make wonderful hot-water bottles.*
(GOOD HOUSEKEEPING, April 1995)

Those restaurant critics of the press who invariably take a companion with them to dine come close to the original meaning of this word, for a *companion* is literally 'one with whom one eats bread'.

Scholars say that by the fourth century the population of the Roman Empire included several million people of Germanic extraction in all walks of life. In addition, commerce between the Empire and Germanic tribes beyond its northern border was also thriving, so that a certain amount of linguistic exchange between Germanic languages and Latin was inevitable. *Companion* is a result of that Germanic influence on Latin. Some of the northern tribes referred to those with whom they rubbed shoulders on a daily basis as 'partakers of bread'. Gothic, for instance, had the word *gahlaiba* where *ga-* means 'with' and *hlaifs* means 'bread'. Likewise Old High German had the compound *galeipo* (from *ga-*, 'with' and *leib*, 'bread'). Vulgar Latin borrowed this concept and made a direct translation of it forming the word *compāniō* (stem: *compāniōn-*), from *com-* meaning 'with' and *pānis*, 'bread'. From this Old French derived *compaignon* which Middle English then borrowed as *compainoun*.

◆ English *company* (13th cent) comes from Old French *compagnie* which also derived from Latin *compāniō*.

Latin *pānis*, 'bread', is also responsible for:

pannier (14th cent): from Old French *panier*, from Latin *pānārium*, 'breadbasket'

pantry (14th cent): from Old French *paneterie*, 'room for storing bread', from *panetier*, 'panter' (13th cent), a servant responsible for the bread', from *pan*, 'bread'◆

Early Latin influences

It would be not unreasonable to imagine that a significant number of Latin words became established in Old English through the Roman conquest of Britain in AD43, especially since the island was under Roman rule for around 400 years after that. Surprisingly, there are very few. Although Latin was the official language and that of the ruling élite, it use could not have been sufficiently widespread amongst the ordinary population to ensure its survival. It is likely that Latin fell into disuse not long after the withdrawal of the Roman troops around 410 and was certainly incapable of surviving the turmoil of the Germanic invasions which began some 40 years later. When the invasions of the Angles, Saxons and Jutes did take place, they completely submerged the Celtic culture that existed on the island at that time. Thus, from the store of over 600 words that the Celts took from Latin, only around five were passed on:

port, 'harbour', 'gate', from Latin *portus*
torr, 'tower', 'rock', from Latin *turris*
munt, 'mountain', from Latin *mōns*
wīc, 'village', from Latin *vīcus*
ceaster, 'camp', from Latin *castra* (evident in place names: *Chester*, *Lancaster*, *Gloucester*, *Manchester*, etc).

By the same token, the stock of Celtic words that came into Old English is equally meagre. That is not to say, however, that there was no more Latin influence on English until French arrived with William the Conqueror in 1066 and until the revival of Classical scholarship and influence in later centuries. A second source was from the invading Germanic tribes themselves. On the Continent they had had considerable trading links with the Roman Empire and there had been a mutual exchange of words through this contact (see, for example, the entries **companion** and **mint**). When the Anglo-Saxon invasion of Britain took place, therefore, the language of the conquerors already contained a stock of Latin words.

From trade came words such as:
cēap, 'trade', 'bargain', 'cheap' (L *caupō*, 'tradesman'); *mangere*, 'monger' (L *mangō*, 'dealer'); *mynet*, 'coin' (L *monēta*, 'mint', 'money'); *pund*, 'pound' (L *pondō*, 'pound weight'); *wīn*, 'wine', (L *vīnum*).

From everyday life:
cytel, 'kettle' (L *catillus*); *pyle*, 'pillow' (L *pulvīnus*); *cycene*, 'kitchen' (L *coquīna*); *cuppe*, 'cup' (L *cuppa*); *disc*, 'dish' (L *discus*); *mortere*, 'mortar (L *mortarium*); *line*, 'line', 'rope' (L *līnea*); *cīese*, 'cheese' (L *cāseus*).

From communications:
stroet, 'street', 'road' (L *strāta*); *mīl*, 'mile' (L *mīlia*).

The third, and greatest, influence of Latin on Old English was the church. From the earliest mission in 597 to the end of the Old English period over 500 years later, a large number of borrowings took place. These were initially to do with church organisation since Old English did not have equivalents of its own to draw upon: *abbot, altar, angel, chalice, deacon, hymn, mass, nun, pope, provost, psalm* and many more. Also borrowed was a further stock of words relating to monastic life, including education and medicine, which then passed into general domestic use.

For other early influences on Old English, see **Viking conquests** (page 263).

consider

1. to be of the opinion
2. to view, regard as
3. to deliberate, give careful thought to
4. to observe, inspect

Why are ye anxious for raiment? Consider *the lilies of the field, how they grow; they toil not, neither do they spin, and yet I say unto you that even Solomon, in all his glory, was not arrayed like one of these.*
(Matthew 6: 28–29)

'Rats! Hang it all! I wish I was dead. I don't know what I do want to do,' he groaned, and cast himself upon his bed. He was sure of nothing but the fact that he was unhappy. He considered *suicide in a dignified manner, but not for long enough to get much frightened about it.*
(Sinclair Lewis, OUR MR. WRENN, THE ROMANTIC ADVENTURES OF A GENTLE MAN, 1914)

The Romans believed that the relative position of the planets influenced earthly events. The endeavours of the astrologers and augurs as they scrutinised the night sky are encapsulated in the Latin verb *consīderāre.* It literally meant 'to study the stars with great care', being a combination of the intensive prefix *com-* and *sīdus*, 'constellation, star'. Soon, however, the verb was used more generally with the sense 'to observe carefully, to examine', before developing the figurative use 'to reflect upon'. Both applications were current when the word came into English through French *considérer* in the fourteenth century.

◆ The verb *desire*, which came into English in the thirteenth century via Old French *desirer*, is also derived from *sīdus.* It comes from Latin *dēsīderāre* which meant 'to regret, to miss' and hence 'to long for'. The original sense of *dēsīderāre* and its connection with 'star' is obscure but Skeat suggests 'to note the absence of the stars' and hence the regret that the auguries were hidden.

Also from *sīdus* comes English *sidereal*, 'concerning the stars', which was borrowed from Latin *sīdereus* in the seventeenth century.

Considerable was borrowed directly from the medieval Latin *consīderābilis* in the fifteenth century. Originally it meant 'capable of being considered', and then 'calling for consideration, noteworthy'. The sense 'worthy of consideration by virtue of size or amount' dates from the seventeenth century. ◆

For another word connected with augurs, see **temple**. See also **disaster** and **influence**.

criss-cross

to move about in intersecting directions, backwards and forwards

The city was crammed with the youth of all nations and coaches criss-crossed *the Moscow boulevards jam-packed with fresh-faced young men and women flaunting national costume and yodelling national songs.*
(SUNDAY TIMES, 24 April 1994)

It is the simplest of preparations and only involves scrambling eggs with a little cream and chives, piling on to buttered toast or, even better, fried bread, and draping over some salted anchovies in a criss-cross *fashion.*
(THE INDEPENDENT, 28 January 1995)

The horn-book was an early primer. It consisted of a thin wooden board on which the alphabet, the numbers and the Lord's Prayer (and sometimes a formula for exorcism) were printed. This surface was protected by a thin sheet of horn *'to save from finger wet the letter fair'* (William Shenstone, THE SCHOOL-MISTRESS, 1742). The board had a handle and was hung from the child's belt. Shakespeare in a longer passage full of plays on words from LOVE'S LABOUR'S LOST, Act 5, scene 1 (1595), gives this exchange:

Armado: [To Holofernes] Monsieur, are you not lettered?
Moth: Yes, yes; he teaches boys the horn-book. What is a, b, spelt backward with the horn on his head?
Holofernes: Ba, pueritia, with a horn added.
Moth: Ba, most silly sheep with a horn. You hear his learning.
Holofernes: Quis, quis, thou consonant?
Moth: The third of the five vowels, if You repeat them; or the fifth if I.
Holofernes: I will repeat them: a,e, I –
Moth: The sheep; the other two concludes it: o, U.

As Armado goes on to comment on this exchange, it is indeed *true wit!*

In the sixteenth century and perhaps earlier, the alphabet itself was known as *Christ-cross-row.* This was because *Christ's cross* (or *Christ-cross*), a character resembling a Maltese cross, preceded it in the horn-book. Before a child repeated the contents of the book, he would recite the formula *Christ's cross me speed* . In A PLAINE AND EASIE INTRODUCTION TO PRACTICALL MUSICKE (1597) Thomas Morely gives an example of such a recitation: *Christes crosse be my speede, in all vertue to proceede, A, b, c, d, e, f, g, h, i, k, l, m, n, o, p, q, r, s, & t, double u, v, x with y, ezod, & per se tittle tittle est Amen. When you haue done begin againe, begin againe.*

When an illiterate person was required to sign his name he would print the Christ-cross as his mark. A character in Smollett's translation of Don Quixote (1755) remarks: *I am even ignorant of the a, b, c; but provided I remember my christ-cross, I shall be sufficiently qualified.* The form *criss-cross* arose in the nineteenth century from *Christ-cross.* When the latter was pronounced, the first syllable was reduced, so that it became known as *criss-cross,* thereby eventually masking the origin.

For further recitations from the horn-book, see **ampersand**.

crocodile

1. a large reptile
2. a file of schoolchildren walking two by two.

Later in the day, the gonged sun almost audibly roared as it poured down heat. The

jungle, so rich a few hours before became motionless and ashen. The animals slept, except for the monkeys. In dry watercourses I saw crocodiles, *squatting on ridiculous bowed legs, that yawned like antique colonels in the sun.*
(Dom Moraes, My Son's Father, 1968)

. . . *a* crocodile *of small chattering children filing through the trees dressed in immaculate blue and white school uniforms.*
(Good Housekeeping, April 1995)

Alligators and crocodiles are closely related but there are nevertheless several differences between the two: the head of the alligator, for instance, is flattish and almost rectangular while the crocodile's is triangular. There is in fact a third member of the Crocodilia order: the gavial, found in India and south west Asia. It has a longer, narrower and weaker jaw.

Although crocodiles are widespread, the name was first applied to the reptiles of the Nile in particular. In the fifth century BC, the Greek historian Herodotus wrote: *The name of* crocodiles *was given them by the Ionians, who remarked their resemblance to the lizards, which in Ionia live in the walls, and are called* crocodiles. Etymologists consider that the original Ionic form may have been *krokodrilos,* meaning 'worm of the pebbles' (from *kroke,* 'pebble' and *drilos,* 'worm'), reflecting the lizard's habit of basking, and that from this source Greek had *krokodilos* and Latin *crocodīlus.*

The word had various forms after its adoption into English from Old French *cocodrille* and medieval Latin *cocodrillus.* Around 1300 the romance King Alisaunder has *cokedrill,* Wycliffe in 1382 *cokedril,* etc. From the sixteenth century onwards the form was standardised after the Latin *crocodīlus.*

For another word whose spelling was standardised after the Latin in the sixteenth century, see **amethyst**.

The crocodile has been the subject of several myths. Surely the earliest must be that referred to by Herodotus: residents near Thebes and Lake Moeris treated them as sacred. One in each place was tamed, adorned with gold, fed with bread and 'a certain number of victims', and embalmed on death. Crocodiles have also been the object of veneration in India.

The story that the crocodile attracted its prey by pitiful moaning before devouring it with hypocritical tears of remorse is very old. In 1356 we find Sir John Maundeville describing '*in a certain countree* . . . cokadrilles,' adding that *'Theise Serpentes slen men, and thei eten hem wepynge'* (Voiage and Travaile). Shakespeare has Othello accuse his wife of shedding *crocodile tears.* It took some centuries for the crocodile to clear its name.

A more recent myth is that crocodile skin is impervious to bullets. This belief may have come about because African tribesmen used the scaly backs of crocodiles in their shields as protection against their enemies' arrows and spears; more likely, bullets from low calibre weapons might on occasion glance off the bony plated hide when they strike at an angle. In all normal circumstances, crocodile or alligator skin offers no protection at all from firearms.

See **alligator** and **lizard**.

curfew

a period when citizens are ordered to be indoors

In eerily silent streets outside Karachi international airport hundreds of troops have taken up position... People cower in

their homes as troops conduct house-to-house searches in the suburb of Shah Faisal Colony, where a curfew *has been in force for 24 hours... Up to 10 people a day die in ethnic, sectarian and criminal shoot-outs. Business is at a standstill in the city of 10 million people, where guards escort middle-class children to school. Mr Francis de Costa, a taxi driver, said: 'I never know when I return home if there will be a murder,* a curfew, *my children will still be there or if water and power have been cut off.'*
(DAILY TELEGRAPH, 7 October 1994)

In medieval times ordinary dwellings were of insubstantial construction and built close together. Their wooden frames and thatched roofs made them a great fire risk. Towns had no high-pressure water supply for fire fighting. Water for this purpose had to be fetched from wells and streams. Demolishing houses or ripping off thatched roofs to make a fire break was more effective and tools for this purpose were kept by the town authorities.

In medieval houses, the fire did not burn in a chimney against a wall but upon a hearth in the centre of the room, the smoke drifting out through a hole in the roof. In days when the convenience of matches was unknown, a fire was precious and generally not allowed to go out and, in many peasant communities, the glowing fire was also a symbol of hearth and home (Emmanuel Le Roy Ladurie, MONTAILLOU, 1978). If precautions were not taken to tend it well, then a slipping log falling on to the straw or rushes that covered the floor might reduce that house and its neighbours to ashes. A medieval law, in force throughout Europe, guarded against this. The regulation was known in Old French as *covre-feu* (later *couvre-feu*), literally 'cover-fire' (from *couvrir*, 'cover' and *feu*, 'fire'), which gave *coeverfu* in Anglo-French and *courfew* or *curfu* in Middle English. Each evening, usually at eight o'clock, a bell would be rung as a signal to either extinguish the fire or cover it with a *cover-fire*. This was a circular metal or ceramic lid with holes in it which covered the embers until morning. In time *couvre-feu* was applied to the bell as well as the regulation. Indeed, in the earliest English references, which date from the thirteenth-century, the word is obviously applied to the signal alone, or to the hour of its ringing.

Using the curfew as a means of controlling the people is very long-established. Tradition has it that the curfew was introduced into England by William the Conqueror who used it to prevent seditious groups meeting under cover of darkness. However, there is no documentary proof to this effect although there is evidence that in medieval towns the *curfew bell* became a way of restricting comings and goings by night, in an attempt to stamp out crime. Christopher Hibbert (THE ENGLISH, 1987) notes that servants in Norwich risked imprisonment if they were not safely back under their masters' roofs by eight o'clock and the same fate awaited inhabitants of Beverley abroad after nine or visitors to the town out after eight o'clock without both a light and a good reason. From this use comes the present-day meaning of *curfew*: an order, usually in times of unrest or danger, obliging people to clear streets and public places and return home by a certain hour.

The *curfew bell* was still sounded long after the need for the fire regulation had passed, when it functioned as a general signal for everything to settle down for the night:

The Curfew *tolls the knell of parting day,*
The lowing herd wind slowly o'er the lea,
The ploughman homeward plods his
weary way,
And leaves the world to darkness and
to me.
(Thomas Gray, ELEGY IN A COUNTRY CHURCHYARD, 1750)

In countless villages farmers locked up their livestock when it rang, while, according to Walsh, in Durham it was the signal for the college gates to be closed and in Newcastle for the shops to shut. The curfew was gradually petering out by the end of the nineteenth century but, even then, was still sounded in many towns and villages and, as late as 1965, was rung at eight o'clock each evening from St Mary's church in Wallingford.

See **focus** for another word with the hearth as its origin. For another word whose etymology includes the French *couvre,* see **handkerchief**.

cynic

1. someone who sees base motives behind virtuous acts, and expects the worst
2. a scornful mocker

I've always been a staunch champion of the idea of asexual friendship between men and women...Knowing, cynical, *sex-obsessed people sneer and say: 'Ha! No such thing! When someone claims a platonic friendship it's just that one of them doesn't fancy the other!'*
(GOOD HOUSEKEEPING, April 1995)

Satire hasn't just run out of steam, but of sacred cows to attack. Irreverence and irony have become institutionalised, contempt and cynicism *the common wisdom of the age.*
(SUNDAY TIMES, 19 March 1995)

According to the Greek philosopher Antisthenes (c.445 – c.360 BC), virtue is the highest good. It can be achieved through exercising self-sufficiency and self-control, which brings freedom from needs and desires. Such a philosophy naturally demands a very basic lifestyle. Antisthenes and his disciples practised what they preached: Diogenes (411 -322 BC) even went so far as to live in a tub, although his self-control did not stop him from showing open disdain for the pleasures enjoyed by society at large. Milton in COMUS (1634) declared:

O foolishness of men! that . . .
. . . fetch their precepts from the Cynic *tub,*
Praising the lean and sallow Abstinence!

The gymnasium where Antisthenes taught was called the *Kynosarges,* meaning 'white dog' (from the story that a white dog had once made off with part of a sacrifice). This name was probably the source of the title *Kynicos,* 'Cynic', but the critical and carping attitude of the philosopher and his followers so coloured popular opinion that *kynicos* was understood in its literal sense of 'dog-like, cur-like'. Indeed *kyōn,* 'dog', became a nickname for 'Cynic', a fact alluded to by Heywood in IRON AGE (1632): *Peace Cinicke, barke not dogge.*

When *cynic* was first used in English in the sixteenth century it properly referred to one who adhered to Antisthenes' philosophy. Almost immediately, however, it became a term for 'a fault-finder, a critic'. Modern usage since the nineteenth century has extended the meaning further so that it now denotes 'one who disbelieves any purity of intent in the actions of others and responds with disdain and sarcasm':

What is a cynic*? – A person who knows the price of everything and the value of nothing.*
(Oscar Wilde, LADY WINDERMERE'S FAN, 1892)

Portmanteau words

The Victorian author Lewis Carroll was fond of the nonsensical and enjoyed coining what he called 'portmanteau words' (a *portmanteau* was a large travelling bag). Carroll explains himself through Humpty Dumpty in ALICE THROUGH THE LOOKING GLASS (1872): *Well, 'slithy' means 'lithe and slimy'... You see it's like a portmanteau – there are two meanings packed up into one word.*

Slithy is mainly familiar through the popularity of the nonsense poem 'Jabberwocky'; other 'portmanteau words', however, have entered into current use. *Mimsy*, according to Humpty Dumpty, is a blend of 'flimsy' and 'miserable'. The OED says that *mimsy* – a dialect word meaning 'clumsy, flimsy' – already existed in Carroll's time. It does, however, accept that *mimsy* may well have been separately invented by him, adding that in any case his use of the word has influenced the meaning.

The verb *galumph* is probably a combination of 'gallop' and 'triumphant' since it originally described the gait of the boy who slew the Jabberwock, severed its head and '*went galumphing back*'. In modern usage it means 'to stomp', 'to gallop about clumsily or heavily'. *Chortle* merges 'chuckle' and 'snort'. The result is a very onomatopaeic term for a rich, throaty gurgle of laughter.

Over the last century there have been a good number of other words invented on similar principles that have been accepted into the language. Several originated in America.

aquacise	aqua + exercise	*guesstimate*	guess + estimate
bit	binary + digit	*identikit*	identity + kit
bo(a)tel	boat + hotel	*mingy*	mangy + stingy
brunch	breakfast + lunch	*motel*	motor + hotel
camcorder	camera + recorder	*sitcom*	situation + comedy
Chunnel	Channel + tunnel	*smog*	smoke + fog
cyborg	cybernetic + organism	*stagflation*	stagnation + inflation
Dormobile	dormitory + automobile	*televangelist*	television + evangelist
franglais	français + anglais	*transistor*	transfer + resistor

It is a pity that others, created for humorous effect, have not made the grade:

ambisextrous, for a bisexual
beerage, for either ennobled leaders of the drinks trade, or for heavy-drinking peers
hoolivan, for the vehicle used by police to monitor unruly crowds
red-tapeworm, for parasitic bureaucracy

Carroll's use of the term 'portmanteau word' also lives on in combinations such as 'portmanteau quotation', 'portmanteau term' and 'portmanteau form'. The jargon of linguistics even has 'portmanteau morph' where a single morph represents two morphemes (as the French *du* stands for *de* + *le*).

deadline

the cut-off point for newspaper copy, payment, the completion of a task, etc.

The notion of lasers in space has captured the imaginations of planners at the Pentagon and the White House. Such a system – a final technological fix to end the escalation in missile production – 'may not be accomplished before the end of the century,' Reagan said.

In fact, even with the Pentagon spending about $ 1000 million a year on research into laser and anti-ballistic missile systems, lasers are unlikely to meet that deadline, *said George Keyworth, Reagan's science adviser and a physicist, last year.*
(NEW SCIENTIST, 1983)

This word originates from the prison-camps of the American Civil War (1861–5). The *dead-line* was a line marked out about 17 feet from the inner fence. Any prisoner who dared pass over the line would be shot down to prevent his escape. Later, *deadline* was applied to the guideline on the bed of a cylinder printing press over which the prepared type surface should not pass. The word was used figuratively by the American press in the first quarter of the twentieth century to denote a time by which all copy had to be ready for inclusion in a particular issue of a publication. The term is now widely applied to any task or payment which has to be completed by a certain date or time.

decimate

1. to kill one in ten
2. to destroy or reduce by a large proportion

Farther south, the millions of seabirds that normally nourish on the famous guano islands are being decimated. *Hardest hit is the guanay cormorant, the most numerous species. Perhaps most important from the human point of view, the Peruvian fishermen face disaster as the anchovies disappear.*
(NEW SCIENTIST, 1983)

The Latin verb *decimāre,* which was derived from *decimus,* 'a tenth', and *decem,* 'ten', meant 'to take one tenth' and had a two-fold application.

The first of these was military and referred to a strategy which Roman generals sometimes employed to keep their men in order. Whenever a general got wind of mutinous rumblings among his troops he would have one in ten of their number picked out by lot for execution, to bring the remainder into line. The practice was not confined to Roman times. In 1599 Elizabeth I appointed Robert Devereux, second Earl of Essex, Lord Lieutenant of Ireland with orders to quell the rebellion there. The Irish, however, put up stiff resistance which dismayed the English troops. During a skirmish at Wicklow on 29 May Sir Henry Harington's company showed cowardice under fire and ran away. In Dublin on 11 July, Essex disciplined the company, imprisoning Harington and executing one soldier in every ten. The earliest recorded use in English of *decimate* with the sense 'to destroy one in ten' refers to this distressing episode. Initially the verb was confined to this meaning and to historical and military contexts; by the second half of the seventeenth century, it was being applied more widely and with the looser sense 'to destroy or remove a large proportion of' – as though nine out of ten had died or been destroyed and one tenth saved. Even today, some writers still reject this second sense.

The second application of *decimāre*

was a fiscal one and meant 'to levy a tax of one tenth'. Its use in English was largely restricted to the exacting of Cromwell's one-tenth tax upon the Royalists in 1655. In his comedy THE WILD GALLANT (1663), for instance, Dryden writes of being '*as poor as a decimated Cavalier*'. *Decimate* in this sense did not survive the eighteenth century and never replaced the old familiar term *tithe* which derived from Old English *tēotha*, 'tenth', in the twelfth century.

derrick

a large crane, hoisting equipment

The long inlet of the main harbor looked eerily deserted, with the floating lamp of a single freighter smoking off the blistered, sagging piers and twisted derricks.
(Harvey Wasserman and Norman Solomon, KILLING OUR OWN, 1982)

The principal place of execution in London from 1388 to 1793 was at Tyburn, close to the present day Marble Arch. Generally large crowds gathered and there was something of a carnival atmosphere, for hanging days were designated public holidays. The grizzly spectacle was intended to serve as a deterrent to the citizens who went to watch. In 1571 a huge triangular gallows was erected at Tyburn where up to twenty-one victims could be hanged at the same time. The prisoners would arrive on a cart which came to a stop under the gallows. Once the rope had been secured around the victim's neck the horse was urged forward and the victim left dangling. Accounts speak of girls offering the condemned prisoners flowers and of crowds pushing forward to touch the corpses once they had been cut down, in some macabre belief that they were imbued with healing powers. Given the immense public interest in executions, the executioner himself must have been a relatively well-known figure. The hangman at Tyburn at the turn of the seventeenth century bore the surname *Derick*. Over the years he was responsible for dispatching over 3000 prisoners, and among them the man said to have once shown him mercy.

The story goes that as a soldier Derick had served at the sacking of Cádiz (1595) under the second Earl of Essex (see **decimate**). Here he was charged and found guilty of rape and would have hanged, had not the earl pardoned him on condition that he became hangman at Tyburn. A few years later Essex, who had lost favour with the queen, tried to provoke an uprising in London and was accordingly charged with high treason and condemned to death in the Tower in 1601. The man engaged to behead him was none other than Derick, who took three blows to sever the earl's head (the nobility were beheaded rather than hanged – see **guillotine**). Essex had been a popular figure and it is said that Derick himself narrowly escaped death at the hands of the mob on the day of the execution. Two street ballads remain to testify to the depth of popular feeling. One of them, entitled UPON THE EARLE OF ESSEX HIS DEATH, runs:

Derick, thou know'st at Coles I sav'd
Thy life lost for a rape there done,
Where thou thyself canst testifie
Thine own hand three and twenty hung.

Such was Derick's notoriety that his name was applied to gallows and hangmen in general. This example comes from an old play: *Pox o' the fortune-teller! Would Derrick had been his fortune seven*

years ago! – to cross my love thus.
(Wentworth Smith THE PURITANE; OR THE WIDDOW OF WATLING STREET, 1607)

References to *derricks* as gallows were superseded in the following century, when the term was applied to 'hoisting equipment'. It was first so used in a naval context – some have suggested that sailors' 'gallows humour' made them see the connection between a device for hanging, and lifting tackle on the mizzen mast. The nineteenth century saw *derrick* applied to a 'crane' and by extension, originally in America, also to the 'framework constructed over an oil-well both to support the drilling equipment and to hoist and lower lengths of pipe'.

The etymology of *derrick*, however, can be taken back far beyond London's boundaries, for the name is of Dutch origin, *Diederik*, *Dierryk* and *Dirk* being variants of the same.

For another word with its origins in execution, see **guillotine**.

desultory

aimless, haphazard, unmethodical

Odd noises began issuing from the underside of the car. At the next village we consulted the blacksmith, a heavy-set, uncommunicative man who sucked his teeth as he gave the axle a few desultory *bangs with a mallet.*
(Alexander Frater, CHASING THE MONSOON, 1990)

The Roman circus, a huge oval building enclosed by banks of seats, was the scene of a variety of spectacles, including horse and chariot races. A *dēsultor* (from Latin *dēsultus*, past participle of *dēsilīre* 'to jump down') was an equestrian acrobat who entertained the crowd by leaping from one swiftly moving horse to another. From this word came the adjective *dēsultorius* which meant 'belonging to a vaulter' and, by extension, 'jumping about, disconnected, superficial'. The adjective was borrowed into English as *desultory* in the sixteenth century with the same sense of 'random, jumping from one thing to another'.

◆ Latin *dēsilīre* is derived from *dē*, 'down' and *salīre*, 'to jump'. *Salīre* is present in a number of other common English words:

assail and *assault* (both 13th cent) ultimately derive from Latin *assilīre*, 'to leap on'.

insult (16th cent): from *insultāre* 'to leap on', from *in-*, 'upon' and *saltāre*, from *salīre*, 'to jump'.

result (15th cent): from medieval Latin *resultāre*, from Latin *resultāre*, 'to jump back', from *re-*, 'back' and *saltāre*, from *salire*, 'to jump'.

salacious (17th cent): from *salāx* (stem *salāc-*), from *salīre*. Applied to male animals jumping up to mate.

salient (16th cent): from *saliēns*, the present participle of *salīre*. Originally used as an heraldic term for 'jumping'.

somersault (16th cent): from Old French *sombresault*, variant of *sobresault*, from unattested Provençal *sobresaut*, compound of *sobre*, 'over' (Latin *sūpra*) and *saut*, 'a jump' (Latin *saltus*, 'a leap')◆

dirge

1. an anthem sung at a service for the dead
2. any sad, mournful music

While I watched the tempest, so beautiful yet terrific, I wandered on with a hasty step. This noble war in the sky elevated my spirits;

I clasped my hands, and exclaimed aloud, 'William, dear angel! this is thy funeral, this thy dirge*!' As I said these words, I perceived in the gloom a figure which stole from behind a clump of trees near me; I stood fixed, gazing intently: I could not be mistaken. A flash of lightning illuminated the object, and discovered its shape plainly to me; its gigantic stature, and the deformity of its aspect more hideous than belongs to humanity, instantly informed me that it was the wretch, the filthy daemon, to whom I had given life. What did he there? Could he be (I shuddered at the conception) the murderer of my brother?*

(Mary Shelley, FRANKENSTEIN, OR THE MODERN PROMETHEUS, 1818)

Not so much in obedience, as in surprise and fear: for on the raising of the hand, he became sensible of confused noises in the air; incoherent sounds of lamentation and regret; wailings inexpressibly sorrowful and self-accusatory. The spectre, after listening for a moment, joined in the mournful dirge*; and floated out upon the bleak, dark night.*

(Charles Dickens, A CHRISTMAS CAROL, 1843)

REQUIEM, n. A mass for the dead which the minor poets assure us the winds sing o'er the graves of their favorites. Sometimes, by way of providing a varied entertainment, they sing a dirge.

(Ambrose Bierce, THE DEVIL'S DICTIONARY, 1911)

In the Latin rite for the Office of the Dead, the anthem '*Dirige, Domine, Deus meus, in conspectu tuo viam meam*' is prescribed for Matins. The line comes from Psalm 5:8 and translates into English as 'Direct, O Lord, my God, my way in thy sight'. From the earliest records, the entire service was referred to by the first word of the anthem, *dirige* (from Latin *dīrigere*, 'direct, guide').

Of course these offices had to be paid for. SELDEN'S TABLE-TALK (published 1689, thirty-five years after his death) includes this piece of ready reckoning: '*The Priest said* Diriges, *and twenty* Diriges *at fourpence a piece comes to a Noble*'. Fortunately one of the benefits offered by medieval guilds was the provision of funeral masses for the souls of its members: '*When any Broder or Suster of this Gilde is decessed oute off this worlde . . . ye Steward of this Gilde shall doo Rynge for hym, and do to say a Placebo and dirige, wt a masse on ye morowe of Requiem*' (1494). And medieval wills sometimes left a sum of money to pay for the funeral feast or dirge-ale (see **ale**): '*Brede & Ale to Spende atte my dyryge*' (1408).

In the sixteenth-century the word, sometimes contracted to *dirge*, was also applied to any funereal music or song of lament. Shakespeare uses it of a swansong in THE RAPE OF LUCRECE (1594):

And now this pale swan in her watery nest
Begins the sad dirge *of her certain ending.*

Thereafter, it was to be much used by other writers in doleful mood. Not surprisingly, Gray's ELEGY WRITTEN IN A COUNTRY CHURCH YARD (1751) describes the funeral of the youth that *Melancholy marked for her own*, borne slowly through the church-way path *with* dirges *due in sad array*.

For a word with a similar origin, see **placebo**.

disaster

a serious misfortune, a calamity

You can fake old tables with early oak floorboards then submit the top to every disaster *you can devise – hot gravy, Indian ink, children gouging with knives – and it will look more authentic.*

(WEEKEND TELEGRAPH, 21 January 1995)

Since the Eighteenth Century, Baring Brothers has been respected as one of the world's most blue-blooded investment banks. All the more shocking then that this great institution should stumble so sudddenly to disaster.
(DAILY MAIL, 27 February 1995)

I have survived enough lambing seasons now to expect an occasional disaster *and come to terms with it; even so, the heart can still grieve a little. We lost a lamb the other night because the ewe decided to give birth exactly in the spot where a puddle of icy water had formed after a wintry downpour.*
(THE TIMES WEEKEND, 11 March 1995)

In past centuries it was believed that the stars influenced both the characters and the affairs of men. *Disaster* is a product of this belief. Its source is an Old Italian adjective *disastrato* which meant 'ill-starred'. This had been formed by adding the pejorative prefix *dis-* to *astro*, 'star' (from Latin *astrum*, from Greek *astron*). From *disastrato* came the Italian back-formation *disastro*, meaning 'bad luck, disaster', the implication being that the misfortune was the result of inauspicious planetary activity. *Disaster* made a late appearance in English at the end of the sixteenth century, probably by way of French *désastre*. Shakespeare linked the new word to its heavenly origins in HAMLET (1601) where Horatio speaks of '*disasters in the sun*'. Again, in KING LEAR (1605), Gloucester's bastard son Edmund mocks his father's conviction that his own problems and those of the world are no fault of man but are dictated by the planets:

This is the excellent foppery of the world, that, when we are sick in fortune, often the surfeits of our own behaviour, we make guilty of our disasters *the sun, the moon, and stars; as if we were villains on necessity; fools by heavenly compulsion; knaves, thieves and treachers, by spherical predominance; drunkards, liars, and adulterers, by an enforc'd obedience of planetary influence; and all that we are evil in, by a divine thrusting on – an admirable evasion of whoremaster man, to lay his goatish disposition on the charge of a star!*
(Act 1, scene 2)

◆ Greek *astron* gave the stem *astro-*, 'star, in the shape of a star'. This was used in Greek compounds such as *astronomos*, literally 'star-arranger' (from *astro-* and *-nomos*, from *nemein*, 'to arrange'), the source of English *astronomer* and *astronomy*.

Astro- is now widely used to form modern compounds relating to the shape of a star (*asteroid, astroid, astrocyte*) or the science of stars and space (*astrochemistry, astrogeology, astronautics, astrophysics*, etc).◆

For other astrological terms see also **consider**, **influence**, and **influenza**.

dismal

gloomy, dreary, woeful

A dismal *screech, as of mere animal terror, rang from the cabinet.*
(Robert Louis Stevenson, THE STRANGE CASE OF DR JEKYLL AND MR HYDE, 1886)

The woods across the line were but the scarred and blackened ruins of woods; for the most part the trees had fallen, but a certain proportion still stood, dismal *grey stems, with dark brown foliage instead of green.*
(H G Wells, THE WAR OF THE WORLDS, 1898)

Media pundits have searched for years for really good news to report about national newspapers instead of dismally *charting*

month by month and year by year the slow but steady decline in sales.
(THE TIMES, 18 January 1995)

Besides saints' days, holy days and festivals, medieval calendars also marked twenty-four Egyptian days, said to be the result of ancient studies by Egyptian astrologers. These were inauspicious, evil days, the medieval equivalents of 'Friday the thirteenth', and there were two of them each month. Medieval Latin called them *diēs māli*, meaning 'evil days', and from this Anglo-French derived *dis mal*. This subsequently appeared as the noun *dismal*, often in the expression *in the dismal*, meaning 'at an unlucky time, in the evil days'. Some medieval writers, Chaucer included, misunderstood the origin of *dis mal*, believing it to derive from French and to mean 'ten evils' and therefore to refer to the ten plagues of Egypt mentioned in the Bible (Exodus Chapters 6–12). Skeat quotes Chaucer's BOKE OF THE DUCHESSE (c.1369). Here the knight, describing the emotional turmoil he was in as he told his tale of love to his lady, says:

I not wel how that I began,
Ful euel rehersen hit I can;
And eek, as helpe me God withal,
I trowe hit was in the dismal,
That was the ten woundes of Egipte.

During the fifteenth century *dismal* was also often appended to the word day as an adjective, the result being a tautological coupling: *Her* disemale daies *and her fatal houres.* (John Lydgate, THE STORY OF THEBES, c.1420)

By the last quarter of the sixteenth century *dismal*, with its overtones of foreboding and disaster, was being widely used to qualify any noun where the sense 'sinister, disastrous or wretched' was intended. The modern sense of 'dark and dreary, depressing' developed in the first half of the seventeenth century.

dollar

a unit of currency, particularly in the United States but also widely in other countries

As we swept away from the shore, I prayed that the inhabitants might long retain . . . their respect for the fiddle and their contempt for the Almighty Dollar.
(Washington Irving, THE CREOLE VILLAGE, 1837)

Almighty dollar, *thy shining face*
Bespeaks thy wondrous power;
In my pockets make thy nesting-place,
I need thee every hour.
(Unknown, THE WORLD'S PRAYER, c.1891)

Mr Evarts, formerly Secretary of State, showed an English friend the place where Washington was said to have thrown a dollar *across the Potomac. The English friend expressed surprise; 'but' said Mr. Everts, 'you must remember that a* dollar *went farther in those days.' A Senator met Mr Evarts next day, and said that he had been amused by his jest. 'But,' said Mr Evarts, 'I met a mere journalist just afterwards who said, "Oh, Mr. Evarts, you should have said it was a small matter to throw a* dollar *across the Potomac for a man who had chucked a Sovereign across the Atlantic." '*
(George William Erskine Russell, COLLECTIONS AND RECOLLECTIONS, 1898)

Alice Mafola, 79 and stooped from work and worry, took her best dress off the steel hanger nailed to a wooden post. When she had it on, she stepped over people still sleeping and walked out into the chill of a morning in which the sun had not yet the strength to

burn off the clouds. A white petticoat with frills hung down six inches below the hem of her dress. But she went down Martinus Smuts Drive, Zone 3, Soweto, like a million dollars, *and it was still before 6am and the walk put her into history.*
(DAILY MAIL, April 27, 1994)

In the sixteenth century the present-day town of Jachymov, situated in the Erzgebirge Mountains, Czechoslovakia, was known as *Sankt Joachimsthal* ('the valley of St Joachim') and was in Bohemia. In 1519 large coins were minted there under the direction of the Count of Schlick, using silver extracted from a nearby mine which had opened three years earlier. A single coin was known as a *Joachimstaler.* This was soon shortened to *taler* or *thaler* in High German and became *daler* in Low German and Dutch. Denmark and Sweden in imitation took *rigsdaler* and *riksdaler* respectively for their coins.

Sixteenth-century English used *daler,* also spelt *dalder, dallor* or *dolor,* when referring to these foreign currencies. English settlers in the North American colonies applied the term similarly to the Spanish *peso,* the unit used in New Spain. Such was the importance of trade between the Spanish colonies and North America that, by the time Thomas Jefferson considered a monetary unit for the United States, he was forced to acknowledge that '*The unit or [Spanish]* dollar *is a known coin and the most familiar of all to the mind of the people. It is already adopted from south to north*' (NOTES ON A MONEY UNIT FOR US, 1782), with the result that, on July 6, 1785, the Continental Congress '*Resolved, that the money unit of the United States of America be one* dollar'.

For notes on another currency, see **sterling**.

draconian

severe, very harsh

Supermarket employee Nicholas Smith . . . was sacked from Safeway for refusing to cut his waist-length mane. He sued the chain and won.

Such long hair, said Lady Olga Maitland, was 'disrespectful to the people you work for and the customers'. The Tories, it seems, have rather Draconian *views about the nation's appearance. A clause in the job seeker's allowance bill, issued by Peter Lilley and Michael Portillo, appears to allow Job Centre officials to withhold benefits if claimants do not look 'presentable' to future employers. Labour spokesman Donald Dewar, said: 'I do not believe the employment service should be in the business of ordering short-back-and-sides haircuts.'*
(THE SUNDAY TIMES, 18 December 1994)

The adjective derives from the name of *Draco* who was chief magistrate at Athens. In around 621 BC he compiled the first written legal code for the city. Justice was no longer to be left up to the individual interpretation of the magistrates since there was now a penalty for every crime. The punishments, however, were so harsh, the death penalty figuring largely for even trivial offences, that in 594 BC they were repealed by Solon who retained only those dealing with homicide. The adjective *draconian* was coined in the nineteenth century (supplanting largely the earlier *draconic*), to denote any measures demanding uncalled-for severity or brutality.

◆ From the late seventeenth to the early nineteenth centuries *draconic* also meant 'belonging to a dragon' or 'dragon-like' from Latin *dracō* and Greek *drakōn.*◆

dunce

a person of poor academic ability

How much a dunce *that has been sent to roam*
Excels a dunce *that has been kept at home.*
(William Cowper, THE PROGRESS OF ERROR, 1780)

'I'm a poor man, your Majesty,' the Hatter began, in a trembling voice, '—and I hadn't begun my tea – not above a week or so – and what with the bread-and-butter getting so thin – and the twinkling of the tea—'

'The twinkling of the what?' said the King.

'It began with the tea,' the Hatter replied.

'Of course twinkling begins with a T!' said the King sharply. 'Do you take me for a dunce*? Go on!'*

(Lewis Carroll, ALICE'S ADVENTURES IN WONDERLAND, 1865)

Three frogs
hopped in the playground, freed by a dunce,
followed by a line of kids, jumping and croaking
away from the lunch queue.
(Carol Ann Duffy, b. 1955, IN MRS TILSCHER'S CLASS, 1955)

It is ironic that a word denoting someone who is incapable of learning should derive from the name of a gifted scholar. John Duns Scotus (c. 1265–1308) was a Scottish-born Franciscan monk of great intellectual ability who, on the strength of his writing and teaching on philosophy and theology, gained a great following in universities at home and abroad. He lectured at the universities of Oxford, Paris and Cologne. Those who subscribed to his school of thought were known as *Scotists.*

Duns Scotus was particularly known for his insistence on the doctrines of the Immaculate Conception and of free will, which he described as a horse under the control of its rider, grace, who could at any moment be unseated. His teaching that human reasoning could prove neither the existence of God nor that of the after-life brought him and the Scotists into conflict with the followers of Thomas Aquinas, who upheld that faith and reason were in harmony, faith building upon reason to a revelation of the one true God.

The Scotists were esteemed until the sixteenth century when, due to their opposition to the revival of classical study that characterised the Renaissance, they met fierce opposition from the humanists and others who accused them of unsound, quibbling and pedantic rhetoric: *'Remember ye not how . . . the old barkyng curres,* Dunces *disciples & lyke draffe called Scotistes, the children of darkenesse, raged in euery pulpit agaynst Greke Latin and Hebrue'* wrote William Tyndale (AN ANSWERE UNTO THOMAS MORES DIALOGE, 1531).

In their tirades the humanists nicknamed the Scotists *Dunsmen* or *Dunses* so that, by the last quarter of the sixteenth century the term *dunce* had become synonymous with 'a pedant who derives no benefit from study', and then 'one who is incapable of any learning'. In Butler's satire HUDIBRAS (1678) and in Pope's ESSAY ON CRITICISM (1711), there is this sense of the word with reference to the sect; Pope entitled one of his major works THE DUNCIAD (1743), an attack on 'Dulness' everywhere.

From the first quarter of the seventeenth century some inns of court even had *dunce-tables* for the less able students preparing for the bar. The *dunce's cap,* a Victorian invention supposed to goad a child into learning through fear of being humiliated, was a conical hat to be worn by the child who could not recite his lessons.

earwig

a small insect

*[*Earwig *is, says Professor Sharp of the Memorial University of Newfoundland], a case of a dropped "e". The original word was* earsewig. *Drop the first letter and you get an insect that wiggles its arse, which seems plain enough.*
(NEW SCIENTIST, 1983)

Consider the persistence of the earwig! *Each afternoon, it feasts on the dahlia blooms. First sight. Each morning, we empty the flower pots and drown the* earwig . . . *But still they come! Nature's remorseless . . .*

If we did this for one million years all over the world, could we make some small dent in the pattern of evolution? Would we produce an earwig *that could swim?*
(John Mortimer, A VOYAGE ROUND MY FATHER, 1982)

Written English references to this insect date back a thousand years. The word is from the Old English *earwicga* (from *eare*, 'ear' and *wicga*, 'insect'). As its name suggests, this lithe little creature was thought to make a habit of scurrying into people's ears as they slept and, from there, penetrating their heads. The French were tormented by the same fear and so were the Germans and the Dutch; French has *perce-oreille*, 'ear piercer', German *ohrwurm* and Dutch *oorworm*, both meaning 'ear-worm'. Happily there was a remedy; in his HISTORIA NATURALIS Pliny the Elder (AD 23–79) suggests spitting into the ear to flush the offender out – not as easy as it sounds.

◆ *Wicga*, 'insect', comes from *wig-* , the same unattested ancient Germanic root responsible for *wiggle*.◆

See **Portmanteau words** (page 92), for other examples of terms made up from two separate words.

easel

a frame to support pictures, blackboards, etc

Everyone always talks about the sky around Taos, and it is astonishing. I had never seen a sky so vivid and blue, so liquid. . . you can certainly see why Taos has always attracted artist and writers – or at least you can until you get to Taos itself. I had expected it to be a sweet little artists' colony, full of people with smocks and easels, *and it was just a tourist trap, with slow-moving traffic and stores selling ugly Indian pottery and big silver belt buckles and postcards.*
(Bill Bryson, THE LOST CONTINENT, 1989)

Easel was borrowed into English in the seventeenth century from the Dutch *ezel*, whose literal sense is 'donkey'. The allusion is to a beast of burden carrying a load. Other languages derive their words for *easel* in the same way. German *esel* is akin to the Dutch word and means 'donkey'. In French, Italian and Spanish, on the other hand, a diminutive of 'horse' is used: *chevalet*, *cavalletto* and *caballete* respectively.

English, of course, also uses *horse* figuratively for various pieces of equipment that support or carry loads; tanning, whaling and clock-making are just some of the trades where such apparatus was used. A carpenter uses a trestle-like support known as *horse* or *sawhorse* to hold the wood while he saws it and in a domestic settings the *clothes-horse*, a wooden frame on which washing is spread to dry, has been in use since the sixteenth century.

eavesdrop

to listen in secretly

With a professional bow and flourish, the maître d' ushers us to our window table in the romantic, nearly empty restaurant . . . Then the young couple appear, minus coats. 'There's a celebratory air about them,' I speculate. Inexplicably, though, they are given the table just two inches from ours – I mean, if we were eavesdropping *types, we'd hear every word.*
(WEEKEND TELEGRAPH, 4 March, 1995)

Alan [Bennett] . . . would sit on the top of buses eavesdropping *on other passengers, very occasionally noting down a memorable phrase in his little black book; when the notebook was full, he would assemble the phrases into a carefully crafted monologue.*
(DAILY TELEGRAPH, 25 March 1995)

The *eaves* are those edges of a roof or thatch which overhang the side of the building so that water is directed away from the walls. (The word ultimately appears to come from *ob-*, the same Germanic root which produced 'over'). In medieval times before gutters were commonly used, an ancient law forbade the construction of any building less than two feet from a boundary in order to protect the adjoining property from water cascading from the eaves. This water was referred to as *yfesdrype*, literally 'eavesdrip', in Anglo-Saxon, but the word was remodelled as *eavesdrop* in Middle English. The regulation strip of land around the eaves was also referred to as the *eavesdrop*. The word *eavesdropper* was derived in the fifteenth century to denote a nosey person who lurked literally within the eavesdrop '*under mennes walles or wyndowes . . . to bere tales*'. (MODUS TENENDI LUŘ BAROŇ VON VISU FRANCI PLEGII, c. 1515) The verb *to eavesdrop* is a back-formation of this coined in the seventeenth century.

engine

1. a mechanical device for converting energy into motion
2. a railway locomotive

But as I grew up, in those far-off days, I saw myself as a child of the future. I was enamoured – little thinking that the object of my passion was doomed, too, soon to become an anachronism – of that roaring, hurtling, up-to-the-minute thing, the steam engine.
(Graham Swift, EVER AFTER, 1992)

To wander around the QE2 in mid-afternoon is to find the pools empty, the lecture theatres almost deserted, the games equipment abandoned, and the only sound the giant susurration of engines *and sea. Hush! The entire ship is snoring.*
(WEEKEND TELEGRAPH, 25 February 1995)

To the contemporary mind the word *engine* might conjure up the mysteries under the car bonnet or perhaps, to those who hanker after a bygone age, a mental picture of a steam train. The term does not originate in mechanics of any kind, however: it derives from the Latin *ingenium*, meaning 'an inborn skill' and source of the word *ingenious*. From this Old French had *engin* or *engien*. This word had several meanings, all of which were borrowed into Middle English.

Initially *engin* retained its Latin sense of 'innate ability'. The twelfth century French writer Wace used it in this sense and, in his CANTERBURY TALES (1387), Chaucer states: *A man hath sapiences thre, Memorie,* engin, *and intellect also.*' (The Second Nun's Tale). From this primary sense emerged the related meaning of 'ingenuity', often with the implication of 'cunning' (Old French had a phrase *mal engien* which meant 'trickery'.) *Engin* was next extended to the 'product of ingenuity', in other words a 'plot or deception'. In the thirteenth century Provençal courtly poem AUCASSIN ET NICOLETTE for instance, the heroine, imprisoned in a tower, wonders by what means or *engien* she might rejoin her forbidden love, Aucassin (*Ele se pourpensa par quel engien ele porroit Aucassin querre*). This sense is reflected in English literature from the fourteenth century. The next step was the application of *engin* to a 'tool or mechanical device' that was the product of such innate ability. At the turn of the fourteenth century it referred to machines of war (a *siege engine*, for instance) but was swiftly extended to all kinds of appliances.

This use of *engine* to mean 'implement' sometimes has quite a comical ring to modern ears. In his poem THE RAPE OF THE LOCK (1714) Pope describes the climactic moment when the lock of fair Belinda's hair is severed thus:

Just then, Clarissa drew with tempting grace
A two-edg'd weapon from her shining case; . . .
He takes the gift with rev'rence, and extends
The little engine *on his fingers' ends;*
This just behind Belinda's neck he spread,
As o'er the fragrant steam she bends her head.

The engine here is, of course, a pair of scissors. It would be another sixty years or so before the gathering momentum of the industrial revolution knew the power of the steam-engine which gradually pushed all these other senses into obscurity.

◆ Latin *ingenium*, 'talent' gave the Medieval Latin verb *ingeniāre*, 'to contrive', and the derivative *ingeniātōr*, 'contriver'. This became *engigneor* in Old French and *enginer* in Middle English. *Engineer* followed the same pattern as *engine*: an 'author, designer or plotter'; 'one who designs and builds military fortifications and machines'; 'one who makes *engines*' (depending here on the particular sense of *engine*); 'one who designs bridges, roads, etc' (*civil engineer* from the eighteenth century).◆

etiquette

a code of prescribed social behaviour

It is common etiquette *for the other guests to arrive before the Queen, but she wouldn't mind if someone was late. She is a very understanding woman. The Queen's private secretary would inform us at what time she planned to arrive. Susie would then ask our other guests to arrive half an hour earlier.*
(DAILY MAIL, 27 September 1994)

A 1913 agony aunt advised girls on mistletoe etiquette: *'Girls should remember that because a man wishes to kiss her under the mistletoe, he does not necessarily mean to propose to her.'*
(THE SUNDAY TIMES, 18 December 1994)

Christmas trees, once the repository of the family collection of baubles and fairy lights, are now a major style statement. . . From the moment your guests stand on your doorstep and see the wreath on the knocker, they will assess how traditional, fashionable, sophisticated or creative you are . . . And new Christmas etiquette

demands that you find out what theme your hostess has chosen so that you can wrap your presents to suit. There's creeping good taste everywhere . . .
(THE TIMES MAGAZINE, 24 December 1994)

Étiquette is, of course, a French word that has been borrowed directly into English. From the verb *estiquier* (related to Dutch *steken* and German *stechen* 'to stick, to fix' – source of the English verb *to stick*), Old French derived *estiquette*, or *etiquet*. The word was variously applied. In its old sense of 'a label' *étiquette* survives in modern French. In this sense also it was adopted into English around 1600, becoming the word *ticket*. Old French also used *estiquette* to denote the written order that assigned a soldier to his billet and again for a short note or notice posted on the door of a court to inform the public of a judicial order.

Later, however, the word was promoted from these humble beginnings to grace royal circles when visitors to the French court were issued with an *étiquette*, a card bearing instructions which outlined correct dress and procedure. By the time it was borrowed into English in the mid-eighteenth century the term had been transferred from the card to the code of behaviour inscribed on it.

Stories abound of the difficulties royal personages have been forced to endure in the name of *etiquette*. In many European courts touching royalty was absolutely forbidden, except to a very few. A story is told of the second wife of Charles II of Spain who was once riding a very spirited horse when the animal tried to throw her. The queen fell to the ground but with one foot caught fast in the stirrup. Irritated, the horse bucked and kicked but no one dared come to the queen's assistance, for no one qualified to touch her was present. Eventually two courageous cavaliers ran to her aid. The saving deed done, both men prepared to flee for their lives until they were informed by a messenger that the queen had interceded with the king on their behalf and they had been freely pardoned.

The modern British monarchy, though much more relaxed, still has its *etiquette* and those who break its rules are heavily censured, if only by the popular press. This happened in the early 1990s when the Prime Minister of Australia slipped an over-familiar, matey arm around the Queen's waist.

From the strictures of court ceremonial *etiquette* was later applied to behaviour in legal, professional and diplomatic circles, and finally to the behaviour expected of any well-bred person in society. In the Victorian era the market for books of etiquette boomed amongst the rising and prosperous middle classes, eager to learn the behaviour of the social élite. Readers were told how to dress and behave on particular occasions, how to order and leave visiting cards, how to greet people of different social classes and how to speak. A keen memory was required to remember one's table manners alone. MANNERS AND RULES OF GOOD SOCIETY (1888) has these niceties on eating cheese:

When eating cheese, small morsels of cheese should be placed with a knife on small morsels of bread, and the two conveyed to the mouth with the thumb and finger, the piece of bread being the morsel to hold as the cheese should not be taken up in the fingers, and should not be eaten off the point of the knife. As a matter of course, young ladies do not eat cheese at dinner parties.

It is easy to imagine that society in the late twentieth century has become so relaxed that etiquette is an out-of-date concept. No so. New acts of courtesy are demanded to suit the changing age:

At one time a man always walked on the right to keep his sword arm free; later he walked nearest the road to protect her from splashes and passing robbers. Today, in cities like New York, men are beginning to walk on the inside to ward off muggers in doorways.
(Moyra Bremner, MODERN ETIQUETTE AND SUCCESSFUL BEHAVIOUR, 1989)

The computer world also has its proper ways of behaving:

THE TENETS OF USENET 'NETIQUETTE'
Newcomers to Usenet should remember that they are about to encounter a different network culture, one with its own rules of behavior. Here's a list of the etiquette *issues involved. . .*
(COMPUSERVE MAGAZINE, January 1995)

For another word signifying a 'code of behaviour', see **protocol**.

exchequer

treasury, financial reserves

The enemies of Cortes had been, for a long time, busy in undermining his influence at court, and in infusing suspicions of his loyalty in the bosom of the emperor... They charged him with appropriating to his own use the gold which belonged to the crown, and especially with secreting the treasures of Montezuma. He was said to have made false reports of the provinces he had conquered, that he might defraud the exchequer *of its lawful revenues.*
(William Hickling Prescott, THE HISTORY OF THE CONQUEST OF MEXICO, 1843)

In the days of the Norman and Plantagenet kings the treasury table was covered by a cloth that was divided up into squares upon which coloured counters were used to keep track of revenue and expenditure. For obvious reasons, the table was referred to as the *eschequier*, the Old French word for a chessboard. This became *escheker* in Middle English, where it had the sense in the twelfth and thirteenth centuries not only of a judicial and financial department of state but still that of a chessboard.

Authorities differ as to whether *eschequier* to denote the treasury department originated in Normandy and came to England or whether it was the inspiration of the kings in England. Certainly the term was to be found in Norman French but, from the time when the duchy was recaptured from the English (1436–50) right up to François I (1494–1547), with the sense 'supreme court'.

The modern spelling with the prefix *ex-* is a result of a mistaken piece of spelling reform. If it was believed a word issued from a Latin original beginning with *ex-*, the prefix was attached to the English form: *eschange* and *esploit* thus properly became *exchange* and *exploit*. However, this should not have applied to *exchequer*. See **chess** for the correct etymology.

See **chancellor**.

excruciate

to inflict extreme pain, physical or mental, to torture

Foppa was decidedly short, always exquisitely dressed in a neat suit, blue or brown, his tiny feet encased in excruciatingly *tight shoes of light tan shade.*
(Anthony Powell, A DANCE TO THE MUSIC OF TIME, 1951–75)

> . . . *he [Pope] suffered* excruciating *torments every time he travelled along the bumpy roads of eighteenth-century England.*
>
> (Pat Rogers, Introduction to Pope's Complete Poetical Works, 1978)

> *The argument of the film . . . is that King George III was not truly disturbed in any psychological sense, but was driven to distraction by the agonising gastric discomfort of porphyria . . . In other words the king was not crazy, he was just mad with* excruciating *abdominal pain.*
>
> (Daily Telegraph, 25 March 1995)

The brutality of ancient Rome is encapsulated in the agonising death that was meted out to low-class criminals. Crucifixion was an horrific execution that originated with the Phoenicians and Carthaginians. Under the Romans, methods of crucifixion varied in different parts of the Roman empire, but each subjected the victim to long, racking torture. In 1968 the skeleton of a crucified man was discovered near Jerusalem. His arms had been nailed to the crossbeam of his cross, the weight of his body probably supported by a strip of wood nailed to the upright. His legs were not straight but had been twisted right back under him at the knee and secured to the upright at the ankles by a single iron nail. Both legs had been broken, a means of hastening death.

The Latin verb *excruciāre*, 'to torture', derives from this brutal punishment, being composed of the intensive prefix *ex-* and *cruciāre*, 'to torment', which itself comes from *crux*, 'cross, stake'. The English verb *to excruciate* was taken into English from Latin in the sixteenth century with the literal meaning 'to subject to torture' and the related meaning 'to inflict extreme pain'. Figuratively it was also used with the sense 'to cause intense mental agony'. In Tamburlaine (1586) Marlowe writes of a matter that '*doth* excruciate *The very substance of my vexed soul*.'

Like many etymologically powerful words, *excruciate* and its derivatives are considerably weakened by overuse and exaggeration.

◆ Other words which have come into English from Latin *crux* (stem *cruc*) are:

cross (10th cent): Middle English *cros*, Old English *cros*, Old Irish *cross*

crucial (18th cent): modern usage (19th cent) emerging from Bacon's phrase *instantia crucis*, 'crucial instance' (Novum Organum, 1620).This was a metaphor from a finger-post at a crossroads and which Bacon used to indicate a point of critical decision

crucible (15th cent): from Medieval Latin *crucibulum*, originally a night-lamp, perhaps one lit before a crucifix, later a melting-pot

crucifix (15th cent): from Old French *crucefix*, from Latin *crucifixus*, 'fixed to a cross'

crusade (16th cent): in the 1500s the French form *croisade* was used (from Old French *croisee*, from the past participle of *croiser*, 'to receive the mark of the cross', from *crois*, 'cross', from *crux*). English *crusade* is an eighteenth-century blend of this and *crusado*, (from the similarly derived Spanish word *cruzada*). Before this, Middle English had *croiserie*, a borrowing of the Old French word which was current at the time. The figurative use of *crusade* to mean 'vigorous opposition to a perceived evil' or 'an enthusiastic movement in support of a cause', dates from the eighteenth century.◆

For a word with a related sense, see **agony**.

explode

1. to go off, blow up
2. to refute, reject

It is not generally known that President Reagan was shot with an exploding *bullet in the assassination attempt on him in 1981, but that it failed to* explode. *Surgeons had to take special precautions when operating, since even the use of ultrasound or microwave diagnostic techniques could have set it off.*
(John May, THE BOOK OF CURIOUS FACTS, 1993)

Unexploded bombs (UXBs) were a constant threat. One in ten of the high explosive *bombs that fell did not* explode *on impact; many by malfunction, some . . . because they contained timing devices. By the end of the first phase of the Blitz a backlog of 3,000 such bombs needed attention.*
(DAILY MAIL, 20 February 1995)

The explosion *of the Valentine's Day industry is a very recent thing. It's just one arm of the greeting-cards monster that has grabbed Mothering Sunday, fingered Father's Day, and conjured Grandparents' Day from up its sleeve.*
(WEEKEND TELEGRAPH, 11 February 1995)

'*Why they did not hiss and* explode *him off the stage*' . . ., wrote Abraham Cowley (VERSES AND ESSAYS, 1663). Cowley was not, of course, suggesting that dynamite should be used to remove the actor from the stage but that he should be clapped off. *Explode* is borrowed from the Latin *explōdere* (from *ex-*, 'out' and *plaudere*, 'to clap'). Theatre audiences in ancient times did not tolerate actors whose performances were not up to scratch. Instead they would make their dissatisfaction obvious by hissing and clapping, so that the players could no longer continue and were forced to leave the stage. Even the basic verb *plaudere*, without the prefix, came to mean 'to express disapproval by clapping, hissing and stamping'. It was in use in this sense by the Christian writer Minutius Felix by AD230.

Figuratively applied, the same Latin verb *explōdere* meant 'to reject scornfully' and it was in this sense that it was taken into English in the sixteenth century. From this evolved the sense 'to cry down', 'to discredit', 'to reject'. David Hume's AN ENQUIRY CONCERNING HUMAN UNDERSTANDING (1748) talks of *exploding* a forgery and a superstition, and contains these lines:

How many stories of this nature have, in all ages, been detected and exploded *in their infancy? How many more have been celebrated for a time, and have afterwards sunk into neglect and oblivion?*

Modern English still speaks of *exploding a myth, hypothesis, theory, fallacy, lie, etc.*

The original theatrical meaning was not adopted into English until the first quarter of the seventeenth century. The learned cleric Robert Burton found use for it in his ANATOMIE OF MELANCHOLY (1621), when he wrote: *Vertue and Wisdom . . . were hissed out, and* exploded *by the common people.*

In the second half of the seventeenth century a new sense began to emerge from the theatrical one when the verb was applied, for instance, to a bullet being expelled from a gun with a sudden report, or coals being spat from a fire with a sharp crack. By the late eighteenth century the word had evolved still further to mean 'to burst apart with great force, to detonate', the familiar modern meaning.

For another word with the same Latin sense, see **plaudit**.

family

1. parents and their children
2. parents, children and relatives

All happy families *resemble one another; every unhappy* family *is unhappy in its own fashion.*
(Leo Tolstoy, ANNA KARENINA, 1873–76)

Pre-industrial societies have little notion of a person as a separate entity. A Nigerian psychiatrist told me that, when a psychiatric clinic was first set up in a rural district of Nigeria to treat the mentally ill, the family *invariably accompanied the sufferer and insisted upon being present at the patient's interview with the psychiatrist. The idea that the patient might exist as an individual apart from the* family, *or that he might have personal problems which he did not want to share with them, did not occur to Nigerians who were still living a traditional village life.*
(Anthony Storr, SOLITUDE, 1988)

Family obviously derives from the Latin word *familia* but the meaning of this word is not what one might expect. In Latin a *famulus* was a 'domestic servant'; *familia* was a collective noun that denoted 'all the servants in a Roman household'. When the word was borrowed into Middle English as *familie* around the turn of the fifteenth century, it was with this original meaning. This sense persisted until the nineteenth century and was variously extended to include the retinue of a nobleman or the staff of a high-ranking military officer.

During the mid-sixteenth century the term was also applied to an 'entire household', that is to everyone who lived under the same roof, from the master, his wife and children to their domestic servants. Not until the 1660s did the modern sense of *family* gradually begin to emerge: father, mother and children, whether or not they were living together.

fanatic

an over-zealous devotee

Of ballet fans *we are the cream,*
We never miss a night;
The ballet is our only theme,
Our Russian accent is a dream,
We say the name of every prim-
A ballerina right; . . .
(Herbert Farjeon [1881–1945], NINE SHARP AND EARLIER)

Fans *have been queuing over-night outside the Royal Opera House for Domingo's* Carmen. *Sleeping bags, blankets and hip flasks are arranged in a neat line along Floral Street.*

Another rather different queue of opera buffs formed at Glyndebourne for the first day of sales of the cheap(er) tickets for its new season which opens on May 28. A kind-faced member of the staff announced that Glyndebourne had laid on coffee and buns for the stout-hearted fanatics. *After the initial excitement the* fans *found that coffee and buns had indeed been provided – but at £1 a time.*
(DAILY TELEGRAPH, 14 May 1994)

Fanatic derives from the Latin adjective *fānāticus* which, in turn, comes from *fānum*, 'temple'. *Fānāticus* had two meanings: 'belonging to a temple' and, by extension, 'inspired or possessed by a divinity'. In sixteenth-century English *fanatic* described either 'irrational, frantic behaviour or speech that might indicate possession by a demon' or a person acting in such a way. By the second half of the seventeenth century the word, with all its implied criticism, was applied to a 'person prompted by excessive enthusiasm' and, more specifically, to the nonconformist congregations who argued against the established church, talked of fellowship with God, claimed to be directed by the Holy Spirit and were motivated by a fervent missionary zeal. Thus *fanatic* became synonymous with 'religious maniac'.

The word was given a new lease of life in late nineteenth-century America where it was applied to zealous baseball supporters who gave every indication of being possessed when they watched a game. From baseball the term was widened to include other sports and still further to apply to non-sporting hobbies and interests. The term, which was almost immediately shortened to *fan*, hit Britain in the second decade of the twentieth century. There are fans these days of anything from pop groups to home-made jam; those who want to set a better tone refer to themselves, with a term borrowed from Spanish, as *aficionados*.

For other words concerning temples, see **anathema, mint** and **temple**.

farce

1. an exaggerated comedy for humorous effect
2. something vain and utterly pointless

For if this book is a joke it is a joke against me. I am the man who with the utmost daring discovered what had been discovered before. If there is an element of farce *in what follows, the* farce *is at my own expense; for this book explains how I fancied I was the first to set foot in Brighton and then found I was the last.*
(G K Chesterton, ORTHODOXY, 1909)

Dumb and Dumber is about a character with broken teeth and a character with a pudding-basin haircut, and all the daft but warm-hearted things they do. It belongs in the tradition of low-denominator farce, *and seems to make folks feel good on afternoons when the weather is bad.*
(DAILY TELEGRAPH, 16 January, 1995)

Satire has encouraged people to see politics as an entertaining spectacle, – always a farce *but never a tragedy.*
(THE SUNDAY TIMES, 19 March, 1995)

French culinary terms seem to crop up in the strangest contexts, in this case ecclesiastical – see **hotch-potch** for another.

The basic meaning of the Latin verb *farcīre* was 'to stuff' and this gave the culinary terms *farcir*, 'to stuff' and the derived *farce*, 'stuffing' when it was borrowed into Old French. *Farse* is accordingly found in Middle English cookery books dating back to the fourteenth century to denote 'force-meat, filling'.

But *farcīre* carried a rather different meaning in the ecclesiastical Latin of the Middle Ages. In parts of southern Europe and England between the thirteenth and fifteenth centuries it had become common to expand the set text of the Latin liturgies with laudatory statements or to interject expository passages in the native language into the Latin chanting of the epistle. In these contexts *farcīre* had the sense 'to insert, to pad out' and the derived *farsa* denoted such an 'interjection'. The Old French *farce* reflected the culinary and ecclesiastical meanings. The liturgical insertions were likened to a stuffing which interlarded and so enhanced the main dish. In similar fashion, the ad libbing, witty remarks and entertaining horseplay that brightened medieval religious dramas were comic interpolations that by the fifteenth century had become an independent type of drama. As 'a short humorous dramatic piece', the word has been in use since the early sixteenth century in England.

Anthony Powell manages to combine a culinary with a dramatic context in this quotation:

Members was fond of quoting a mot of his master's to the effect that dinner at the Huntercombes' possessed 'only two dramatic features–the wine was a farce *and the food a tragedy'.*
(A DANCE TO THE MUSIC OF TIME, 1951–75)

The NEW SCIENTIST (1983) demonstrates another sense of the word that dates back to the seventeenth century where something that is a pretence or mockery is compared to a theatrical farce:

The End Users' Certificate system, whereby arms sales are supposedly made only when the end user is known, is a farce. *There is no way of monitoring arms once they are sold.*

fiasco

a total disaster, a débâcle

The United Nations fiasco *in Bosnia has set off predictable calls to pull out, since the war there is 'nothing to do with us'.*
(DAILY MAIL, 18 April 1994)

The new traffic scheme at Buckingham Palace was condemned as a fiasco *in the House of Lords last night . . . a succession of peers complained that they, like the Queen, taxi drivers and commuters, had been caught up in the roadworks set up six weeks ago.*
(THE TIMES, 8 March 1995)

Having only recently got the job, Peter Sullivan, editor of the Johannesburg daily newspaper The Star, *might be wishing he was still a humble hack after yesterday's* fiasco. *For Sullivan fled, under police protection, hordes of angry readers who were up in arms about a* Star *competition. They all thought they had won, but Sullivan had the unpleasant task of telling them they hadn't – their winning numbers were the result of a printing error.*
(FINANCIAL TIMES, 16 March, 1995)

Fiasco is an Italian word for 'a bottle' or 'a flask'. Its use to denote an 'embarrassing failure' arose from an Italian idiomatic expression *fare fiasco* (literally 'to make a bottle'), which meant 'to break down, to fail in a performance'. It was apparently traditional in Italian opera houses for the audience to cry '*Ola, Ola, fiasco!*' when a singer sang a false note or generally failed to please. Walsh quotes from an issue of the SATURDAY REVIEW which carried a piece about an Italian critic who used this custom in an ingenious visual way to assess each performance:

An Italian contemporary, in reviewing the past musical season, adopted recently a system of symbols which we may commend to the notice of English journalists. Appended to the notice of each new opera was the picture of a wine-flask, which varied in size with the degree of failure achieved by the particular work. Every one who remembers that the word fiasco *– popularised as a synonym with failure – is really the Italian for a flask, will perceive the convenient possibilities opened up by this method. At present the critic is often condemned to write whole columns of which the gist might be comprised in two words. How much better it would be if we adopted the delightfully terse symbolism thus suggested! One column would be reserved every week, the names of the pieces set down, and opposite we should put a finely-graded series of wine-flasks, showing the precise degree of good and ill success attained.*

Etymologists have pondered long and hard over exactly how *fiasco* came to be synonymous with 'failure'. Some have suggested that an empty wine bottle fails to please. Others have turned to the skilful Venetian glass makers for inspiration. They advance the theory that whenever a flaw was discovered in the bulb of a beautiful piece of glassware the blower would simply turn it into an ordinary bottle, a *fiasco* and, therefore, a failure.

◆ *Fiasco* derives from Late Latin *flascō*. The stem *flascōn-* gave Old French *flacon* and Middle English *flagon* (15th cent).

Flascō is a variant of Late Latin *flasca*. This became *flasque* in Old French and was borrowed into English as *flask* (14th cent).◆

filibuster

to obstruct legislation by delaying tactics, usually very long speeches

Even if the tort reform package survives the trial lawyers' assault in the House, opponents are threatening a filibuster *in the Senate. If there had been fine print in the* Contract With America, *it might have included language any trial lawyer would understand: 'Outcome may vary due to legislative maneuvering.'*
(James Popkin, U.S. News & World Report, 13 March 1995)

The history of this word is complex and its passage from language to language somewhat obscure. Etymologists agree, however, that its source is the Dutch *vrijbuiter*, from which English derived the word *freebooter*, a pirate who lived by free booty or plunder.

The trading history of the New World records how, in the seventeenth century, pirate adventurers attacked cargoes bound for Spain from the Indies and Central America. Alexander Esquemeling (sometimes Oexmelin) was a Dutch physician who lived among the buccaneers (see **buccaneer**) between 1668 and 1674. In the second edition of his subsequent account of their lives, De Americaensche Zee-Roovers (1686), he uses the word *flibuster* to describe French, English and Dutch piratical rovers who haunted the waters of the Spanish colonies. Esquemeling's statement that this corruption of the Dutch *vrijbuiter* is of English origin is entirely possible. Whatever its source, the word passed into French as *flibustier*, perhaps because of its frequent use in the English West Indian colonies. From French the word travelled again, this time into Spanish as *filibustero*.

In the mid-nineteenth century new groups of adventurers targeted Spanish–American territories. This time they came from the United States with a view to inciting revolution. In 1850–51, for instance, Narciso Lopez brought forces against the Cuban government and between 1855 and 1858 William Walker led expeditions to the State of Sonora, in Mexico, and to Nicaragua. An issue of The Gentleman's Magazine of 1856 called Walker *'the* filibustering *chief of Nicaragua'*. Both men were eventually captured and executed. When referring to such an adventurer English discarded the French form *flibustier*, which it had adopted at the end of the eighteenth century, in favour of *filibuster* from the Spanish *filibustero*.

The verb *to filibuster* developed in an entirely different context. In the early nineteenth century, members of the American senate gave the presiding officer powers to curtail lengthy or irrelevant speeches. In 1872 these powers were revoked. This move opened the door to that favourite weapon of legislative assemblies, delaying tactics. Senators employing them were accused of subverting and destabilising normal process, just as the adventurers had been doing south of the border. In short they were *filibustering.* These new possibilities for delay through enormously long speeches gave more precise definition to a verb that had already been in use since the middle of the century. Since then the verb has crossed the Atlantic and is freely used in Britain to describe the same practice of obstruction and delay. One who uses these methods is known as a *filibusterer.*

For another word arising from questionable political practice, see **gerrymander**.

flabbergast

to amaze totally, render speechless, gobsmack

'But to be killed like that? With a gun? Sten gun, no? In broad daylight? How can that happen? What the hell is going on?' Gomes was a Radio Ceylon man, continuously flabbergasted *by everything around him. He could only speak in a tone of high-pitched incredulity.*
(Romesh Gunesekera, REEF, 1994)

Flabbergast was a slang term that was either an invention or a dialectal borrowing of fashionable society in the eighteenth century. It was first recorded as a new word in 1772. The inspiration behind the coinage is not known for certain but most authorities reasonably suggest a humorous combination of *flabby* and *aghast.* The result is a word that speaks of a loose, gaping mouth and eyes opened wide-eyed in amazement.

Agast was originally a verb which meant 'to terrify'. It is found from the early thirteenth century onwards and goes back to the Old English *gæstan,* 'to frighten'. The contemporary *aghast* is the only survivor, from the past participle (shortened from *agasted*). The *h* was inserted from the early fifteenth century in Scotland and became the standard spelling from the end of the sixteenth century.

Flabby was a late seventeenth-century adaptation of *flappy,* itself a derivative of the verb *to flap. Flap* is an onomatopoeic word which, in the fourteenth century, meant 'to give a blow with a broad instrument or weapon' and also 'to applaud'. The sense 'to sway about limply', often implying that the movement is made with a slapping noise, developed from this in the first half of the sixteenth century. In the 1590s, therefore, someone described as *flappy* had swinging folds of spare flesh. To the seventeenth-century mind, however, the sharp sounding *flappy* was not evocative enough of round rolls of flaccid flesh and so the word was modified to *flabby,* to give a heavier ring. Three hundred years on, fighting the *flab* has become a national pastime, the derived noun emerging with this particular sense in the 1950s.

flower

1. a bloom, blossom
2. a plant with blooms

For general garden displays leave sweetpeas to their own devices, picking off dead flowers *each week. Leaving old* flowers *on the plants to set seed will prevent further* flowers *from forming. For big blooms, however, with long stems to pick as cut* flowers, *grow your sweetpeas as single stemmed cordons, pinching off sideshoots and tendrils.*
(WEEKEND TELEGRAPH, 4 March 1995)

How does your garden grow?

The common names of plants make a fascinating study. Some flowers are named for their appearance – *snowdrop, bluebell* and *sunflower* for instance. Others are more fanciful:

Carnation Originally in the sixteenth century the plant was called the *coronation*, a reference either to its jagged flower which resembled a little crown or to its use in floral garlands. Towards the close of the century, however, the name was confused with *carnation*, a colour term meaning 'flesh-colour' (from French *carnation*, 'flesh-colour', from Italian *carnagione*, from Latin *carnātiō*, 'fleshiness', from *caro*, 'flesh'), doubtless because the flowers were sometimes of this colour.

Coltsfoot The shape of the leaves suggests the hoof of a colt. Other animals occasionally lent their names to it: *fole foote, horse houe* or *bull foote*. Should the allusion seem too tenuous, French has *pas-d'âne*, 'ass's foot'.

Cranesbill This name, which is now applied to various species of geranium, though originally only to the *geranium dissectum*, is a translation by sixteenth-century herbalists from German and Dutch terms. It alludes to the long, pointed beak of the fruit.

Dandelion Middle English *dent-de-lion*, from an Old French translation of medieval Latin *dens leonis*, 'lion's tooth', an allusion to the jagged leaves. Vulgarly the plant was called *pissabed*, in French *pissenlit*, because of its diuretic properties.

Foxglove (Old English *foxes glōfa*, 'fox's glove') So called because the individual flowers look like finger-stalls. The reference to the fox is obscure but Norwegian has *revbjelde*, 'fox bell'. The modern Latin name for the plant is *digitalis*, from Latin *digitālis*, 'of the fingers', and was bestowed by the German herbalist Fuchs in 1542 after the German name *Fingerhut*, 'thimble'.

Garlic The Old English compound is *gārlēac* where *lēac* means 'leek' and *gār* 'spear', descriptive of the shape of the leaves.

Orchid The Greeks named the plant *orkhis*, 'testicle', because of the shape of the tubers. The English word is formed from the Latin borrowing *orchis*. Seventeenth-century botanists erroneously believed the Latin stem to be *orchid-*, thus introducing the final *d*.

Pansy This viola was popularly called *pensée*, 'thought', by the French, possibly because its markings resemble a face with a thoughtful look. English borrowed the word at the turn of the sixteenth century, but the modern spelling did not evolve until the eighteenth.

continued over page

How does your garden grow? continued

Snapdragon To the sixteenth-century imagination the two-lipped flowers of the antirrhinums were fashioned like a dragon's mouth.

Tulip Originally named for its resemblance to a turban. Sixteenth-century English from New Latin *tulipa*, from *tülibend*, a vulgar Turkish borrowing of unattested Persian *dulband*, 'turban'.

Other plants were named for the place in which they grew. Sixteenth-century botanists list the *wallflower* and *cornflower*, for instance, but other names are less obvious:

Cowslip In Old English the plant was *cūslyppe* or *cūsloppe* where *cū* meant 'cow' and *slyppe* 'a slimy dropping'. Thus the plant was named for its proliferation in fields abundantly fertilised by grazing cattle.

Houseleek In Old English this was probably *hūslēac* (from *hūs*, 'house', and *lēac*, 'leek'), giving *howsleke* in Middle English. The plant was so named because it was often grown on roofs, perpetuating the belief held by the Romans that it offered the household protection against lightning and evil. For this reason it was also known as *Jove's beard*, Jove (or Jupiter) being the god of the elements.

Oxlip The name was formed like cowslip from Old English *oxan*, 'of an ox', and *slyppe*, 'dung', giving *oxanslyppe*.

Rosemary This is a native of southern Europe and was known as *rōs marīnus*, 'sea dew', in Latin (from *rōs*, 'dew', and *marīnus*, 'of the sea', from *mare*, 'sea'), supposedly because the plant grew profusely on the coast. The word came into Middle English as *rosmarine* via Old French *rosmarin* and Late Latin *rosmarinum*, but its form was soon altered because of the elements' similarity to *rose* and *Mary*, the name of the Virgin.

Other plants were named for the uses to which they were put. The *euonymus*, for instance, was commonly known as the spindle-tree as its wood was excellent for making spindles (see **spinster**).

Thyme The Greeks evidently used this herb as a sweet-smelling burnt offering. Its name ultimately derives from Greek *thuos*, 'sacrificial incense', and *thuein*, 'to offer a burnt sacrifice to the gods'. Thus Greek *thumon* was named for its sweet sacrificial smell. From it Latin derived *thymum* and Old French *thym*, borrowed into Middle English as *tyme*.

Many of the uses to which plants were put were of course medicinal and this is reflected in their names: *feverfew*, *fleabane* and *sneezewort*, for instance.

Sage *Sauge* in Middle English, a borrowing from Old French *sauge* and from Latin *salvia* which means 'the healing plant' (from *salvus*, 'healthy').

According to medieval belief, plants with particular medicinal properties bore a signature, that is a mark, feature or colouring, which indicated their usefulness.

Thus the *lungwort*, which has white-spotted leaves reminiscent of a diseased lung, was thought to heal pulmonary disorders. The *viper's bugloss*, on the other hand, was deemed efficacious against the viper's bite because its seed looked like a viper's head, while its stem resembled snake skin. Wounds from agricultural implements were treated with *self heal*, a herb whose flower bears a petal shaped like a billhook.

Plants might also be named after a particular characteristic they displayed:

Daisy The Middle English forms *daisie* and *dayeseye* derived from the Old English *doegesēage*, literally 'day's eye' (from *doeg*, 'day' and *ēage*, 'eye'), an allusion to the fact that the petals open in the day to reveal the flower's yellow eye and close again in the evening.

Honeysuckle Old English had *hunigsūce* (from *hunig*, 'honey' and *sūcan*, 'to suck') which gave *honysouke(l)* in Middle English. Originally the word was used of any flower, especially the clover, which readily yielded nectar for honey and then, in the sixteenth century, to the climbing woodland shrub familiar to modern gardens.

Lupin The plant was originally grown for animal fodder and for its seed, which was used as a vegetable. The Romans called it *lupīnum*, derived from *lupīnus*, meaning 'wolf-like' (from *lupus*, 'wolf'). Ancient belief held that, just as the wolf was a greedy, ravenous creature, so the *lupin* destroyed the soil, sucking out all the goodness.

Nasturtium This is a kind of cress with edible leaves. According to Pliny, their pungent taste gave rise to the plant's Latin name, *nāsturtium* (from unattested *nāsitortium*, from *nāsus*, 'nose' and *tortus*, from *torquēre*, 'to twist'). The allusion is to the burning felt at the back of the nose when the plant is eaten. (French has *nasitort*.)

Soapwort '*The stalkes of Sope-woort are slipperie*,' declared the herbalist John Gerarde (HERBALL, 1597). The plant is named because a lather forms when its stems are rubbed. Dutch and German have similar names for the plant and the English term is perhaps fashioned after these.

The Indo-European root *bhlō-*, meaning 'to flourish', influenced both Latin and the Germanic languages so that 'floral' words which appear very different are, in fact, cognates. *Bhlō-* was responsible for Old English *blōstm*, a general word for 'flower' which has become *blossom* in Modern English. It is also the ultimate source of Middle English *blom* or *blome*, meaning 'bloom', so that, eventually, a finer distinction was drawn between 'blossom', which heralded fruit, and 'bloom', which was considered the ultimate glory of the plant.

Latin *flōs*, 'flower', was also derived from *bhlō-*. *Flōs* had the stem *flōr-* from which the Romance languages derived their words for 'flower'. Old French had *flor* or *flour*, both of which were borrowed into Middle English.

In the thirteenth century the word also developed a specific use to denote 'the finest quality meal, from whatever grain, that could be separated off by sieving', and eventually became a general term for 'ground grain'. When the variant spelling *flower* arose in the first half of the sixteenth century, the forms *flour* and *flower* were used interchangeably in both senses of the word. By the end of the sixteenth century *flower* was being regularly used to denote 'bloom', although either form continued to be used for 'milled grain'. In his DICTIONARY OF THE ENGLISH LANGUAGE (1755), however, Dr Johnson refused even to recognise the spelling *flour*, let alone make a distinction in meaning between the two forms and indeed, as late as 1806, a travel book about France advised '*in a long voyage* . . . flower *will not keep.*'

◆Other words deriving from Latin *flōr-* include:

flora (from Latin mythology, Flora, goddess of flowers)

floral (17th century)

florist (17th century)

flourish (14th century, through Old French *florir*, 'to flower')

florid (17th century, through French *floride*)◆

focus

a central point, a point of convergence

The family tree is the emotional focus *of Christmas – an altar for presents in the eyes of small children, a shrine of memories for their elders. Penny Rigby, owner of Tomlinsons and The Dulwich Trader shops, is still forced to put on the loo-roll angels her sons made when they were small (they're now 15, 19 and 24).*
(THE TIMES MAGAZINE, 24 December 1994)

On a winter Saturday morning, the real focus *of attention is the dance floor itself, constructed, so the blurb tells you, of 57,000 individual blocks of mahogany and oak.*
(INDEPENDENT WEEKEND, 28 January 1995)

When central heating became widespread in the 1960s, people blocked up their chimneys and many houses were built with no chimney at all. It was soon recognised that rooms lacked a focal point and so, in the 1980s and 90s, the fireplace was reinstated. Those designers and architects who describe the hearth as the *focus* or *focal* point of a room are reviving the word's origins for, in Roman times, *focus* meant 'fireplace, hearth'.

Our modern uses of *focus* arise from scientific and geometric applications of the word. In the science of optics in the seventeenth century, *focus* was aptly chosen to denote 'the point at which rays converge when reflected', in other words 'the burning point of a lens'.

Although this use is first recorded in the 1680s it is thought to have been in circulation rather earlier and to have inspired the German astronomer Johannes Kepler's geometric application of the word in 1604 to 'one of the points from which the distances to any point of a given curve are connected by a linear relation', the burning point of a curved mirror and its geometrical focus being at the same point.

Extended scientific uses apart, in the late eighteenth century *focus* also began to develop the sense of 'centre of energy or activity'; it was used to denote the eye of a storm, earthquake or eruption, for instance. From the early nineteenth century this was figuratively extended to denote 'the seat of intrigue or initiative' and then, more widely, 'the centre of attention, interest, concern, etc.'

◆ From *focus* Medieval Latin derived *focārium*, 'hearthstone'. This was borrowed into French as *foyer* which embraces all the senses of English *focus* as well as the Latin ones of 'hearth and home'. From the notion of the family gathered under one roof, French extended the use of *foyer* to denote the 'green-room' of a theatre, where actors not required on stage could congregate. Later the term was applied to the lobby used by the audience during intervals and, in this latter sense, it was borrowed into English in the nineteenth century.

Over the centuries Latin *focus* came to mean not only 'hearth' but also the contents of the hearth, the fire itself. Today it is found in Spanish *fuego*, Portuguese *fogo* and Italian *fuoco*. It is also the root of the French *feu*, 'fire'. This last has come into English in various guises. See **curfew** for one of its appearances. Another is in *fuel*. Latin *focus* spawned the Vulgar Latin *focālia*. This was used in the medieval Latin of both France and England as a legal term for a particular right to demand fuel. From it was derived the thirteenth-century Old French blend *feu* + *aille*, literally 'material for a fire', *-aille* being a collective noun suffix. A century later, this word had been borrowed into English as *fuel*.◆

freelance

a self-employed professional, often a writer or artist

ONLY SIX WITH RINGS. . .

Sally Stephens is a freelance *writer living in San Francisco. Her last story for* ASTRONOMY *was* Telescopes that Fly,' *November 1994.*

(ASTRONOMY, April 1995)

In the fourteenth to the sixteenth centuries mercenaries operated throughout Europe, knights who, being free of any particular allegiance, would take their lances into battle for whichever prince or state had paid most for their services. Nineteenth century authors writing about the period coined the term *freelance* when referring to them. In IVANHOE (1819), for example, Scott refers to knights as *lances*: *I can form no guess – unless he be one of the good* lances *who accompanied King Richard to Palestine.*

They form a company:

He is a monarch by whom Fitzurse and De Bracy hope to rise and thrive; and therefore you aid him with your policy, and I with the lances *of my Free Companions.*

Finally they demonstrate one of the earliest uses of the term that we know today:

'Ay,' said Fitzurse, 'such is indeed the fashion of Richard – a true knight-errant he, and will wander in wild adventure, trusting the

prowess of his single arm – What dost thou propose to do, De Bracy?"

'I? – I offered Richard the service of my Free Lances, *and he refused them – I will lead them to Hull, seize on shipping, and embark for Flanders; thanks to the bustling times, a man of action will always find employment.'*

During the second half of the century the word was figuratively applied to a rogue politician who, being independent of party loyalty, was free to side as inclination took him. The modern application of 'one who works for himself' arose in the last quarter of the nineteenth century.

funny bone

1. the part of the elbow where the ulnar nerve is easily stimulated
2. a sense of humour

SHOW PEOPLE: IN YOUR FUNNYBONE *RATHER THAN YOUR FACE: PUNT AND DENNIS*

After nearly 10 years in the business, Punt and Dennis deserve the chance. Their humour is sharp, but not show-off. They may make jokes about Titus Andronicus and Chaucer, but they also like a good fart gag. Indeed, the day we met, they had been involved in an exchange with the BBC authorities over the use of that particular F – word – 'one of the funniest words in the English language,' according to Punt. Theirs is a playful, amiable sort of comedy, not so much in-your-face as in-your- funnybone.

(INDEPENDENT ON SUNDAY, July 3 1994)

They have pulled you down flat on your back!
And they smack and they thwack,
Till your funny-bones *crack*
As if you were stretched on the rack.
(R.H. Barham, INGOLDSBY LEGENDS: BLOUDIE JACKE OF SHREWSBERRIE, 1840)

Etymologists – not normally given to an outbreak of that British idiosyncrasy, the pun – have boldly declared in seeking an explanation for *funny bone* that it is so named because it is part of the humerus. In reality the word *funny* should probably be understood in its sense of 'strange,' and it refers here to the unpleasant prickling sensation that is felt when the ulnar nerve, which passes over the end of the humerus, receives a sharp knock.

gargantuan

huge, colossal, of vast proportion

Anyone who feels like investing in a few grams of silver should call up a certain Carroll Jones in his office in Washington. Jones, an official in the US government's General Services Agency, has $2,000 million worth of the stuff that he would dearly love to get rid of. Likewise, if it is tin that you hanker for, Jones is in charge of 150,000 tonnes of the material that his political masters have decided they no longer need. The tin – worth another $2000 million – will reside in government warehouses until the US Congress decides to sell. The gargantuan *quantities of tin and silver are part of the stockpile of strategic materials that, since 1950, the American government has stored away, squirrel-like, in case of an emergency such as a world war.*

(NEW SCIENTIST, 1983)

. . . many thousands of kilometres of water mains are corroding. . . The task of maintaining and improving Britain's crumbling system of sewers and water mains is gargantuan.

(NEW SCIENTIST, 1983)

Ageing rockers and balding hippies will remember the moment with horrid clarity. At virtually every gig in the late Sixties and early Seventies, the band would gradually

drift off stage, leaving only the drummer and his gargantuan *kit. There was no doubt about it, we were in for the drum solo. . .*
(DAILY TELEGRAPH, 26 January, 1994)

Gargantua was the name of a giant celebrated in medieval French folklore. In 1534 François Rabelais further popularised the character when he wrote LA VIE INESTIMABLE DU GRANT GARGANTUA, PÈRE DE PANTAGRUEL, based on a chapbook of legends about him. The story was a peg upon which to hang a bawdy and irreverent satire on the systems and society of sixteenth century France; the church, the law, politics, education and social conventions were all ridiculed by Rabelais, who promoted the humanistic thinking and learning that was emerging in Europe at that time.

Gargantua's name was probably derived from Spanish *garganta*, 'throat'. It was particularly apt since he was portrayed as a being of enormous, insatiable appetite: on one occasion he accidently swallowed five pilgrims along with the rest of his dinner. Shakespeare made reference to a throat that could gulp down such a meal with ease in AS YOU LIKE IT (1599):

Rosalind: Answer me in one word.
Celia: You must borrow me Gargantua's *mouth first before I can utter so long a word: 'tis a word too great for any mouth of this age's size.* (Act 3 scene 2)

Indeed, the giant *Gargantua* was so colossal in stature that his horse sported the stolen bells of Notre Dame about its neck and flattened a forest with a swish of its tail. Small wonder, then, that his larger-than-life exploits captured popular imagination and gave rise to the French adjective *gargantuesque* and our own *gargantuan*, to describe anything of vast proportion.

gerrymander

to change electoral boundaries for political advantage

The Court condemned the school district as an improper gerrymander, *tailored solely for the convenience of a particular religious group. In the Court's view, the New York state law creating the school district had improperly singled out the Satmar Hasidim for a special privilege not available to other groups.*

But, it should be noted, the Supreme Court has never been much troubled by gerrymandering *when the beneficiaries were minorities it has deemed deserving. In 1977, for example, the Court . . . upheld a scheme expressly designed to increase the number of districts that would elect black representatives in Brooklyn. In 1993 (in Shaw v. Reno), the Court, in a 5–4 decision, did voice doubts about a racially*-gerrymandered *district in North Carolina because its eel-shaped configuration was too 'bizarre.' But here, too, the Court held that race could legitimately be considered in drawing electoral maps as long as it was not the only factor taken into account. Moreover, the dissenting Justices insisted that such racial* gerrymandering *was fully in accord with the Constitution, at least when done for the benefit of an officially recognized 'minority' group.*
(Jeremy Rabkin, COMMENTARY, November 1994)

The new authorities and electoral wards have been created not by the impartial Boundary Commission but by the Secretary of State for Scotland. Despite his shameless gerrymandering, *the Tories will be trounced.*
(GUARDIAN, 4 April 1995)

The word was coined in part from the name of Elbridge *Gerry* who, in 1811, was re-elected Governor of Massachusetts for the Republicans. At that time the legislative assemblies were both Republican, though only by a slender majority. In order to give their party increased representation in the State Senate, the Republicans rearranged the state district boundaries so that Federal majorities would occur in only one or two and a Republican landslide would be assured. The act authorising these changes was duly signed by Governor Gerry on 11 February 1812.

The story goes that, in his Boston office, Benjamin Russell, editor of the Federalist newspaper the COLUMBIAN CENTINEL, was pondering over a map of the nonsensical divisions proposed for Essex county which hung on his wall. Suddenly the painter Gilbert Stuart, who was in the office at the time, seized his pencil and rapidly transformed the outline of the new county boundaries into a creature by adding a head, wings and claws. 'That will do for a salamander,' he said. '*Gerrymander*!' retorted Russell.

Whether or not these are the exact circumstances under which *gerrymander* was produced, the caricature was appropriated for the Federalist cause. Soon the term *gerrymander* was transferred from the creature itself to the tactics and, within a few months, had also become a verb.

In spite of this popular propaganda, however, the gerrymandering led the Republicans to victory. The Federalists polled a greater total vote but won only 11 seats to the Republicans' 29. It was, perhaps, a crumb of comfort to the Federalist party, however, that Gerry was a casualty of the election and that the bill of 1812 was repealed the following year.

For another term denoting a questionable political practice, see **filibuster**.

giraffe

a large African cud-chewing animal, with long neck and legs, and a spotted skin

Anarchism adjures us to be bold creative artists, and care for no laws or limits. But it is impossible to be an artist and not care for laws and limits. Art is limitation; the essence of every picture is the frame. If you draw a giraffe, *you must draw him with a long neck. If, in your bold creative way, you hold yourself free to draw a* giraffe *with a short neck, you will really find that you are not free to draw a* giraffe. *The moment you step into the world of facts, you step into a world of limits.*
(G K Chesterton, ORTHODOXY, 1909)

Down in the dustbowl crate . . . game is plentiful, and you can expect to see most species (except giraffe, *who find the walls a tad too vertical).*
(GOOD HOUSEKEEPING, April, 1995)

The Greeks called the giraffe *kamēlopardalis.* This was a compound of two words, *kamēlos,* 'camel' and *pardalis* (variant of *pardos*), 'leopard' and was formed because the creature has a head like a camel's and the patterned skin of the leopard. Latin borrowed this as *camēlopardalis,* which became *camēlopardus* in Medieval Latin. The word came into English as *cameleopard* in the late fourteenth century, the spelling erroneously influenced by that of *leopard.* It was regularised as *camelopard* in the seventeenth century.

In the late sixteenth century, however, *camelopard* was put under pressure by a new term which eventually won out. Italian had *giraffa* and French *giraffe,* words derived from Arabic *zarāfah,* which may ultimately be of African origin. Sixteenth- and seventeenth-century texts show evidence of borrowing from both Italian and French sources, so it is difficult to establish which language English borrowed from, although by the eighteenth century the French spelling was settled upon. Ironically, Modern French now has *girafe.*

gorilla

a very large, strong African ape

Notwithstanding her youth, she was large and powerful – a splendid, clean-limbed animal, with a round, high forehead, which denoted more intelligence than most of her kind possessed. So, also, she had a great capacity for mother love and mother sorrow. But she was still an ape, a huge, fierce, terrible beast of a species closely allied to the gorilla, *yet more intelligent; which, with the strength of their cousin, made her kind the most fearsome of those awe-inspiring progenitors of man.*
(Edgar Rice Burroughs, TARZAN OF THE APES, 1914)

Gorillas *are four times the size of chimps. Their brains are larger in absolute terms than those of chimps but relative to body size, they are considerably smaller . . . if you consider the order of primates as a whole, you find there is a significant relationship between relative brain size and diet...the genera that eat fruit have larger brains in proportion to their body size than those that eat leaves. . . The diet of a* gorilla *consists of nearly 90 per cent foliage, while chimpanzees eat mainly fruit.*
(NEW SCIENTIST, 1983)

Evidence for this word, like that of *canary,* rests on a later surviving translation of a lost original. In this case an account of a voyage, the *Periplūs* or 'circumnavigation', written in Punic, has come down to us in Greek. When Hanno, the Carthaginian navigator, sailed the west coast of Africa in the fifth or sixth century BC he returned wide-eyed with tales of an island inhabited by a tribe of hairy women who, he was informed, were called *Gorillai.* Many centuries later in 1847 Dr Thomas S. Savage, an American missionary and naturalist, was excited by the discovery of great apes while on an exploration of West Africa and suggested naming the creature *Trogolodytes Gorilla.* It is possible, of course, the wild hirsute tribeswomen Hanno came across may have been gorillas all along, in which case Dr Savage's observation was a mere rediscovery.

gossip

1. a person, usually a woman, who talks about others behind their backs
2. idle rumour
3. a chat, a natter

Mrs. Cole, acting admirably the good old prating gossip, *who lets every thing escape her when her tongue is set in motion, cooked him up a story so plausible of me . . . as finished him finely for her purpose, whilst nothing could be better counterfeited than her innocence of his.*
(John Cleland, FANNY HILL, 1749)

The men of the new regiment watched and listened eagerly, while their tongues ran on in gossip *of the battle. They mouthed rumors that had flown like birds out of the unknown.*
(Steven Crane, THE RED BADGE OF COURAGE, 1895)

'I always speaks fair of folks when I can,' continued Mrs Pringle self-righteously, putting down her dustpan and settling herself on the front desk for a good gossip.
(Miss Read, OVER THE GATE, 1964)

Gossip derives from Old English *godsibb,* a compound noun made up of *god* and *sibb*. While *god* is readily understood in modern English, *sibb* meant 'kinsman, relative' and is apparent today in the word *sibling*. The word was composed in the eleventh century to denote a 'godparent, one who agreed to assist the spiritual nurturing of the child'. Richard Verstegan, antiquary and zealous Catholic, writing at the beginning of the seventeenth century, expressed the relationship thus:

Our Christian ancestors understanding a spiritual affinity to grow between the parents, and such as undertooke for the child at baptisme, called each other by the name of Godsib, *that is, of kin together through God: and the child in like manner called such his godfathers and godmothers.*

If Verstegan is right, the bond of spiritual kinship did not only exist between the child and its sponsors but involved the whole family. Since friends would be invited to enter into this special relationship, it is not surprising that, by the fourteenth century, *godsib* had come to mean a 'familiar friend'.

Friends generally enjoy a good chat in each other's company and so by the second half of the sixteenth century a *gossip* also denoted 'someone who indulges in tittle-tattle'. In John Heywood's comedy JOHAN JOHAN, THE HUSBANDE, TYB HIS WYFE, AND SYR JHĀN THE PREEST (1533), the wife's *gossyp*, 'good friend', is aptly named, since Margery, together with other derivatives of Margaret, was used of a talkative woman (see **magpie**):

Truely Johan Johan we made a pye
I and my gossyp *Margery.*

Gossips were usually women – possibly because a woman's particular chums were usually invited to attend her in childbirth (the term *gossip* was used in this context also), but more likely through an already centuries-old reputation women had for talkativeness – and the word carries this gender bias even to the present day. Surprisingly, *gossip* as a term for 'idle chit-chat' or 'a juicy rumour' has only been current since the early nineteenth century.

grape

a small round fruit, growing in clusters on a vine, often used to make wine

THE FOX AND THE GRAPES
One hot summer's day a Fox was strolling through an orchard till he came to a bunch of Grapes *just ripening on a vine which had been trained over a lofty branch. 'Just the thing to quench my thirst,' quoth he. Drawing back a few paces, he took a run and a jump, and just missed the bunch. Turning round again with a One, Two, Three, he jumped up, but with no greater success. Again and again he tried after the tempting morsel, but at last had to give it up, and walked away with his nose in the air, saying: 'I am sure they are sour.'*

It is easy to despise what you cannot get.
(AESOP'S FABLES, 6th century BC)

Hot-country whites [wines] need cold-country treatment. You have got to try to harvest your grapes *at their coolest. The warmer the* grapes, *the bigger the risk of oxidation and oxidation produces flat, decayed flavours and dull, dark colours.*
(WEEKEND TELEGRAPH, 25 February, 1995)

Grapes have been cultivated since late prehistoric times, not so much for their fruit as for the production of wine. The early English word, Old English *wīnberige*, literally 'wineberry', reflects this preoccupation. The thirteenth-century borrowing *grape* which replaced it takes its name from a tool used in viticulture. *Grape* in Old French meant 'vine-hook' and came from the unattested Germanic root *krappon*, 'hook'. *Graper* was a derived verb which meant 'to gather clusters of grapes with a hook'. From this came the further noun *grape* which denoted 'a bunch of grapes' (Modern French has *grappe*, 'bunch of grapes'), and this was the sense in which it was first borrowed into Middle English. The new word, however, was often used in contexts which demanded the plural, *grapis*, so that eventually it was taken to refer to the number of berries in the bunch. Thus – logically, if erroneously – *grape* came to denote a single berry.

◆ Further derivatives of Old French *grape*, 'hook', which have been borrowed into English are:
grapnel (14th cent) from Old French *grapon*
grapple (16th cent) from Old French *grapelle* ◆

great

1. large, big
2. important, prominent

And for an hour I have walked and prayed
Because of the great *gloom that is in my mind.*
(W B Yeats, A Prayer for My Daughter, 1919)

He originated nothing, he could keep the routine going – that's all. But he was great. *He was* great *by this little thing that it was impossible to tell what could control such a man. He never gave that secret away.*
(Joseph Conrad, The Heart of Darkness, 1902)

In the ninth century the opposing adjectives *great* and *small* had the meanings 'stout' and 'slender' respectively. The concept 'large in size' was denoted by *mickle*, an adjective which is now rarely heard. The sense 'of wide girth' is evident in the early thirteenth-century application of *great* to women in the advanced stages of pregnancy. This use is familiar through old translations of the Bible:

And all went to be taxed, everyone into his own city. And Joseph also went up from Galilee, out of the city of Nazareth, into Judaea, unto the city of David, which is called Bethlehem... to be taxed with Mary, his espoused wife, being great *with child.*
(King James Authorised Version, 1611, Luke 2:4–6)

Great acquired the general sense 'large' around the beginning of the fourteenth century, its importance as an adjective of size and stature increasing steadily to supersede *mickle*. In the same period the word was also applied figuratively to people or events to give the meaning 'distinguished', 'eminent', 'prominent'.

Towards the end of the thirteenth century a new and powerful little word, possibly of Norse origin, started to appear in the works of writers in the north-eastern counties. *Big* originally meant 'strong', 'powerful', 'mighty'. This sense still lingers in the coupling *big and strong*. Strong men and cities are usually of substantial proportion, however, and so by the sixteenth century *big* had developed the sense 'of large size'. In Modern English *big* has usurped *great* just as *great*, in earlier centuries, superseded *mickle*.

Great still reigns, however, as an adjective with a meaning of pre-eminence and status; there is a world of difference between a *great* man or woman and a *big* one.

guerrilla

an independent soldier in an irregular group

Documentary footage shows guerrillas *planting their flag, Iwo Jima-style, as they storm an Israeli position. Israeli troops load casualties onto stretchers and into helicopters. 'Thousands upon thousands are waiting for their martyrdom,' says Nasrallah of his forces.*
(TIME, 6 March 1995)

Guerrilla is a Spanish word, a diminutive of *guerra*, meaning 'war'. It came into English during the Peninsula War (1808–14), which Britain, together with Spain and Portugal, fought against the Napoleonic invasion of Iberia. Here it referred to the independent tactics of the resistance movement. In one of his despatches early in the war (1809), however, Wellington applied the term to individuals thus engaged rather than to the warfare itself. This is generally how it has come to be used in English where a *guerrilla* is one who is involved in *guerrilla warfare.*

guillotine

a device for beheading criminals, political opponents, etc.

With no income prisoners turned their hands to their trained crafts . . . and bartered their products for extra food and medicines. Later, supplies of bone from the prison kitchens were supplemented with materials brought in by visitors, and markets were established within the prisons. . . . [Bone] models of the guillotine *are probably the most dramatic works made by the Napoleonic prisoners. The gruesome detail, as in the example in Mr Pilcher's collection, includes a decapitated head. Last December, Phillips Edinburgh, the auctioneers, sold a two-storey example with two figures, a working blade and a basket for £750, plus 15 per cent buyer's premium. Outstanding models of* guillotines *can make £5000.*
(THE TIMES, 7 May 1994)

Cracked, battered and wet, [the icons] lay exposed to the snow and sleet, their faces confused, like those of aristocrats the wrong side of the guillotine.
(Leslie Wilson, Market Choice, in GOOD HOUSEKEEPING, November 1994)

Who was who?

An eponym is a word that goes back to a name. In this book there is the story of *bloomers, guillotine, sandwich, tantalise, wellington.*

There are several categories of eponyms: most go back to individuals, but some refer to places (see **gypsy**) and some to trade names (see **jeep** and **tabloid**), but there are many more of all types. The general tests of their acceptance into the vocabulary are various, for example:

- the initial capital is no longer used (*aspirin*, not Aspirin).
- the word is employed even for a competitor's product (how many people realise the contradiction when they *xerox* a document with a machine that does not come from the Xerox Corporation?).
- one is surprised to discover the word once referred principally to a proprietary product (*brassière, celluloid, codswallop, trampoline, zip*).

Just before her execution in 1536 Anne Boleyn is said to have remarked with thankfulness that she had a little neck: she knew that decapitation with an axe or sword seldom rushed the victim into swift oblivion. Two hundred and fifty years later, this suffering stirred a politician to action, and gave the world a new word.

In common with other European countries, France had a two-tier system of execution. Beheading was the prerogative of the nobility; the common people suffered the gibbet. This inequality together with concern for the agonies endured by victims troubled a certain Joseph Ignace *Guillotin*. Guillotin was a physician and a Deputy of the Constituent Assembly. On 10 October 1789, he voiced his concern during an assembly debate on reforms in criminal jurisprudence. He proposed that '*in all cases where the law shall pass sentence of death upon a convicted person, the punishment shall be the same, whatever the nature of the offence of which he shall be found guilty. Such punishment shall be decapitation, and the execution shall be carried out by a simple machine.*'

Guillotin probably already had a 'simple machine' in mind, for contraptions similar to the *guillotine* had already been used in Scotland during the sixteenth and seventeenth centuries, and in thirteenth- and fourteenth-century Italy. When, in 1792, his reform was finally adopted, Guillotin consulted with a surgeon, Dr Antoine Louis who came up with the *louison* or *louisette*, a machine originally named for its inventor, but which soon became known as the *guillotine* after its champion. This was a shortening of *la machine guillotine* or of the popular term *Madame Guillotine*. The miscreant who had the honour of trying out the efficiency of the contraption was a highwayman named Pelletier, who knelt beneath the gleaming blade on 25 April 1792. What he thought of it has not been recorded.

Ironically, Dr Louis in some accounts was beheaded subsequently by his own invention and Dr Guillotin only just escaped. Over two centuries earlier, the Earl of Morton in 1571 had the Maiden (an early guillotine) brought from Halifax in Yorkshire to Edinburgh, to execute rebellious noblemen. In 1581, he too was beheaded by his own machine.

The word *guillotine* entered English in 1793. This was not surprising since the year was marked by two deeply shocking events. Firstly it saw the beginning of the Reign of Terror when the guillotine was used for the systematic execution of thousands who were charged with opposing the revolution. Secondly 1793 brought the execution of King Louis XVI and his queen, Marie Antoinette.

It is rumoured that after the French Revolution, the original guillotine was sold by the public executioner to Curtius who then sold it at a profit to his niece Madame Tussaud. That good lady recouped the price and more by displaying it in her Chamber of Horrors. Dr Guillotin is supposed to have tried to disassociate his name from the terrible machine after the horrific use to which it was put, but to no avail. Upon his death in 1814 his children did the next best thing and sought legal permission to change their name.

Since the early nineteenth century *guillotine* has been used in a wide variety of industries to refer to any number of devices which cut with a slicing movement. Also since that century the word has been prominent in parliamentary procedure to describe a means of limiting the discussion of a bill by naming a day when the Committee stage must close.

For another word deriving from the executioner's scaffold, see **derrick**.

gypsy

1. an itinerant trader of the Romany people
2. a rootless wanderer

Then, in high summer, more gipsies *come, bearing gaudy flowers made of woodshavings and dyed all the colours of the rainbow.*
(Miss Read, OVER THE GATE, 1964)

There is no winning either way for the Gypsy *horse traders of the Cotswolds. They have been doing business in Stow-on-the Wold since the 15th century, so when the town's antique shop proprietors, hoteliers and residents complained that their caravans were cluttering up the grass verges and lay-bys, they bought a field of their own.*

Now, they have been told to stop using it or be prosecuted for 'congestion and disturbing the appearance and tranquillity of the local area generally'.
(THE GUARDIAN, 11 May 1994)

When *gypsies* first appeared in England, people looking at their dark skin and black hair and listening to their foreign chatter assumed that they were from Egypt and referred to them as *Egyptians*. In speech, however, the soft, unstressed initial vowel was often lost, reducing the word to *Gypcians*. In a letter dating from 1537, Lord Cromwell wrote that:

The Kings Maiestie, about a twelfmoneth past, gave a pardonne to a company of lewde personnes within this realme calling themselves Gipcyans, *for a most shamfull and detestable murder.*

By the end of the century *gipcyan* had become *gipsie*. This form was generally accepted, although as late as the mid-eighteenth century *Egyptian* was still insisted upon by sticklers for correctness. This was ironic because the *gypsies* had not, in fact, come from Egypt at all. They were a wandering people of low-caste Indian origin who migrated first to Persia and then to continental Europe during the fourteenth and fifteenth centuries. Traditionally they have earned their way by tinkering, fortune-telling, handicrafts and horse-dealing, which persists to the present day as the quotation above from THE GUARDIAN shows.

Even today, centuries later, the spelling has not yet finally settled down. An *i* or *y* in the first syllable is commonly found.

haggard

tired and drawn, through anxiety or hunger or aging

He could plainly see how old all the rest of his family and acquaintance were growing. Anne haggard, *Mary coarse, every face in the neighbourhood worsting, and the rapid increase of the crow's foot about Lady Russell's temples had long been a distress to him.*
(Jane Austen, PERSUASION, 1818)

Here, for a moment, the fog would be quite broken up, and a haggard *shaft of daylight would glance in between the swirling wreaths.*
(Robert Louis Stevenson, THE STRANGE CASE OF DR JEKYLL AND MR HYDE, 1886)

He gets to his seat and moves unsteadily forward to answer questions from the audience. To say that Senator Edward

Kennedy staggers would be harsh, but to say that he waddles would be kind. His appearance is extraordinary: bloated, blotchy, raddled, haggard. *This is the Portrait of Dorian Gray in reverse. Instead of a painting hidden in the attic which changes and ages hideously, while the man himself remains young and beautiful despite a life of depravity, Ted Kennedy seems in his face and form to bear witness not only to his own misspent manhood, but to all his family's misdemeanours and miseries.*
(INDEPENDENT ON SUNDAY, 6 November 1994)

Hawking, or falconry, is the ancient practice of hunting with a trained bird of prey. The hawks were not originally bred in captivity but were taken as nestlings or captured as adults. In the sixteenth century, birds caught after they had gained their adult plumage were known as *haggards,* from Middle French *hagard.* The source of this word is unknown but, since the *haggard* had the freedom of the hedgerows before its capture, it has sometimes been connected with a French dialect word deriving from *haie,* 'hedge' (and ultimately, therefore, from the same Germanic root as English *hedge*).

Initially the newly-captured wild birds resisted confinement and training with all their might, so that *haggard* made an evocative metaphor when applied to a person of difficult and wayward disposition. Thus, when Petruchio compared the mastery of Katerina to the manning of a falcon in Shakespeare's THE TAMING OF THE SHREW (1596), he was making a very topical comparison:

My foulcon now is sharp, and passing empty,
And 'till she stoop she must not be full-gorg'd,
For then she never looks upon her lure.
Another way I have to man my haggard,
To make her come, and know her keeper's call;
That is, to watch her, as we watch those kites
That bate, and beat, and will not be obedient.
She eat no meat today, nor more shall eat;
Last night she slept not, and to-night she shall not.
(Act 4, scene 1)

The terror and bewilderment of a wild creature newly captured and anxious for its freedom prompted a new application of the adjective in the seventeenth century when it described a 'wild, despairing look haunting the eyes' or a 'face marked by the ravages of want, fatigue or dread'. These senses are still current. In the nineteenth century the word also came to mean 'gaunt', originally through aging, an application that was apparently influenced by the similar sounding *hag,* 'hideous old woman'.

For another word from falconry, see **mews**.

ham

the upper thigh of a pig or other animal, prepared for food

'I shall take a mere mouthful of ham *and a glass of ale,' he said, reassuringly. 'As a man with public business, I take a snack when I can. I will back this* ham,*' he added, after swallowing some morsels with alarming haste, 'against any* ham *in the three kingdoms. In my opinion it is better than the hams at Freshitt Hall – and I think I am a tolerable judge.' 'Some don't like so much sugar in their* hams,*' said Mrs. Waule. 'But my poor brother would always have sugar.' 'If any person demands better, he is at liberty to do so; but, God bless me, what an aroma! I should be glad*

to buy in that quality, I know. There is some gratification to a gentleman' – here Mr. Trumbull's voice conveyed an emotional remonstrance – 'in having this kind of ham *set on his table.'*
(George Eliot, MIDDLEMARCH, 1872)

Well, my father was a large man, a very large man and he decided he'd buy a suit. He went along and measured and fitted and fitted and measured, week after week. He talked of nothing else, first the trousers then the waistcoat and finally the jacket. The great day came at last and the suit came home! We had the best cups out and ham *for tea and cream buns and two kinds of jam – all for the suit.*
(Vivienne C. Welburn, JOHNNY SO LONG, 1967)

Ham was not always a sandwich filling. Evidence from old Anglo-Saxon, Dutch, German and Norse words has led etymologists to assume an Old Germanic root *hamm-*, 'to be crooked'. Derived from this, Old English *hamm* originally denoted the 'hollow at the back of the knee', a sense which lingers in the compound *hamstring*, the name for any one of the tendons which run through this part of the leg. In the mid-sixteenth century the term was extended to refer to the back of the thigh and then to the whole of the upper leg. The seventeeth century saw the word applied to the 'thigh of a slaughtered animal', more especially to that of a pig which had been cured, and from there to the meat itself.

The word *hamburger* has nothing to do with ham whatsoever but is short for *Hamburg steak*, a delicacy made of spiced minced-beef that originated in the German city of Hamburg. German immigrants introduced the dish into the United States in the mid-nineteenth century where it proved extremely popular. By the late 1880s it was known as a *Hamburger steak* and twenty years later was often just referred to as a *hamburger*. Since the end of the Second World War, Modern American and British English has been

From swine to pork

When the victorious Normans communicated with the conquered Saxons it was presumably with much arm waving and broken attempts at each other's language. Although French and English did gradually merge it was a process which took three or four centuries. For a long time French was the language of the social élite, while English was confined to the uneducated masses. A farmyard-to-table study bears witness to this. The animals that the peasants reared and tended have retained their Old English names: the meat that was served to the Norman masters is known by French equivalents:

Old English	French
swine (Old English *swin*)	
pig (Old English *picga*)	pork (Old French *porc*, 'pig')
ox (Old English *oxa*)	beef (Old French *boef*, 'ox')
sheep (Old English *sce-ap*)	mutton (Old French *moton*, 'sheep')
calf (Old English *cealf*)	veal (Old French *veel*, later *veau*, 'calf')

even more economical, clipping the word to a mere *burger.*

It must be a great comfort to the travelling American that he can now enjoy what has become his national dish at fast-food outlets worldwide. Indeed, even the quaintest of British high streets boasts at least one brash burger bar. Congratulations, therefore, to the TIMES journalist who, in an article dated 30 January, 1960, timorously predicted that '*the mounting number of* hamburger *bars suggests that it is here to stay*'.

handicap

1. a hindrance to performance or success
2. a disability, physical or mental

You can no longer say that only Standard English is socially acceptable (and a slight Irish or Scottish accent). However, you can't say that Standard English is ever a handicap, *and there still are professions in which you can't do without it.*
(John Braine, WRITING A NOVEL, 1974)

'Mummy, why have I got Down's Syndrome?'
We were driving home from a weekend away. Lizzie woke up, bright as a button after a short sleep. It was dark now and the street lights shone on her glasses as she turned to me and said, 'Mummy, I am mentally handicapped. *That is not the same as physically* handicapped, *is it? That friend, Edward, he's the same as me, and Penny (referring to another friend). Physically* handicapped, *that means you can't walk. . .'*
(Caroline Philps, MUMMY, WHY HAVE I GOT DOWN'S SYNDROME?, 1991)

The word is a contraction of the phrase *hand in the cap* or *hand i' cap.* This was a game of chance based upon bartering. One person would challenge another for a particular possession and offer something of his own in exchange. If the challenge was accepted an umpire would be appointed and all three would place forfeit money into a hat, keeping their hands in the cap. The umpire would then consider the value of the proposed articles and would decide what extra payment should be offered by the owner of the inferior item to make the exchange fair. The two players then withdrew their hands; holding on to one's money indicated that the deal was off, an empty hand signalled acceptance. If both players were in agreement, the exchange was made or cancelled accordingly and the umpire took all the forfeit money. If the players disagreed no exchange was made but the one who had indicated a willingness to trade took all the forfeit.

The game was an old one. It is described in the Middle English poem PIERS PLOWMAN where a hood was offered for a cloak, the 'noumpere' (umpire) judging that the owner of the hood should also give a cup of ale. In the fourteenth century, however, the game was known as *Newe Faire.* The name *hand in the cap* is of later date and is not found in written records until the seventeenth century. In his diary entry for 18 September, 1660, Samuel Pepys called the game *handicap,* adding that he had never heard of it before but that he had enjoyed playing it immensely.

In the 1680s the rules of *handicap* were applied to certain horse races, although they were not referred to as *handicap matches* until the mid-eighteenth century. In these races the appointed umpire decided upon the extra weight that should be carried by the stronger horse and the system of forfeits operated as before. In the following century *handicap* was extended to any kind of race or competition where superior competitiors were penalised in some way to create an evenly-matched contest.

By the second half of the nineteenth century, besides its use in sporting contexts, the verb *to handicap* was also generally applied in the sense of 'to place someone at a disadvantage'. In the early twentieth century the past participle, *handicapped*, became an adjective to describe anyone hindered by a mental or physical defect.

For other words originating in games, see **hazard** and **rigmarole**.

False division

Mostly it is very clear how to divide a word up into its different elements. *Impossible*, for instance, is *im-* + *possible*. In some places a false division can hint at some very misleading – but diverting – origins. Quite a number of wits have capitalised on this for humorous effect.

allegro chorus line
antimony inheritance from aunt
bedrug bed covering
counterspy shop detective
firecracker burnt biscuit
forestress female forester
incommode engaged, occupied
largesse capital S
lawsuit judge's attire
locomotion faint noise
mandate male partner
maritime wedding day
nitrate overnight tariff
shamrock counterfeit diamond
stalemate boring partner
stowaway sailor with large appetite
tenet group of 10 singers

handkerchief

a square of cloth, carried in the pocket, for wiping the nose, etc

Handkerchief, *a small square of silk or linen used at funerals to conceal one's lack of tears.*
(Ambrose Bierce, THE DEVIL'S DICTIONARY, 1911)

She read the notice warning people that the llamas spat.

'Nannie won't let me spit. She says it's common to spit. She didn't say about llamas.'

'She's quite wrong to tell you never to spit. You must never swallow phlegm. If you've forgotten your handkerchief, *always spit it out. Wouldn't you like to spit at the llamas?'*
(Dane Chandos, ABBIE, 1947)

In the Middle Ages women covered their heads with a cloth known as a *coverchief*, 'headscarf'. The word was borrowed from Old French *couvrechief* or *cuevrechief* (from *couvrir*, 'to cover' and *chief*, 'head', from Latin *caput*). In the Middle English of about 1300 the word was often contracted to *curchef* or *kerchef*. Sometimes kerchiefs were also worn about the neck or to cover the breast. In the sixteenth century *kerchief* became part of a new compound, *handkerchief*, to denote a 'square of fabric carried in the hand to mop the face or nose'.

The common-or-garden *handkerchief* does not today have all the associations that it had in past centuries. It was in the seventeenth century something of a family heirloom and very precious. Therefore, when Shakespeare's Othello discovered that his wife Desdemona had passed on to Cassio *a Handkerchiefe Spotted with Strawberries* (OTHELLO, 1604)) that he had given her as a symbol of his love, it was enough to incite the jealous rage in which he smothered her. And in his diary (1666) Samuel Pepys takes his wife to task for buying a laced handkerchief without his permission.

Sometimes *handkerchief* and *kerchief* were used interchangeably. In this passage from Henry Fielding's JOSEPH ANDREWS (1742), Joseph has been wounded while rescuing Fanny from an attacker. Her handkerchief has been torn from her shoulders:

This modest creature, whom no warmth in summer could ever induce to expose her charms to the wanton sun, a modesty to which perhaps they owed their inconceivable whitenesss, had stood for many minutes bare-necked in the presence of Joseph . . . at last, when the cause of her concern had vanished, an admiration at his silence, together with observing the fixed position of his eyes, produced an idea in the lovely maid, which brought more blood into her face than had flowed from Joseph's nostrils. The snowy hue of her bosom was likewise changed to vermilion at the instant when she clapped her handkerchief *round her neck.*

The ordinary pronunciation of *handkerchief* was for centuries reflected in the common alternative spelling *handkercher*. Voltaire (1694–1778) commented to his countrymen on the discrepancy between spelling and pronunciation in this word. Eventually, the pronunciation and spelling that is standard today asserted itself, although the old variant still persists in dialects.

The abbreviation *hanky*, at first very properly spelt *handky*, dates from the late nineteenth century.

For another word whose etymology includes the French *couvre*, see **curfew**.

harbinger

a forerunner, one who announces something shortly to happen

Liberals interpreted the violence as a form of political protest against poor housing, high unemployment and the lack of opportunity. Radicals saw it as the harbinger *of a revolutionary uprising by the black under-class, and welcomed it accordingly. Conservatives tended to agree with radicals that the violence was insurrectionary, and were horrified.*
(INDEPENDENT, 1 May 1992)

In February, as things were looking desperate, a new single, Girls and Boys, was released. An irresistibly catchy thing celebrating the English ritual of spending holidays copulating in Benidorm, it – Fluke! – sped to No 8 in the charts and proved a harbinger *of the album to come.*
(GUARDIAN, 10 November 1994)

Rows of hunting prints adorn the walls and these, in my experience, are harbingers *of doom – portending dry meat, overcooked vegetables and all the other appurtenances of Middle England at lunch.*
(WEEKEND TELEGRAPH, 4 March 1995)

Today *harbinger* is a rather literary, even poetic, word found in phrases like the *harbinger of spring*. It is hard to believe that for a part of its history it was a military term. Its source is a Germanic word related to Old High German *heriberga*, meaning 'an army encampment' (from *heri*, 'army' and *bergan*, 'to protect').

This term had already gained the extended meaning of 'lodging, hostelry' when Old French borrowed it, together with both its senses, as *herberge*. (Modern French has *auberge* for 'inn'.) The derivative *herbergere* therefore meant 'one who provides lodgings, a host', and this was borrowed directly into Middle English in the twelfth century.

By the late medieval period, the term was undergoing a change in both form and meaning. As with the words *messenger, scavenger* and *passenger*, a letter *-n-* was introduced in the fifteenth century to give *herbengar*. A variant spelling of the first syllable, *har-*, began to take hold in the following century though the emergence of *harbinger* was not complete until the 1630s.

As for the job itself, a *harbinger* was no longer simply a host or the keeper of a lodging house but had become 'one who was sent on ahead of an army or a royal progress to procure accommodation for the entire party'. His task was not an easy one since the scale of such operations was often enormous: as many as 30 coaches, 300 carts and 1000 pack-animals might be needed to move the Elizabethan court from place to place, for instance. The royal *harbinger* had to inspect the places to be visited along the route. Would most of the party need to be lodged in tents or was there sufficient accommodation available in nearby towns? Were there enough provisions available locally to feed such a vast company for the length of their intended stay? Was the neighbourhood free of disease? People needed time to prepare and advice on how to welcome the Queen with due state. The role of *harbinger* was still in force in the reign of Charles II, as this passage from William Hawkin's LIFE OF BISHOP THOMAS KEN (1837) shows:

On the removal of the court to pass the summer at Winchester, bishop Ken's house which he held in the right of his prebend, was marked by the harbinger *for the use of Mrs Eleanor Gwyn; but he refused to grant her admittance and she was forced to seek for lodgings in another place.*

Although the harbinger's task had long since changed from host to that of billet officer and tour manager by the seventeenth century, Francis Bacon kept the medieval meaning when he wrote '*There was a* harbinger *who had lodged a gentleman in a very ill room*' (APOPHTHEGMS, 1624). The figurative use of the word, the only one with which we are now familiar, was already well-established by that date. It is rather odd that a lowly soldier should find favour in the lofty language of great poets, but he did. Shakespeare has Puck describe the coming of the dawn in these terms:

For night's swift dragons cut the clouds full fast,
And yonder shines Aurora's harbinger*;*
At whose approach, ghosts, wandering here and there,
Troop home to churchyards.
(Shakespeare, MIDSUMMER NIGHT'S DREAM, c.1595)

while Milton compared Dalila (to us, Delilah of Judges, Chapter 16) to a stately galleon in SAMSON AGONISTES (possibly 1647):

With all her bravery on, each tackle trim,
Sails fill'd, and streamers waving,
Courted by all the winds that hold them play,
An amber scent of odorous perfume
Her harbinger.

◆ *Harbour* shares the same Germanic roots. Originally it meant 'a place of shelter', the verb *to harbour* meaning 'to provide shelter, to quarter soldiers'. *Harbour* in the sense of 'port' or 'safe haven' was used by extension.◆

hazard

risk, chance, peril

In west Surrey, autumn leaves fall into two distinct camps. First, there are those that tumble to the ground and remain dry: these are treated as litter and swept up by Waverley Borough Council. Then there are those that flutter down from the trees and get wet, presumably when it rains. If enough of them stick together to constitute a hazard *for road users, they suddenly become the responsibility of the highways people at Surrey County Council.*
(WEEKEND TELEGRAPH, 25 February 1995)

But Mr Paulsen . . . sees a man broken with grief after one of his team [of dogs] is killed by a moose, one of the recurring hazards *of the race, along with ice collapsing on river, lake and sea, precipitous descents, raging blizzards and the appalling cold, in which freezing point is described as 'warm'.*
(DAILY TELEGRAPH, 8 March 1995)

In the twelfth century a force of crusaders, engaged in the siege of a Palestinian fortress called *Hasart* or *Asart*, invented a game of chance played with dice to while away their moments of inactivity, naming it *hasart* for the castle. This, at any rate, is the account offered by William of Tyre. Unfortunately *'Ain Zarba* is thought to have been the actual name of the castle, which rather spoils the story. Instead the name of the game is believed to have derived ultimately from a vulgar Arab word *al-zahr*, meaning 'luck, chance'. (See **Words from Arabic** (pages 10–11) for a discussion of *al-*.) This passed into Spanish as *azar*, 'a throw of the dice, chance'. References to the game as *hasart* in Old French texts date back to the first half of the twelfth century although, by the time it was introduced into England from France at the turn of the fourteenth century, the spelling *hasard* was current.

Over the years the game increased in popularity, as did the size of the stakes. By the eighteenth century vast fortunes could be won or lost in London's fashionable clubs. In one of his letters Horace Walpole tells how, '*At the Cocoa-tree Lord Stavordale, not one-and-twenty, lost eleven thousand last Tuesday, but recovered it by one great hand at* hazard' (1770).

These associations with chance made *hazard* an obvious candidate for figurative use, so that by the mid-sixteenth century, in French and then in English, it had also come to mean 'peril or risk'.

◆ *Haphazard* (16th cent), is a tautological compound of *hap*, 'chance, luck' (from Old Norse *happ*, 'chance') and *hazard*.◆

For other words originating in games, see **handicap** and **rigmarole**.

hearse

a vehicle for carrying a coffin

'Are you tired?' I asked.
'Just a little.'
'Perhaps we should talk. What is the best thing about being a hearse *driver?'*
'Widows,' said Dalip. 'Yaarraghaa!' he went, yawning again.
(Alexander Frater, CHASING THE MONSOON, 1990)

The old Grey Hearse *goes rolling by,*
You don't know whether to laugh or cry;
For you know some day it'll get you too,
And the hearse's *next load may consist of you.*
(Anon)

Surprisingly *hearse* began as *hirpus*, an Oscan term for 'wolf'. (The Oscans were an ancient people who lived on the Italian peninsula.) The connection has nothing to do with the victims of these animals being borne away on hearses; the route to the present meaning is far more tortuous and contains a couple of imaginative twists.

The first of these occurred when the fanciful Romans borrowed the word as *hirpex* (stem *hirpic-*) and then applied it to the large rake or harrow they used for breaking up the soil – an allusion, it would seem, to the jagged teeth of the wolves. The term came into Old French as *herce* or *herse*, retaining its agricultural meaning (the Modern French is *herse*). In medieval times, however, it was customary to erect a triangular frame with spikes to hold candles over the bier of an important person. And here we have the second twist: since the shape and teeth of the harrow bore a resemblance to this spiked framework, Old French used *herse* to refer to it. It was in this sense of 'taper hearse' that the word was first borrowed into English in the fourteenth century. Edward Hall's THE UNION OF THE FAMILIES OF LANCASTER AND YORK (1542) illustrates how richly these *hearses* were often decorated:

The body was taken out, and caried into the Quire, and set under a goodly Herce *of waxe, garnished with Banners, Pencelles, and Cusshions.*

Hearses of one sort or another, fixed and temporary, were commonly used well into the second half of the seventeenth century but that century also saw a change in the application of the word. During the first fifty years or so it was used rather generally to denote a 'coffin' or 'tomb' but the second half of the century saw *hearse* applied in the modern sense to a 'vehicle constructed for carrying a coffin'.

For another word from the same source, see **rehearse**. For words on the same funereal theme see **cemetery**, **coffin**, **dirge** and **sarcophagus**.

hibernation

the state of dormancy some animals and plants assume during winter

Since 1926 Timothy [a tortoise] has lived at the same place, Powderham Castle in Devon. The castle's human inhabitants, the Earls of Devon, have come and gone, but Timothy has remained. Every autumn he puts himself to bed for hibernation, *and every spring he wakes up again in time for the castle's Easter opening to the public.*
(WEEKEND TELEGRAPH, 2 July 1994)

The postulated Indo-European root *gheim-* is the ultimate source of the Latin *hiems*, 'winter'. From this word Latin derived an adjective *hībernus*, 'wintery', and from this a noun *hīberna*, meaning 'winter quarters'. Further derivatives were the verb *hībernāre*, 'to spend the winter', and *hībernātiōnem*, 'the action of overwintering'.

The noun *hibernation* (from *hībernātiōnem*) was borrowed into English in the seventeenth century to denote 'the passing of the winter in suitable quarters or conditions'. This applied equally to plants in the greenhouse or vizirs searching for a congenial place to spend the season. However, it was the British naturalist Erasmus Darwin, grandfather of Charles Darwin, who brought the term into prominence at the very beginning of the nineteenth century when he used it in a scientific sense to describe the torpor in which many animals and plants spend the winter. At the same time Darwin was responsible for the introduction of the verb *hibernate* (from *hībernāre*) into English.

The ability of animals to remain dormant over very long periods of time has been a matter of fascination and investigation for many years. The toad was an early subject of research. A Frenchman, Hérissant, encased three live toads in plaster in 1777. When he looked at them again in the archives of the French Academy of Sciences 18 months later, two were still alive. This experiment did not work forty years later when Dr Edwards took the additional step of putting the plaster blocks into water. The key lies in access to at least minimal oxygen. Francis Buckland in 1825 placed twelve toads in dense sandstone, twelve in porous limestone. Over a year later, all the first were dead, all the second alive.

◆ *Gheim-* is responsible for Sanskrit *hima*, 'snow', which is evident in *Himalayas*.◆

hobnob

to be on familiar terms with

Louisiana is also a case-history of stupefyingly bad leadership. The state legislature is notoriously corrupt... Governors are little better. Since the example set by Huey Long, most have appealed to populist instincts even as they hobnob *with local businesses.*
(The Economist, 10 December 1994)

This informal modern verb appears as a phrase in Shakespeare who uses it in the sense 'give or take': Hob, nob, *is his word: giu't or take't.* (Twelfth Night, 1601)

It seems to be a variant of the earlier phrases *hab nab* and *hab or nab*. These had the general sense 'whatever might happen' and are recorded from the mid-sixteenth century. The expressions, however, must be much older than this since they clearly derive from *habbe* and *nabbe*, subjunctive forms of the Middle English dialect verbs *habben*, 'to have' and *nabben*, 'not to have'. However, since these forms were obsolete by the mid-sixteenth century it must be assumed that *habbe nabbe* and *habbe or nabbe* (meaning literally 'have he [I, we, etc] or have he [I, we, etc] not') were Middle English expressions which survived in spoken language.

In the eighteenth century a social application of the variant phrase began to emerge. *To hobnob* meant 'to drink to each other, to toast one another by clinking glasses', and the phrase *hob and nob* was used by two people drinking in this way. In Great Expectations (1861) Dickens describes one such exchange between Mr Pumblechook and a sergeant:

'Have another glass!'

'With you. Hob and nob, *' returned the sergeant. 'The top of mine to the foot of yours – the foot of yours to the top of mine – Ring once, ring twice – the best tune on the Musical Glasses! Your health'.*

In the nineteenth century such scenes of conviviality gave rise to a more general sense of *hobnob*, when it came to mean 'to be on familiar terms with somebody socially', the sense that the verb has retained in modern English.

holocaust

a terrible period of widespread destruction and loss of life

Once elected, the pressure group spokesman becomes a politician, whose business is

compromise, not ideological purity. Any transition from bearing witness to holding power, however limited, will probably alienate the idealistic Green rank and file from the people they have elected. Where this will leave either is hard to say. So there may well be eco-freaks in office in France and Germany come Monday. Not to panic. But also not to stop worrying about acid rain or nuclear holocaust, *just yet. . .*
(NEW SCIENTIST, 1983)

Humiliation is still the most dominant emotion I feel when thinking about the Holocaust. *Not rage, a desire for revenge, or hatred, but a bitter and inconsolable humiliation that such things were done to people. . . I am on my own with this humiliation, as with the terrible fears the* Holocaust *has imprinted on my psyche; the total, almost mythic insecurity about the possibility of a future; of my children having a future.*
(THE OBSERVER, 29 January 1995)

HOLOCAUST *HORROR*
An Israeli shop of horrors from the Nazi Holocaust *in Tel Aviv has cancelled plans to auction a bar of soap which its owner said was made from the bodies of Jews killed in a death camp following protests by the Chief Rabbi.*
(GUARDIAN, 4 April 1995)

The word derives, via Old French and Late Latin, from Greek *holokaustos* and literally means 'burnt whole' (from *holos*, 'whole', and *kaustos*, 'burnt'). It denoted a pagan sacrificial offering that was completely consumed by fire, 'a whole burnt offering'. Within the Christian tradition, it is used in mid-thirteenth-century English of the offering of Isaac by Abraham. From the end of the fifteenth century *holocaust* also had the figurative application of 'a heartfelt sacrifice', of loyalty or devotion, for instance. It was in the second half of the seventeenth century, however, that the word came to be used of widespread destruction and large-scale massacre. Milton was the first to use it in this way; it subsequently regularly retained its original sense of destruction by fire.

During the Second World War (1939–45) Nazi Germany attempted to systematically annihilate the European Jewish population whom they accused of infesting their territories. Six million Jews were subjected to intense cruelty before meeting a hideous death in extermination camps. Throughout the war *holocaust* was a word frequently chosen to describe these atrocities. When it ended historians referred to this savage treatment of the Jews as the *Holocaust* (often written with a capital letter) and it is by this specific term that this period of history is known today.

◆ The two elements that constitute the root of *holocaust* have both provided other words in English. *Holos* is clearly to be seen in *holograph, holism* and even in *whole*. It is less evident, but still true, that it forms part of *catholic* which means 'universal, all-embracing' (from *kata*, 'concerning, in respect of', and *holos*, 'entire'). There is even a connection of *holos* with *safe*. The English word finds its root, via French, in the Latin *salvus*; this word corresponds in root and suffix with the Greek *holos*.

Caustic comes from *kaustikos*, 'capable of burning'. *Caustic soda* literally burns, while *caustic comments* sear the soul.◆

For other words concerning temple or sacrifices, see **anathema, thyme, mint, scapegoat** and **fanatic**.

holy

sacred, set apart

'Holy father,' said the knight, 'upon whose countenance it hath pleased Heaven to work such a miracle, permit a sinful layman to crave thy name?' 'Thou mayst call me,' answered the hermit, 'the Clerk of Copmanhurst, for so I am termed in these parts — They add, it is true, the epithet holy, *but I stand not upon that, as being unworthy of such addition.'*
(Sir Walter Scott, IVANHOE, 1819)

Holy derives from the Middle English word *hool* (from Old English *halig*), meaning 'whole' in its archaic sense of 'in robust health' and therefore 'complete'. *Holy* is simply *hool* with the suffix *-y* added, giving the Middle English forms *holi* and *holy* and conveying a sense of wholeness and perfection as well as subsequent Christian senses.

Holy in its different forms makes up part of several other common words. In THE CANTERBURY TALES (c. 1387), Chaucer refers not to *holidays* but to *holy days.* The church's calendar was marked by such anniversaries. They were set apart for church attendance and festivities and no work was done. *Holy days,* therefore, meant enjoyment and, at a time when the right to a fortnight off with pay was unheard of, became associated with rest and recreation. For over five hundred years the term was written either as two words or in a combined form but, during the sixteenth century, when a day's recreation was no longer restricted to church festivals, the need was felt to make a distinction. Thus a *holy day* (or *holyday*) had religious significance while a *holiday* denoted a day's leisure.

It was customary in the church to abstain from meat on *holy days* and to eat fish instead. Middle English had the word *butte,* a general term for 'flatfish'. This, combined with *haly* ('holy') in the fifteenth century, gave *halybutte,* then *halibut,* the term for the largest of the flatfish and an excellent holiday dish. Languages from the same root have similarly constructed words for the fish. Swedish, for instance, has *helgflundra* from *helg* ('holidays') and *flundra* ('flounder').

The *hollyhock*'s name also derives from *holy* (Middle English *holihoc,* from *holi,* 'holy' and *hoc,* 'mallow'). Some authorities have erroneously suggested that it came originally from the Holy Land and was brought to England during the Crusades. A more likely reason why the hock, or mallow, was deemed to be holy is that in both Welsh and medieval Latin it was known as a 'blessed mallow'. Moreover the plant had also previously been known as 'St Cuthbert's cole' after a seventh- century monk who lived on Holy Island. With all these holy associations, it is perhaps not surprising that the *hock* metamorphosed into the *hollyhock,* with a reputation, amongst some at least, for medicinal and healing properties which made people whole again.

hoodlum

a young thug

GET SHORTY (MGM). After PULP FICTION, John Travolta plays another cool-jerk hoodlum, *this time in Elmore Leonard's tale of a crook who becomes a Hollywood player.*
(MACLEAN'S, 9 January 1995)

Ward has his own demons, and when he returns to Moat County to follow a lead about a local hoodlum *wrongfully convicted for the murder of the sheriff, his*

own secret life is forced to the surface with violent and irrevocable results.
(PEOPLE WEEKLY, 30 January 1995)

In the early 1870s the streets of San Francisco were haunted by bands of young thugs intent on crime. The BOSTON JOURNAL (1877) had this to say about them:

You at the East have but little idea of the hoodlums *of this city [San Francisco]. They compose a class of criminals of both sexes . . . travel in gangs; and are ready at any moment for the perpetration of any crime.*

These young toughs had been referred to locally as *hoodlums* since about 1869. When their notoriety spread to other parts of America, interest was shown in the term but, by then, the origin was lost. This spurred correspondents with various newspapers into offering suggestions to account for it. Here are some of them:

A newspaper man in San Francisco, in attempting to coin a word to designate a gang of young street Arabs under the beck of one named 'Muldoon', hit upon the idea of dubbing them 'noodlums,' that is, simply reversing the leader's name. In writing the word the strokes of the n *did not correspond in height, and the compositor, taking the* n *for an* h, *printed it* 'hoodlums'.
(THE CONGREGATIONALIST, 26 September 1877)

Before the late war there appeared in San Francisco a man whose dress was very peculiar. The boys took a fancy to it, and, organizing themselves into a military company, adopted in part the dress of this man. The head-dress resembled the fez, from which was suspended a long tail. The gamins called it a 'hood,' and the company became known as the 'hoods'. The rowdy element in the city adopted much of the dress of the company referred to, who were soon designated as 'hoodlums'.
(SAN FRANCISCO MORNING CALL, 27 October 1877)

A gang of bad boys from fourteen to nineteen years of age was associated for the purpose of stealing. These boys had a place of rendezvous, and when danger threatened them their words of warning were, 'Huddle 'em! Huddle 'em!' An article headed 'Huddle'em,' describing the gang and their plan of operations, was published in the San Francisco Times. The name applied to them was soon contracted into hoodlum.
(LOS ANGELES EXPRESS, 25 August 1877)

hotch-potch

a mixture of ill-assorted ingredients, a mess

Perhaps the most impressive building in the bay is the Granville Hotel, built in about 1880 by Earl Granville, who was largely responsible for property development on the cliff. It is a wonderful Victorian hotch-potch *of gables, turrets and covered wooden balconies with extensive views towards France.*
(TELEGRAPH, 9 May 1992)

Hochepot is first recorded in the Anglo-French of 1292 as a law term. In legal vocabulary up to the present day it applies to the collecting together of various properties and funds. The term especially applies to the estate of an intestate parent, where substantial sums that might have been bestowed during the deceased's lifetime are recalled so that they can be fairly distributed to all the beneficiaries.

The word is a French compound from *hocher*, 'to shake' and *pot*, 'pot'. Possibly the legal use was a figurative application of a French culinary term for a ragout or stew, where a variety of ingredients was stirred and mixed together in one big cooking pot. However, *hochepot* is recorded as a cookery term only from the first half of the fifteenth century, some two hundred and fifty years after its use in law .

An interesting example from 1606 not only combines legal and culinary uses but also exhibits what had become, through rhyming assimilation, the established new shape of the word:

Nay, thats plaine in Littleton, for if that fee-simple and the fee taile be put together, it is called hotch-potch*; now this word* hotch-potch *in English is a pudding, for in such a pudding is not comonly one thing only, but one thing with another.*
(Returne from Pernassus, 1606)

Fee-simple and *fee taile* are both legal terms connected with inheritances; the first means that the estate is open to all beneficiaries for ever; the latter that the estate is limited to one class of heirs. Obviously, if the two are put together, the result is a *hotchpotch*.

A variety of other forms appeared, including *hodge-podge* in the sixteenth century. This corruption was based on the name *Hodge*, an altered form of *Roger*, which was used to denote a typical rustic. In England *hodge-podge* is an alternative but in Scottish and American usage it is the preferred form. Walsh, an American, gives this Scottish example:

During the earlier visits of the royal family to Balmoral, Prince Albert, dressed in a very simple manner, was crossing one of the Scotch lakes in a steamer, and was curious to note everything relating to the management of the vessel, and, among other things, cooking. Approaching the 'galley', where a brawny Highlander was attending to the culinary matters, he was attracted by the savory odors of a compound known by Scotchmen as 'hodge-podge,' *which the Highlander was preparing.*

'What's that?' asked the prince, who was not known to the cook.

'Hodge-podge, *sir,' was the reply.*

'How is it made?' was the next question.

'Why, there's mutton intil't, and turnips intil't, and cairots intil't, and—'

'Yes, yes,' said the prince, who had not learned that 'intil't' meant 'into it', 'but what is intil't?'

'Why, there's mutton intil't, and turnips intil't, and cairots intil't, and—'

'Yes, I see; but what is intil't?'

The man looked at him, and, seeing that the prince was serious, replied,—

'There's mutton intil't, and turnips intil't, and—'

'Yes, certainly, I know,' urged the inquirer; 'but what is intil't – intil't?'

'Ye daft gowk!' yelled the Highlander, brandishing his big spoon, 'am I no telling ye what's intil't? There's mutton intil't, and—'

Here the interview was brought to a close by one of the prince's suite, who was fortunately passing, and stepped in to save his royal highness from being rapped over the head with the big spoon.

Figurative use of the word for 'a mixture of disparate elements, a jumble' began with Chaucer but became increasingly common from the mid-sixteenth century.

◆ There is no connection between *hotchpotch* and *hot pot*, despite their similarity in form and their joint reference to culinary matters. The latter first came into use about 1700, as a slang term for hot beer with spirit added: Its common meaning today of a stew of mutton or beef is only found from the middle of the nineteenth century onwards.◆

hypocrite

one who speaks or acts apparently virtuously, but at variance with his true, baser motives

The Dean was observed to be extraordinarily moved, and said his prayer of thanksgiving in a voice that was not at all steady. Frank Ashworth, halfway down the nave, remarked this to himself with a kind of disgust; to him, the Dean's hypocrisy *knew no bounds.*
(Joanna Trollope, THE CHOIR, 1988)

Satire flatters its audience into thinking that they are the chosen ones who alone see through the hype and hypocrisy *of people in power. . .*
(THE SUNDAY TIMES, 19 March 1995)

In the theatre of ancient Greece an *hupocritēs* was an actor, someone skilled in playing a part, in feigning emotion, in promoting opinions he did not share. The term derived from the compound verb *hupokrinein* (from *hupo*, 'under' and *krinein*, 'to separate') which originally meant 'to decide, judge' and then 'to answer' and finally 'to play a part'. Figuratively the verb meant 'to pretend'. Not surprisingly *hupocritēs* also gained the figurative application of 'dissembler' and with this meaning it passed into ecclesiastical Late Latin as *hypocrita* to denote 'one who gives an outward display of piety that belies his true character or way of life'. In this very particuar religious sense the word was taken into Old French as *ypocrite* and into Middle English as *ipocrite* or *ypocrite.* The ANCRENE RIWLE, the thirteenth-century devotional manual that was used by those called to a solitary religious life, calls the false recluse an *ipocrite,* and in his translation of Matthew 23:13-15 Wycliffe uses *ypocritis* in Jesus's three-fold denunciation of the scribes and pharisees. Soon, however, the contexts in which the word was found became more varied and applied to any situation where virtuous behaviour was a screen for base motives. In the mid-sixteenth century attempts were made to regularise the spelling and, in both French and English, the word was pulled back into line with its classical roots and spelt with an initial *h.*

idiot

1. a fool, a person of poor judgement
2. a person of very limited intelligence

'. . Say, gee, I ain't talking too nutty, am I?'
*'"Nutty"? You mean "*idiotically*"? The slang's changed since — Oh yes, of course; you've succeeded in talking quite nice and "*idiotic*".'*
(Sinclair Lewis, OUR MR. WRENN, THE ROMANTIC ADVENTURES OF A GENTLE MAN, 1914)

Show me a good loser and I'll show you an idiot.
(Leo Durocher, in Mark Fisher, THE MILLIONAIRE'S BOOK OF QUOTATIONS, 1991)

When the devout Augustinian friar, John Capgrave, described the twelve apostles as '*twelue ydiotes*' his intention was neither to shock nor to offend. He was using the word in one of its early senses and simply meant that '*thei not lerned were*' (LIFE OF ST CATHERINE, c. 1440).

In ancient Greece *idiōtēs* (from *idios*, 'private') denoted a 'private person' in the sense that he was excluded from public office, and therefore from public notice, because he lacked professional qualification or education.

From here, quite logically, the term came to denote a 'man-in-the-street', a 'plebian' and eventually an 'uneducated, ill-informed person'. It was in this final sense that Latin borrowed the word as *idiōta.* From there it was absorbed into the Romance languages, coming into English at the turn of the fourteenth century by way of French *idiot.* Written records of the period show three kinds of *idiot*: the 'unlearned' person, the 'mentally deficient' and the 'fool'. Of these the first sense is now obsolete.

During the sixteenth century *idiot* was sometimes written *nidiot,* the *n* being transferred from the indefinite article: *an idiot – a nidiot* (see **umpire**). *Nidiot* itself was sometimes corrupted to *nidget* so that Thomas Heywood writes of '*a company of fooles and* Nigits' (THE WISE WOMAN OF HOGSDON, 1638). This variant became obsolete around the mid-nineteenth century.

imp

1. a demon, an evil spirit
2. a mischievous child

Children are notoriously risky. The freckle-faced imp *scoffing the newest breakfast cereal may turn out to be the pick-pocket champion of Greater London, scourge of the shopping malls. They may go off the rails after making the ads.*
(INDEPENDENT WEEKEND, 28 January 1995)

When Chaucer, in the prologue to the *Monk's Tale* (CANTERBURY TALES, c. 1387) wrote '*Of fieble trees ther comen wrecched ympes*' he did not mean that an *imp* was some sort of woodland sprite but a 'shoot', for the word was originally a horticultural one. Old English had *impa* to denote 'shoot of a plant, sapling', from the verb *impian* 'to graft on'. This was probably from an unattested Romance verb *impotare,* a derivative of Medieval Latin *impotus,* 'graft', itself from the Greek adjective *emphutos,* 'implanted', and *emphuein,* 'to implant'.

Records of *imp* as a horticultural term date from the writings of King Alfred in the ninth century until the early eighteenth century:

She'll tell you, what you call virginitie
Is fitly lik'ned to a barren tree,
Which, when the gardner on it pains bestows
To graffe an impe *thereon, in time it growes*
To such perfection, that it yeerly brings
As goodly fruit as any tree that springs.
(William Browne, BRITANNIA'S PASTORALS, 1613)

[Ivy] is a sneaking insinuating Imp.
(Andrew Marvel, THE REHERSAL TRANSPROS'D, 1672)

During the fourteenth century, however, the word was also figuratively applied to a child, the sense being 'an offspring from the parent stock'. In his CHRONICLE OF THE FAMILIES OF LANCASTER AND YORK (1548), Edward Hall described Prince Edward as *'that goodly* ympe', while the Epitaph to Lord Denbigh in Beauchamp Chapel, Warwick (1584) reads *'Heere resteth the body of the noble* Impe *Robert of Dvdley... sonne of Robert Erle of Leycester.'*

Imp gained a sinister new dimension in the sixteenth century when it denoted a 'child of the devil', 'a little demon'. In the seventeenth century these satanic associations combined with the now dwindling sense of 'child, offspring' to lend *imp* yet another new meaning, that of a 'sprightly, mischievous child'.

Otherworldly influences

The stars and planets were once held to be influential in shaping people's characters (see **influence**). John Gaule was the Minister of Great Staughton in Huntingdonshire and warned his flock against the dangers in THE MAG-ASTRO-MANCER OR THE MAGICALL-ASTROLOGICAL-DIVINER POSED, AND PUZZLED (1652). In Chapter 20, a particular target are the *physiognomists, metoposcopists* and *chiromantists,* who believe that people are shaped by their stars:

And how is it that? by first judging and pronouncing the man, or the member, to be saturnine, jovial, martial, solar, venereal, mercurial, lunar.

These adjectives may no longer hold astrological significance in modern English, but their present-day meanings reflect these ancient beliefs.

Jovial (late 16th cent) from French *jovial,* from Italian *gioviale,* 'born under the planet Jove', from Latin *jovialis,* 'pertaining to Jove', from *Jovis,* 'Jove'). The Roman deity Jove, also known as Jupiter (a classical Latin contraction of *Jovis Pater,* 'Jove Father'), was the majestic lord of heaven and the well-spring of happiness. The largest known planet was named in his honour and those born under its influence rejoiced in a cheerful, convivial disposition.

Martial (14th cent) from Old French *martial,* from Latin *mārtiālis* 'pertaining to Mars', from Latin *Mārs,* reduced form of early Latin *Māvors.* Mars had a savage, passionate nature. In Rome, where he was worshipped as the god of war, he was second only to Jupiter, and his name was given to the blood-red planet. When the adjective *martial* was borrowed into English it meant 'fit for war, belonging to warfare'. A person described as *martial* had the valiant character of a warrior. Today the adjective is widely used of anything war-like.

Mercurial (14th cent) from French *mercuriel,* from Latin *mercuriālis* 'belonging to Mercury', from *Mercurius,* 'Mercury'. The name of the Roman god Mercury derives from *merx,* 'merchandise', since, amongst his other responsibilities, he was responsible for commerce. He was also something of a thief and those who were *mercurial,* that is to say 'born under the planet Mercury', were eloquent and vivacious with a shrewd head for business and a tendency to devious practice. In seventeenth-century English, however, *mercurial* started to develop the sense 'having a volatile or changeable nature'. Although this new sense initially arose out of the older one, it is commonly perceived as being influenced by the characteristics of the metal mercury, the planetary name given to quicksilver in medieval times.

Saturnine (15th cent) from unattested medieval Latin *Sāturnīnus* 'of Saturn', from Latin *Sāturnus*). The establishment of civilisation (springing from agriculture, of which he was god) was attributed to this deity. In spite of the riotous revelry which took place at his festival, *Sāturnālia* (see **carnival**), Saturn had a gloomy, dour and taciturn nature, which he generously passed on to all born under the influence of his planet.

Solar (15th cent) from Latin *sōlāris*, 'pertaining to the sun', from *sōl*, 'sun'. According to astrology, the solar man was impressive and did everything on a grand scale. He was dignified, magnificent, proud and generous. Sadly we no longer describe distinguished, energetic people as *solar*. The adjective is now confined to things pertaining to or coming from the sun.

Venereal (15th cent) Middle English *venerealle*, from Latin *venereus*, from *Venus*, 'love, Venus'. Beautiful Venus was the Roman goddess of sexual love. The Latin adjective *venereus* meant 'concerning sexual desire or pleasure'. This was borrowed into Middle English as *venerealle* with the same meaning. It is still occasionally found today in this sense. Those born under the influence of Venus were said to be 'lecherous and lustful', but *venereal* was rarely applied in this way and this sense has been obsolete since the eighteenth century. Today the adjective is most commonly found in the coupling *venereal disease*, which has been current since at least the second half of the seventeenth century.

influence

an indirect power to affect, an ability to bring about change in a person, state of affairs, etc.

Charm was a quality of which Frederick deeply disapproved. Affronted that his sister-in-law should accuse his son of possessing such a characteristic, his resolve to save both his boys from Winifred's undesirable influence *increased.*
(Roy Hattersley, THE MAKER'S MARK, 1990)

As I walked back across that field, the moon bright enough to cast a shadow, I thought how silly even to suspect that the arrival of the new moon had somehow influenced *the flock. A truly loony idea.*
(THE TIMES WEEKEND, 18 March 1995)

Influence was originally an astrological term for a supernatural fluid that was thought to flow from the stars and sway the destiny and character of mankind:

> *What euill starre*
> *On you hath frownd, and pourd his*
> influence *bad?*
> (Spenser, THE FAIRIE QUEEN, 1590)

The word derived from Medieval Latin *influentia*, 'a flowing in' (from Latin *influens*, present participle of the verb *influere*, 'to flow in', from *fluere*, 'to flow'), and came into Middle English in the fourteenth century via Old French. Not until the end of the sixteenth century did the modern sense of *influence* 'a person or thing exercising an intangible or imperceptible power over another', begin to emerge.

◆ The past participle of *influere*, *influxus*, 'a flowing in', gave English *influx*.

Latin *fluere* is evident in *effluent* (from *effluere*, 'to flow out'), and *fluent*.◆

For another word deriving from this source, see **influenza**. For other words with astrological origins, see **consider**, **disaster** and **zodiac**.

influenza

a common infectious viral disease

Just before the end of term Petrova had influenza. *She had the worst kind, that is gastric, and makes you sick all day. She felt so miserable for a week that she did not care about anything.*
(Noel Streatfeild, BALLET SHOES, 1936)

Against this flu-*inducing squall, we had insulated ourselves with layers of wool, water-proofing, hats and thermal undergarments.*
(INDEPENDENT WEEKEND, 28 January 1995)

Such is the 'flu *epidemic among London singers that Covent Garden and the Coliseum are now having to share a tenor.*
(DAILY TELEGRAPH, 4 March 1995)

The Medieval Latin word *influentia*, 'a flowing in, an influence', originally referred to celestial power attributed to the stars and in this astrological sense it was taken into the various Romance languages, coming into English as *influence* through Old French (see **influence**). In Italian it became *influenza* where, in addition to the various meanings it shared with other languages, it had gained, by the early sixteenth century, the further sense of an 'outpouring of a disease, an epidemic', such outbreaks being seen as ordained by the stars. In 1743 there was an epidemic of a cold-like fever which gripped Italy and swept through the rest of Europe. An issue of the LONDON MAGAZINE for that year reports *'news from Rome of a contagious Distemper raging there, call'd the* Influenza*'*, and a letter dated 12 February, 1743, from the diplomat Horace Mann to his friend Horace Walpole informs that '*Everybody [in Rome] is ill of the* influenza, *and many die*'.

Today many people diagnose themselves as having *influenza* when they are really afflicted by nothing more terrible than a bad cold. Our forebears were no different, vying for sympathy and recognition by declaring themselves amongst the first victims of '*the new* influenza' (Samuel Foote, 1770). The authors of a nineteenth-century medical work identified '*The practice, so common among the higher classes in this country, of designating as* influenza *any catarrhal attack that happens to be painful and distressing*' (Fagge & Pye-Smith, THE PRINCIPLES AND PRACTICE OF MEDICINE, 1886).

In modern English *influenza* is rarely used in every-day communication. *Flu* is a much easier term to croak for anyone with a sore throat, aching limbs and a raging temperature. The word was shortened in the first half of the nineteenth century, some careful writers apologising for trimming it down by inserting an apostrophe, *'flu*. Today *flu* is so familiar and overused that this convention has generally been dropped.

For another illness with an Italian name, see **malaria**.

interloper

an interfering outsider

'It seems to me,' began the Scarecrow, when all were again assembled in the throne room, 'that the girl Jinjur is quite right in

claiming to be Queen. And if she is right, then I am wrong, and we have no business to be occupying her palace.'

'But you were the King until she came,' said the Woggle-Bug, strutting up and down with his hands in his pockets; 'so it appears to me that she is the interloper *instead of you.'*

(L Frank Baum, THE MARVELOUS LAND OF OZ, 1904)

The close relationship between the forest's living and mineral resources, the wood or charcoal and the seams of iron ore and coal, has been understood by generations of foresters. At times this balance was threatened by greedy interlopers, *as in the 17th century when Sir John de Winter leased the crown lands from Charles I and set out to convert the entire forest into charcoal to feed more and more blast-furnaces making iron for the Royalist arsenal.*

(WEEKEND TELEGRAPH, 4 March 1995)

The word was made up of the Latin prefix *inter*, meaning 'between' and *lope*, an English dialect word derived from the Middle English *lepen*, 'to leap'. This in turn was from a Middle Dutch verb *loopen*, 'to run'. Thus *interloper* meant 'to jump or run between'. In sixteenth-century English there were already familiar derogatory words in existence that used these component elements in different combinations: '*inter*-meddler', for instance, meant 'one who interferes in another's business', while a 'land-*loper*' was literally 'one who ran up and down the land', in other words 'a vagabond'. These two elements were cobbled together in the late sixteenth century to form *interloper*, a word which initially referred to 'a trader or ship illegally trespassing on another's trading rights'. The first known use, which is found in a navigational account dated around 1590, relates to foreign infringements upon the trading rights of the Moscovy Company, an English chartered company formed in 1555 which had been granted a monopoly on commerce with Russia. The East India Company, chartered in 1600, also had to repel *interlopers* who tried to seize some of their trade.

The meaning was extended in the first half of the seventeenth century to refer to a 'person who interferes in the affairs of others'.

◆ *Interlude, internecine* and *intervene* are just three of very many words formed from *inter-*. On the other hand, the original root of *loper* has not otherwise been very productive in English; it may be in **loophole** (see that entry), and in one or two other rare words, and that is all.◆

intoxicate

to inebriate, produce the effects of alcohol or drugs

The Mole never heard a word he was saying. Absorbed in the new life he was entering upon, intoxicated *with the sparkle, the ripple, the scents and the sounds and the sunlight, he trailed a paw in the water and dreamed long waking dreams.*

(Kenneth Graham, THE WIND IN THE WILLOWS, 1908)

Solitary drinking is a strange and dangerous thing. You can drink all night and not feel the remotest sense of intoxication, *but when you rise you discover that while your head feels clear enough, your legs have suddenly decided to go in for a little moonwalking or some other involuntary embarrassment.*

(Bill Bryson, NEITHER HERE NOR THERE, 1991)

The origin of this word lies with warfare in the classical world where arrows were commonly smeared with poison before being loosed. The Greek expression for this compound was *toxikon pharmakon*. *Pharmakon* meant 'drug or poison' and *toxikon* was the neuter of *toxikos*, an adjective meaning 'of or belonging to a bow/archery' (from *toxon*, 'bow'). When the Greeks inevitably economised on effort by clipping the expression to *toxicon* the word was inbued with the sense 'poison' that had properly belonged to *pharmakon*. Thus *toxicon* became a noun meaning 'poison to put on arrows'. The word was borrowed into Latin as *toxicum* with the same meaning, though later it became a general term for 'poison'. As such Medieval Latin derived the adjective *toxicus* from it to mean 'poisoned' which English took as *toxic* in the seventeenth century.

Medieval Latin coined the verb *intoxicāre*, 'to poison' from Latin *toxicum* and the prefix *in*, 'into'. This was borrowed into English as *intoxicate* in the sixteenth century but by the 1590s the word was already being used in its modern sense to describe the 'effect produced by a drug or, more especially, alcohol'. Some of our forebears must have had a rough time of it judging from some of the potions they unwittingly swallowed in search of good strong ale:

Under the Cathedral-church at Hereford is the greatest Charnel-house for bones, that ever I saw in England. In AD 1650 there lived amongst those bones a poor old woman that, to help out her fire, did use to mix the deadmen's bones: this was thrift and poverty: but cunning alewives putt the Ashes of these bones in their Ale to make it intoxicateing.
(John Aubrey 1626–1697, Brief Lives)

But even this is preferable to a poisoned arrow.

◆ Every science must have its *ology*. The study of poisons is no exception – it is called *toxicology*. Other technical terms have also developed: *detoxicate*, for instance, means 'to render poison harmless'.

From the early Greek connection to archery, the sixteenth-century educationist Roger Ascham coined the word *Toxophilus* and used it as the title of his book on archery (literally 'lover of the bow'). His fame as an archer even led to the cabinet for archery equipment being called an *ascham*. His repute certainly reached into the nineteenth century, when *toxophilite* ('archer') and *toxophily* ('the practice of archery') were born, from the title of his book. The words are still alive today:

Robert Hardy has had a lifelong interest in the longbow. He belongs to the Royal Toxophilite *Society, the British Longbow Society and the Men of Arden, an archery association founded in the 18th century.*
(Weekend Telegraph, 25 February 1995)◆

jargon

the specialised, technical language of a social sub-group

Jargon *words like 'judgemental', 'divisive' and 'viable' are irritating. 'Unacceptable' is rapidly becoming one of the most unacceptable of the lot. It's never made clear just what is unacceptable to whom. A spokesman for the Clinton administration said the reason for going into Somalia had been to make an orderly withdrawal, because staying there would have been 'unacceptable'. Let's hope at least that the cameramen got some 'acceptable' pictures.*
(Evening Standard, 6 May 1994)

I was lost within minutes of getting on board. . .The signs and the stewards talked

about aft and forward, port and starboard, quarterdeck and boat-deck, but what did they mean? And these sea-going types are so slippery with their jargon, *for as soon as you pluck up courage to ask for the bow, they say: ' Sharp end? It's back the other way, sir.'*
(WEEKEND TELEGRAPH, 25 February 1995)

This word appeared in Middle English as *iargoun, gargoun,* a borrowing from Old French *jargoun, gargon.* Originally medieval *jargon* was the sound of birds. It described not so much a songster's melodious warbling as the twittering, tweeting and chattering of sparrows and starlings. This original sense was easily transferred to human utterance of the same order. According to Chaucer, the old knight, January, was as garrulous as a magpie as he made love to his pretty young wife, May:

He was al coltissh ful of rageryе
And ful of jargon *as a flekked pye.*
('The Merchant's Tale', CANTERBURY TALES, c.1387)

Figuratively, then, *jargon* soon came to mean 'mindless prattle'. By the fifteenth century the word was no longer used of chirping birds but was confined to chattering people. From the end of the sixteenth century onwards *jargon* became a convenient term to describe any symbols, ciphers, languages or dialects which were meaningless to an outsider. The term was then further stretched to include particular terminology, such as that used by scientists, philosophers, cloistered academics, and even the cant of trades, sects and social classes.

The DICTIONARY OF JARGON by Jonathon Green takes its examples of specialist language from a wide variety of sources, ranging from dog breeders to baseball. Many of the coinings are very diverting. The *jargon* of CB (citizen band) radio, for instance, affords

bears	police
smokey	policeman
motion lotion	fuel
anklebiter	child
handle	CB nickname

Jargon has clearly come a long way since medieval birds twittered on the bough.

For a word with similar origins, see **cajole**.

jeep

a small, tough all-terrain vehicle, originally in military use

A very much modified Cheerokee Jeep, *big and dark blue: 427 cubic-inch turbocharged aluminium Chevy racing engine. Bosch fuel injection, massive high flotation tyres, quartz-iodine lights, bullet proofed.*

A very modified vehicle packed with state-of-the-art computerised radio and navigation gear. All-weather, all-terrain cross-country capability with 100+ on-road cruising.

Engine idling, it loitered in deep forest cover facing the East/West border.
(Steven L Thompson, COUNTDOWN TO CHINA, 1982)

With an average winter snowfall of 41 feet, Idaho can be a skier's dream, but a motorist's nightmare. The locals have a simple solution. Don't drive an ordinary car. Drive a Jeep *Cherokee.*
(Advertisement for Jeep, TELEGRAPH MAGAZINE, 18 February 1995)

In 1937 the American motor industry was busy with plans for a four-wheel-drive, multi-purpose army vehicle. When it was finally unveiled the vehicle was coded G P, signifying 'general purpose'. In speech the last of the two letters was generally clipped short to give a word of one syllable. This altered pronunciation, together with the subsequent spelling, *jeep*, probably came about through the unlikely influence of a cartoon star. On 16 March of the previous year Elzie Crisler Segar had introduced readers of the popular newspaper cartoon strip THIMBLE THEATRE to a little animal called *Eugene the Jeep*, the pet of Popeye's girlfriend, Olive Oyl. True to his name, this amiable and resourceful creature communicated by calling '*jeep*'. Such was his popularity that, before long, he had the honour of influencing the name of a versatile vehicle that, after widespread military use throughout the Second World War, is still in demand today.

jingoism

excessive, belligerent patriotism

It was the same with respect to war: how shameful to speak to children about the jingoistic *France that is so fond of*

Acronyms

The word acronym was coined in the United States around the 1940s. Some of the older acronyms – words made up of the initial letters or syllables of other words – are so much a part of modern speech that their origins are largely forgotten. *Radar*, for instance, stands for '*ra*dio *d*etection *a*nd *r*anging', and *sonar* for '*so*und *na*vigation and *r*anging'. Similarly *laser* is short for *l*ight *a*mplification by the *s*imulated *e*mission of *r*adiation.

More modern is the medical term *AIDS* (*A*cquired *I*mmune *D*eficiency *S*yndrome). Dating from the early 1980s, it is too new for its origin as an acronym to be forgotten, although it trips easily off the tongue like a normal word, and so it is still almost always written in upper case letters.

The world of computing has contributed the programming language *BASIC* (*B*eginners' *A*ll-purpose *S*ymbolic *I*nstrucion *C*ode) to the steadily increasing bank of acronyms. Computer users work in the land of *LAN*s (*L*ocal *A*rea *N*etworks) and *WAN*s (*W*ide *A*rea *N*etworks), as they struggle with *wysiwyg* (*w*hat *y*ou *s*ee *i*s *w*hat *y*ou *g*et) on their screens.

Organisations, political or otherwise, are often more comfortably known by their acronyms than by their cumbersome full titles. One of the earliest examples is *Gestapo*, which stands for *Ge*heime *Sta*ats-*Po*lizei, 'Secret State-Police'. The Gestapo was organised by Hermann Göring in Prussia in 1933 and covered all Germany by the following year.

A great deal of time and breath has been saved since 1949 by shortening the *N*orth *A*tlantic *T*reaty *O*rganisation to the compact *NATO* and when the *C*onciliation and *A*rbritration *S*ervice, set up in 1974, had its tongue-twister of a title prefixed by the word *A*dvisory the following year, *ACAS* saved many newspaper column inches. The same can surely be said of that American animal the *quango*, which grew to

uniforms, that is never wrong. From the time I was a child, I abominated all the pages of our history books summoning us to remember only military victories and names of heroes.
(Emilie Carles, tr Avriel H Goldberger, A WILD HERB SOUP, 1991)

But his [the Prince of Wales's] speech yesterday was a good, old-fashioned appeal to British jingoism – *all part of his current rehabilitation campaign, in the wake of the Camillagate scandal, to win back the hearts and minds of the British people. The speech was a typically superficial, misjudged attempt to win public applause by reducing a complex issue to simple extremes.*
(DAILY MAIL, 5 May 1994)

In the second half of the seventeenth century '*Hey Jingo*!' or '*High Jingo*', along with '*Hey presto*', '*Abracadabra*!' and '*Hocus Pocus*!', was a piece of conjuring jargon with supposedly supernatural connotations. The fact that Motteux chose *by jingo* to translate *par Dieu* ('by God') in his rendition of

fit its acronym. In 1967 it was known simply as a *qu*asi *n*on-government(al) *o*rganisation; by 1976 its name had swollen to *qu*asi *a*utonomous *n*on-*g*overnmental *o*rganisation. Curiously, although the original title and the organisations themselves were of American inspiration, credit for the acronym *quango* is claimed by a lecturer at the University of Essex in the late 1960s.

Some organisations begin with a punchy acronym and then work out an appropriate title to fit. *ASH*, for instance, stands for the *A*ction on *S*moking and *H*ealth. A tear is a potent symbol of the compassion and social concern of the church, so in its very early days the *EAR* fund changed to *T*he *E*vangelical *A*lliance *R*elief Fund and made its mark as *TEAR* Fund.

The full form of *VIP*, like those of *radar* and *laser*, is never heard, the acronym being so well assimilated into the language. *VIP* dates back to the 1930s and is American in origin. It stands for '*v*ery *i*mportant *p*erson' and may have begun as military slang for a high-ranking guest. It has been in use as an adjective (as in *VIP lounge*) since the mid-1940s. Also from America comes *UFO*, '*u*nidentified *f*lying *o*bject', in use since the 1950s.

When present-day society is not probing for life on other planets, its interest focuses on market forces and spending power. Since the boom years of the 1980s this has spawned a whole clutch of economic acronyms such as *yuppie*, '*y*oung *u*rban (or *u*pwardly-mobile) *p*rofessional', and *dinkie*, '*d*ouble *i*ncome *n*o *k*ids'. But what of the recession-ridden nineties? It seems that granny holds the economic key and has been labelled accordingly:

With children off our hands and no mortgage, we are now the glammies *(greying, leisured, affluent, middle-aged spenders) and* woopies *(well-off older* people*). And we still believe we are young despite physical evidence to the contrary!* (DAILY EXPRESS, 16 March 1995)

Rabelais (1694) has led to the conjecture that the term may have been a euphemism for 'by Jesus!'. An alternative view is that it was a borrowing of the Basque *Jinko* or *Jainko* ('God') and was picked up from sailors. According to the OED, this origin is not impossible, but cannot be supported by evidence. From conjuror's cant to popular parlance, by the eighteenth century by *jingo* (or often by the *living jingo*) was generally used as an exclamation:

All of a sudden the lightning let go a perfect sluice of white glare, and somebody sings out:
'By the living jingo, *here's the bag of gold on his breast!'*
(Mark Twain, THE ADVENTURES OF HUCKLEBERRY FINN, 1884)

In 1878 Russia and Turkey were at war and Russian troops were advancing on Constantinople. Disraeli was strongly advocating intervention on behalf of the Turks. His bully-boy tirades against the Russians were echoed in sentiment in a popular music-hall song, the refrain of which was:

We don't want to fight, but, by Jingo, *if we do,*
We've got the ships, we've got the men,
We've got the money too.

Walsh quotes a contemporary parody of the song which appeared in the PALL MALL GAZETTE:

We don't want to fight, but by Jingo, *if we do,*
We've Protestant and Catholic, Turk, infidel, and Jew;
We've 'God' and 'Mammon,' 'Allah,' 'Buddha,' 'Brahma,' and 'Vishnu':
We've collared all the deities, so what can Russia do?

Jingo (plural *jingoes*) was subsequently plucked from the first line of these refrains and used by the Liberal party as a sarcastic epithet for Disraeli and his belligerent followers who, in turn, tried to lend the term dignity by attempting to make it synonymous with right-minded patriotism. The Liberals won the day, it seems, for *jingoism* (coined in the same year) remains to describe the spirit of a warmongering politician, an indiscriminate patriot. *Jingoistic* was in use by the middle of the next decade.

See **chauvinism**.

juggernaut

1. a very heavy lorry
2. an irresistible force

A group of old fakirs were capering and making a wild ado round the statue; these were striped with ochre, and covered with cuts whence their blood issued drop by drop – stupid fanatics, who, in the great Indian ceremonies, still throw themselves under the wheels of Juggernaut.
(Jules Verne, AROUND THE WORLD IN EIGHTY DAYS, 1873)

From the tangled forest came the sound of cracking limbs and crashing trunks – Tantor was coming down upon them, a huge Juggernaut *of the jungle. The priests were becoming uneasy. They cast apprehensive glances in the direction of the approaching elephant and then back at La. 'Fly!' she commanded them and then she stooped and cut the bonds securing her prisoner's feet and hands.*
(Edgar Rice Burroughs, TARZAN AND THE JEWELS OF OPAR, 1916)

Impressed just this side of awe as I am by the Department of Transport and its fearless tackling of such problems as juggernaut *lorries and EEC regulations, I must nevertheless confess some disquiet about a recent plan.*
(NEW SCIENTIST, 1983)

The [house] market is the most delicate mechanism for the allocation of resources we have; but it does not always serve the needs of the old and the infirm, the very poor and the very young. It's a juggernaut *that needs brakes.*
(THE SUNDAY TIMES, 19 March 1995)

Juggernaut has been in English since the 1630s when it was used in purely cultural contexts to describe the *Juggernaut* festival. Its spelling reflects an attempt to transcribe the Hindi word *Jagannāth*, a title given to Krishna, one of the avatars or incarnations of the deity Vishnu. The word is of Sanskrit origin, from *Jagannātha* which means Lord of the Universe (from *jagat*, 'world' and *nātha*, 'lord').

The Indian town of Puri in the north-eastern state of Orissa is the site of a magnificent temple where *Jagannāth* is worshipped. Each year the journey Krishna took from Gokul to Mathura is commemorated when the images of Jagannāth and his two siblings are removed from the main temple and mounted on colossal, ornate cars. It takes 4000 men to drag the unwieldy cars the kilometre or so to the Gundicha Mandir, another temple, where the images reside for seven days before being hauled back again.

Europeans were first alerted to this magnificent procession by Friar Odoric whose account of his travels in the East was published around 1321. The good friar's narrative included stories of devotees who fanatically sacrificed themselves to the god by throwing themselves beneath the wheels of the car. These and subsequent accounts are now thought to have been exaggerated; nevertheless, in the mid-nineteenth century they were instrumental in lending a figurative dimension to *juggernaut*, so that it came to mean 'any belief or institution which attracts unquestioning, sacrificial devotion', 'an overwhelming, irresistible force'.

In modern British English the word also commonly denotes a 'large, heavy vehicle'. This use also arose in the nineteenth century when Thackeray, in the SECOND FUNERAL OF NAPOLEON (1841) wrote: *Fancy, then, . . . the body landed at day-break.and transferred to the car, and fancy the car, a huge* Juggernaut *of a machine.*

But it was the increasing menace of huge articulated lorries on the roads in the 1960s that brought the word to prominence in this context.

kidnap

to seize someone in order to exact payment for his safe return

. . .we're calling in L and F. They're a sort of insurance outfit that advises people on how to negotiate with kidnappers. *Lots of chaps travelling round the world advising grieving relatives and anxious companies on how to get the ransom down a bit. Call themselves Lost and Found.*
(Alan Judd, SHORT OF GLORY, 1984)

On the whole, those with the money to buy a £700 coat are more worried about kidnapping *than assassination. Only a few are prepared to invest in high-quality jackets for their bodyguards, who normally have to make do with ordinary bullet-proof vests.*
(WEEKEND FINANCIAL TIMES, 14 January 1995)

Kidnap is a compound word. The first element, *kid*, has been a slang term for a 'child' since at least the turn of the seventeenth century and was frequently heard in colloquial speech in the nineteenth century. It is, of course, a figurative use of *kid*, meaning 'young goat', which derives from an Old Norse word *kidh* with the same meaning. The second element, *nap*, was another piece of seventeenth-century slang, a cant term for 'to steal'. It is related to the more familiar *nab* and to other words in Scandinavian languages meaning 'to snatch'.

The two elements were combined in the second half of the seventeenth century to describe a particular crime, that of abducting young children and carrying them off or selling them to work as servants or labourers in the American colonies. By the time Dr Johnson had compiled his DICTIONARY OF THE ENGLISH LANGUAGE in 1755 the term had been extended to cover the abduction of a person of any age, such as men who were dragged away to serve as sailors when there were insufficient recruits. They were pressed men.

Escaped negro slaves in America were also prime targets for kidnapping, to return them to their southern masters from the abolitionist north. Frederick Douglass was one such; he escaped from the south and took up residence in New Bedford. In 1841 he addressed an anti-slavery convention in Nantucket, and in 1845 published NARRATIVE OF THE LIFE OF FREDERICK DOUGLASS, AN AMERICAN SLAVE WRITTEN BY HIMSELF. These were his feelings on arriving in the north:

I felt like one who had escaped a den of hungry lions. This state of mind, however, very soon subsided; and I was again seized with a feeling of great insecurity and loneliness. I was yet liable to be taken back, and subjected to all the tortures of slavery . . . I was afraid to speak to any one for fear of speaking to the wrong one, and thereby falling into the hands of money-loving kidnappers, *whose business it was to lie in wait for the panting fugitive, as the ferocious beasts of the forest lie in wait for their prey.*

kowtow

1. to bow deeply and humbly in submission
2. to curry favour with, to show excessive deference

The Marquess kotooed *like a first-rate Mandarin, and vowed 'that her will was his conduct'.*
(Benjamin Disraeli, VIVIAN GREY, 1826)

Having lost an editor to a small independent company at the end of this year, the prospect of having to kow-tow *to the same defector must be particularly galling to ITN. Charles Stuart-Smith, who left ITN to set up media firm Luther Pendragon, is news and editorial consultant to The Big Breakfast, Bob Geldof's TV company which won Channel Four's early morning slot two days ago. Stuart-Smith. . thinks he might be able to direct a little business ITN's way. 'It would be nice to help them save a few jobs,' he muses.*
(DAILY TELEGRAPH, 12 June 1992)

Kow-tow is an anglicised attempt at Mandarin Chinese *kē tóu*, an act of obeisance showing submission or deep respect, such as a subject might have towards his Emperor, for instance. *Kē* means 'bump, knock' and *tóu* 'head', and the reverence is performed by prostrating oneself and touching the ground with one's forehead. The term entered English as a noun in the early nineteenth century with reference to the bow. In the 1820s its figurative potential was exploited when it was used as a verb, with the sense 'to behave in an ingratiating manner'.

Words from Chinese

English has taken a number of Chinese words into its vocabulary, besides *kowtow* and *tea* which have entries of their own in this book.

Japan (16th cent): Chinese *Jih-pun* (from *jih*, 'sun' and *pun*, 'origin') is a translation of Japanese *Ni-pon*, 'sunrise'. This was borrowed into Malay as *Japang* and from there was taken into the European languages.

kaolin (18th cent): a specific type of clay (China clay), used for the manufacture of porcelain, originally came from a mountain in Jiangxi Province called *gao lĭng* (from *gao*, 'high' and *lĭng*, 'mountain').

ketchup (17th cent): this originally referred to the 'brine of pickled fish, known in the Amoy Chinese dialect as *kôechiap* (from *kôe*, a kind of fish, and *chiap*, 'juice'). This was borrowed into Malay as *kichap* and into English as *catchup*, then *ketchup*.

silk (9th cent): probably from Chinese *sī*, 'silk'. Its exact route into English is not known. Part of its history, at least, involves Greek *Sēres*, 'the oriental people from whom silk was obtained', and *sērikos*, 'silken'. The Latin derivatives are *Sēres* and *sēricum*.

soy (17th cent): Chinese *shi-yu* was a sauce made from soya beans (from *shi*, 'salted beans' and *yu*, 'oil'). This was borrowed as *sho-yu* in Japanese, which formed the contracted colloquial form *soy*. The Japanese form was the source of Dutch *soya*, which was borrowed into English in the eighteenth century.

typhoon (16th cent): this is from the Cantonese dialect *daai feng*, 'big wind', (corresponding to Mandarin *dàfēng*), though the spelling was influenced by Greek *Tūphōn*, the mythical hundred-headed monster who begot the winds (early English forms are *touffon*, *tuffon* and *tuffan*).

yen (19th cent): from Cantonese Chinese *yin-yān*, 'craving for opium' (from *yin*, 'opium' and *yān*, 'craving'). Chinese immigrants took the term to America in the mid-nineteenth century where it entered the slang vocabulary as *yen-yen*, later shortened to *yen*. By the early twentieth century it was generally used as a term for a craving of any sort. The word for Japanese currency is unrelated to this *yen*.

lackadaisical

uncommitted, unenthusiastic, languid

Certainly, the backdrop of spreading oaks and white-rail pastures, fitted my mental image of polo. But not the persistent October drizzle, and definitely not balancing atop an upturned milk-crate swiping with a stick at a line of balls. 'One, two and follow through,' shouted Peter Grace. 'Cock your wrist, don't let that arm go wimpy.' I strove to imitate his effortless sweep and final, lackadaisical *twirl, but the balls lurched bumpily off at haphazard angles, usually accompanied by a spray of clover and an excitable terrier eager to retrieve.*
(THE SUNDAY TIMES, 7 November 1994)

'*She's dead, deceas'd, she's dead; alack the day,*' wails Nurse when Juliet cannot be roused (ROMEO AND JULIET, 1597). *Alack the day* or *alackaday* was a common sixteenth-century exclamation of sorrow or reproach which meant 'Woe to the day!' or 'Shame to the day!'. By the eighteenth century the form *lack-a-day* (and its extended form *lackadaisy*) was more common, the expression having lost its initial unstressed vowel. *Lackadaisical* emerged as an adjective in the second half of the eighteenth century, becoming increasingly popular in the nineteenth. It denoted the limp, languid speech and bearing of one who, overwhelmed by life's little problems and challenges, was given to sighing '*Lackaday!*'

laconic

brief and sparing in expression, usually in speech

'Pack!' was his laconic *greeting to Zarinska as he passed her lodge and hurried to harness his dogs. A few minutes later he swept into the council at the head of the team, the woman by his side.*
(Jack London, SON OF THE WOLF, 1900)

Like most men of action, [Lord John Roxton] is laconic *in speech, and sinks readily into his own thoughts, but he is always quick to answer a question or join in a conversation, talking in a queer, jerky, half-humorous fashion.*
(Sir Arthur Conan Doyle, THE LOST WORLD, 1912)

. . . we went back to the Canapina ('room small and bare' say my notes laconically, *'shower sprays all over bathroom') and ate wallpaper-paste gnocchi with 50 school-children on a field trip.*
(WEEKEND TELEGRAPH, 11 February 1995)

The people of *Laconia* (a state in ancient Greece) had a reputation for rigorous austerity. This was even evident in their speech and writing which were brief and to the point. A well-known story illustrates their succinct style. It tells of Philip of Macedon whose threat, '*If I enter Laconia, I will raze Sparta to the ground*', met with the terse, laconic reply, '*If.*'

The adjective *Laconic* (from Latin *Laconicus* and Greek *Lakōnikos*) was borrowed in the sixteenth century to refer to all things pertaining to that region. Soon it was also written with a lower-case letter to denote 'concisely expressed', whether spoken or written. An early instance of this (1589) is recorded in a hurriedly composed letter of James VI of Scotland. He apologises for its sparse style thus, '*excuis me for this my* laconike *writting,*' adding as his excuse, '*I ame in suche haist.*'

The people of the state capital, *Sparta,* were considered especially frugal and well-disciplined. The adjective *Spartan,* borrowed from Latin *Spartānus* in the fifteenth century, follows a similar pattern to *laconic.* Initially it referred only to the city or its people but in the seventeenth century its use was extended to their austere, frugal characteristics. Thus Milton speaks of mollifying a '*Spartan surlinesse*' (AREOPAGITICA, 1644) and Cowper of a '*Spartan soul*' (EXPOSTULATION, 1781). Today, *spartan furnishings, a spartan meal,* or a *spartan lifestyle* are all evocative of the simple, spare life of the inhabitants of the Laconian capital.

◆ There are quite a number of pithy replies and comments that have reached the books of quotations:

- The magazine PUNCH's advice to couples contemplating marriage was simple: 'Don't'.
- During the Battle of the Bulge in the World War II, the Germans called on General McAuliffe to surrender. He replied 'Nuts!'
- 'How can they tell?' (Dorothy Parker's response to the news that Calvin Coolidge was dead.)
- 'Politics is a blood sport.' (Aneurin Bevan)

Remarks worthy of the Laconians themselves!◆

lampoon

a biting satire upon a person or institution

Kenneth Clarke borrowed one of the most memorable phrases in politics yesterday when he mocked Gordon Brown as a 'silly billy'. Or did he? For in common with Jim Callaghan's memorable phrase, 'Crisis? What crisis?', the words 'silly billy' were attributed rather than spoken. The Dennis Healey tag was merely an invention of TV comedian Mike Yarwood, who loved to lampoon *the Chancellor during the dark days of the IMF. But in later years, Healey has become fond of the phrase, and is sometimes heard muttering on the campaign trail: 'Oh, I am a silly billy. That's what you want me to say, isn't it?'*
(THE TIMES, 9 December 1994)

Former victims of the satirical programme Spitting Image, who might have been expected to celebrate its passing, queued up yesterday to mourn the announcement that it was running out of saliva after 11 years of merciless lampooning.
(THE TIMES, 13 March 1995)

It is a well-known fact that drinking loosens the tongue, bringing private thoughts to public attention. This would seem to be the background of *lampoon.* The term *Lampons,* 'Let's drink' (from French slang *lamper,* 'to gulp down, to swig') was a common refrain in French drinking songs of the sixteenth and seventeenth centuries. The verses themselves must often have been of a biting, personal nature, to account for the coining of *lampoon* from this source. The word, as noun and verb, was first used in English from the middle of the seventeenth century.

In his LIVES OF THE POETS (1779–1781), Samuel Johnson denounces Pope as '*a lampooner, who scattered his ink without fear or decency.*' Pope is indeed infamous for invective against those who crossed him. This is part of the portrait of Atticus, otherwise Joseph Addison, with whom he quarrelled:

Damn with faint praise, assent with
civil leer,
And without sneering, teach the rest to
sneer;
Willing to wound, and yet afraid to
strike,

Just hint a fault, and hesitate dislike;
Alike reserv'd to blame, or to commend,
A tim'rous foe, and a suspicious friend;
(EPISTLE TO DR ARBUTHNOT, 1735)

The taste for abusive attacks has not diminished since, although the form it takes may vary. Grotesque cartoons and caricatures were added to in the twentieth century by the rise of satirical TV shows, such as 'That Was The Week That Was' and 'Spitting Image'.

A gentler sense has developed in recent years, which is more good-humoured. *Lampoon* here is rather the mocking of shared human foibles, an affectionate teasing of the target.

For another word originating in a drinking refrain, see **carouse**.

Months of the year

The final version of the ancient Roman calendar is traditionally credited to Numa Pompilius, the (possibly mythical) second king of Rome after Romulus. The original Roman year began at the spring equinox and was divided into ten months, each beginning at the full moon. This allowed for 304 days, which left the remaining 61 days mysteriously unaccounted for. Numa Pompilius added the missing two months.

The Roman year followed the agricultural cycle and began in spring. The first month was named *Martius*, being dedicated to *Mars*, the protector of agriculture and cattle. Old French had *marz* from which northern dialects derived *marche*. This was taken into Anglo-French, becoming *March* in Middle English.

April's origins are more obscure. The month was possibly named for Venus, the goddess of love – perhaps because of much activity from the birds and the bees at this time of the year. The suggestion is that Latin *Aprīlis* was derived from Etruscan *Apru*. This in turn had been borrowed from Greek *Aphrō*, short for *Aphrodite*, whom the Romans identified with *Venus*. Middle English *April* comes directly from Latin.

Some ancient writers have connected *Maius* with *Maia*, an Italic goddess of the spring whom the Romans identified as the eldest and most beautiful of the Pleiades. *Maius* was borrowed into Old French as *mai* and Middle English as *May*.

Latin *Jūnius* was consecrated to *Juno*, queen of heaven. She was the guardian of womanhood and her month was the most auspicious for marriage. Old English borrowed *Junius* from Latin. Middle English also had *Iuyn*, from Old French *juin*.

The remaining months in the ancient Roman calendar were rather unimaginatively numbered:

July, for instance, was originally *Quintilis* from *quintus*, 'fifth'. However, after Caesar's death in 44 BC it was renamed *Jūlius* in his

Lent

a forty-day period from Ash Wednesday to Easter

The original meaning of Lent *was 'holy spring'. Traditionally, at this time of year, Christians prepared themselves for Easter by asking God to show them their failures and by repenting of their wrong-doings. People new to Christianity were made ready for their baptism which would also take place at Easter. So* Lent *is a time of preparation: a spiritual spring-cleaning; a challenge to combat evil in our lives. And* Lent *is a time to turn back to God.*
(Joyce Huggett, APPROACHING EASTER: MEDITATIONS FOR LENT, 1987)

Abstemious types can really let themselves go, Lent *permitting, at a luncheon on*

honour, *Quintilis* having been his birth month. Anglo-French had *julie* (rhyming with Modern English *duly*) and this pronunciation persisted as late as the eighteenth century. Skeat suggests the change was to eliminate any possible confusion with *June.*

August was originally *Sextilis* from *sextus,* 'sixth', but was renamed to honour *Augustus* Caesar, the first Roman emperor (63 BC–AD 14). The adjective *augustus* meant 'venerable, magnificent'. In 27 BC it was taken as a title with the sense 'Imperial Majesty' by Julius Caesar's heir, Octavian, two years after he was named emperor.

Latin *September* was derived from *septem,* 'seven'; *October* was from *octō,* 'eight'; *November* from *novem,* 'nine'; and *December* from *decem,* 'ten'. The Old French *septembre, octobre, novembre* and *decembre* influenced Middle English forms but these were later revised with Latin spellings.

The two months required to complete the year, *January* and *February,* are the ones traditionally credited to Numa Pompilius. *Jānuārius* (Middle English *Januarie*) was named after *Janus,* god of gateways and of beginnings, to whom Numa Pompilius built a temple in Rome. *Februa,* a word of Sabine origin, was a festival of purification which fell in mid-February and Latin *februārius* derived from this. It came into Middle English as *feveryer* through Old French *feverier* and Late Latin *febrārius,* but was later remodelled on the original Latin.

In 46 BC Julius Caesar had the Roman calendar revised. The new Julian calendar confirmed that a year should have 365 days but added an extra day every fourth year to compensate for astronomical difference. The beginning of the year was shifted to 1 January, the two-faced god Janus keeping a watchful eye over the departure of the old year and the arrival of the new. However, since the new calendar retained the months in their original order, this step made a nonsense of those names with a numerical derivation.

For characteristics of classical gods, see **Otherworldly influences** (page 142).

March 23 that wine merchant John Armit is holding for wine critic Robert Parker. Champagne is included as an aperitif and six fine wines during luncheon.
(THE TIMES, 13 March 1995)

Lent was *lenten* in Middle English and comes from the Old English *lencten*, meaning 'the spring'. This, in turn, was supposedly from the Old English word *lang* ('long'), because days become longer at this time of the year. *Lenten* still remains in limited use today, though only as an adjective.

There are cognate forms in many other Germanic languages, where the sense is just 'spring'. English alone has developed an ecclesiastical meaning. From medieval times onwards, *lent* signified a period of forty weekdays from Ash Wednesday to the eve of Easter, a figure which reflects the length of time Jesus Christ fasted in the wilderness (Matthew 4:1–11). This was viewed as a time of abstinence, penitence and spiritual renewal in preparation for Easter:

Is this a Fast, to keep
The larder lean
And clean
From fat of veals and sheep?
Is it to quit the dish
Of flesh, yet still
To fill
The platter high with fish?
No; 'tis a Fast to dole
Thy sheaf of wheat
And meat
Unto the hungry soul.
It is to fast from strife
From old debate
And hate
To circumcise thy life.
(Robert Herrick, NOBLE NUMBERS, 1647)

Interestingly, a season running up to Easter had been established in the ecclesiastical calendar throughout Christendom centuries before the medieval concept of Lent took hold. From the days of the early church in the second century, Easter was a time of baptism for new converts. For this they were prepared by a series of classes on the meaning of baptism, communion, the creeds, the Lord's Prayer and so on. Justin the Martyr in Rome and Pantaenus, Clement and Origen in Alexandria were early teachers of these courses. There are still in existence records of the addresses given to these new converts. Over the centuries, this period of intensive teaching and discipline for new converts before baptism became formalised into a forty-day period of spiritual preparation for Easter for all believers, a season that has been called *Lent* or *Lenten* since about AD1000.

See **carnival** and **Shrovetide**.

lewd

indecent, obscene, licentious

He had, he said, been the greatest of sinners. He had scoffed; he had wantonly associated with the reckless and the lewd. *But a day of awakening had come, and, in a human sense, it had been brought about mainly by the influence of a certain clergyman, whom he had at first grossly insulted; but whose parting words had sunk into his heart, and had remained there, till by the grace of Heaven they had worked this change in him, and made him what they saw him.*
(Thomas Hardy, TESS OF THE D'URBERVILLES, 1891)

Written history of this word dates back to the ninth century. Old English had the unattested adjective *lǣwede*, meaning 'of the laity', to distinguish laymen from clergy. Since the clergy were educated and most of the laity were not, Middle English *lewede* had, by the thirteenth century, picked up the sense of 'unlearned, untutored'. The ignorant were generally regarded as society's dregs and so, by the fourteenth century the word had picked up the sense 'common, vulgar' and, by extension 'vile, wicked and good-for-nothing'. One of the Paston letters, chronicling English social life in the fifteenth century, reads:

> *Plese zow . . . to forgeve me, and also my wyffe of owr* leude *offence that we have not don ower dute.*
> (PASTON LETTERS III, c.1481)

In a passage about the biblical parable of the talents, the puritan Arthur Golding describes the man who wasted his by burying it in the ground as 'a *leaude servant*', meaning 'worthless', 'good-for-nothing' (HEMINGE'S POSTILL, tr 1569), while Sir Henry Savile renders a statement from Tacitus's HISTORIES (tr 1591) as '*A state gotten by* lewde *meanes cannot be retayned.*'

The modern meaning, 'obscene', 'lascivious', was a further development of the word in the fourteenth century. Chaucer speaks of 'lewed *dronken harlotrye*' (CANTERBURY TALES, 'The Miller's Prologue', c.1386) and young ladies of the period were warned against forward behaviour:

> *If thou sit by a right goode manne,*
> *This lesson look thou think upon.*
> *Under his thigh thy knee not fit,*
> *Thou art full* lewd, *if thou does it.*

In the sixteenth century, Shakespeare wrote of '*lulling on a* lewd *Loue-Bed*' (RICHARD III, 1594), while a few decades later Samuel Pepys, dipping into L'ESCHOLLER DE FILLES, a pornographic book from France, thought it '*the most bawdy,* lewd *book*' but persevered with it '*for information sake*' (Christopher Hibbert, THE ENGLISH, 1987).

Often the word is used as an insult. This is how Gloucester deals with the Bishop of Winchester in Shakespeare's HENRY VI, Part 1, Act 3, scene 1 (1592):

> *No, prelate; such is thy audacious wickedness,*
> *Thy* lewd, *pestiferous, and dissentious pranks,*
> *As very infants prattle of thy pride.*
> *Thou art a most pernicious usurer;*
> *Froward by nature, enemy to peace;*
> *Lascivious, wanton, more than well beseems*
> *A man of thy profession and degree.*

Aphra Behn was much too outspoken for many to handle. To one critic she was that *lewd Harlot*; a contemporary, *Gould*, sardonically derided her play THE CITY HEIRESS (1682) in one of his own THE PLAY HORSE, A SATYR:

> *. . . that clean piece of Wit*
> *The City Heiress by chaste Sappho Writ,*
> *Where the* Lewd *Widow comes with Brazen Face,*
> *Just seeking from a Stallion's rank Embrace,*
> *T' acquaint the Audience with her Filthy Case.*
> *Where can you find a Scene for juster Praise,*
> *In Shakespear, Johnson, or in Fletcher's Plays?*

Very little about the word *lewd* has changed in the following centuries.

lizard

a reptile

The place was a small clearing in the center of a palm grove. In this was one of those boiling mud geysers which I have already described. Around its edge were scattered a number of leathern thongs cut from iguanodon hide, and a large collapsed membrane which proved to be the dried and scraped stomach of one of the great fish lizards *from the lake. This huge sack had been sewn up at one end and only a small orifice left at the other.*
(Sir Arthur Conan Doyle, THE LOST WORLD, 1912)

Alice looked at the jury-box, and saw that, in her haste, she had put the Lizard *in head downwards, and the poor little thing was waving its tail about in a melancholy way, being quite unable to move.*
(Lewis Carroll, ALICE'S ADVENTURES IN WONDERLAND, 1865)

Middle English had *liserd* or *lesard*, a borrowing from Old French *lesard* or *laisarde*, which came from the Latin *lacertus* (feminine form *lacerta*). The words *lizard* and *alligator* thus share the same origin. The term is first found in PIERS PLOWMAN by Langland (c. 1377) and in Wycliffe's translation (1382) of Leviticus 11:30 which lists a number of creeping creatures that the Israelites were forbidden to eat.

Since the Latin word *lacertus* means both 'the upper part of the arm' and 'a lizard', it has been assumed by many that the reptile was so named because of its resemblance in shape to the forearm. If this is so, it is another instance of people's propensity to associate animals with parts of the body. (See **muscle**.)

See **alligator** and **crocodile**.

loophole

1. a narrow slit in a wall for shooting or looking through
2. a way of escaping an obligation

The politicians, in a nook apart,
Discuss'd the world, and settled all the spheres;
The wits watch'd every loophole *for their art,*
To introduce a bon-mot head and ears;
(Byron, DON JUAN, 1821)

Captain Smollett made no change in his arrangements. If the mutineers succeeded in crossing the stockade, he argued, they would take possession of any unprotected loophole *and shoot us down like rats in our own stronghold.*
(Robert Louis Stevenson, TREASURE ISLAND, 1883)

Two drunken brawls on board different charter flights returning to Britain in the past few weeks have highlighted a legal loophole *that allows mid-air offenders to avoid justice. Passengers flying into Britain who commit offences on board can be arrested on arrival only if they were on a British plane or if the offences were committed while the plane was in British air space – which is sometimes only for the last 15 minutes of a flight.*
(WEEKEND TELEGRAPH, 11 February 1995)

In medieval fortifications *loupes* were slits set in the thick stone walls that gradually widened out on the inside. These narrow apertures were difficult for enemy archers to penetrate but allowed the defenders within to loose their projectiles with ease over a wide area of territory outside. The word was also applied to similar apertures made to peep through and observe the lie of the land. Milton's poetic use in PARADISE LOST (1667) reflects this sense:

So counselled he, and both together went

Into the thickest wood; there soon
they chose
The fig-tree;
. . . a pillared shade
High over-arched, and echoing
walks between:
There oft the Indian herdsman,
shunning heat,
Shelters in cool, and tends his
pasturing herds
At loop-holes *cut through*
thickest shade.

The aperture might be designed to admit light and air:

I inquir'd a little into the practice of the Moravians: some of them had accompanied me, and all were very kind to me. I found they work'd for a common stock, eat at common tables, and slept in common dormitories, great numbers together. In the dormitories I observed loopholes, *at certain distances all along just under the ceiling, which I thought judiciously placed for change of air.* (The AUTOBIOGRAPHY OF BENJAMIN FRANKLIN, 1793)

Loupe was first recorded in the fourteenth century and has a probable connection with the Middle Dutch verb *lūpen*, 'to lurk, to spy'. In the late sixteenth century the same word, now spelt *loope*, appeared in the compound *loophole*, with exactly the same meaning.

The figurative use of *loophole* dates from the second half of the seventeenth century. It alludes to the narrow opening or outlet in an otherwise impregnable stone wall and denotes 'a way out, an escape'. The sense may also have been influenced by the Dutch *loopgat*, the first part of which is the stem of the verb 'to run'. These days the expression usually applies to a small flaw in the wording of a law, regulation or contract that makes legal avoidance possible. A *loophole* is a way out or escape from an obligation. As W C Fields lay on his death-bed he was asked why he was reading his bible. '*I'm looking for a* loophole,' came the answer.

magazine

1 a weekly or monthly periodical
2. a broadcast programme of general interest
3. an arsenal

Laura, when dressed, was (as I sang before)
A pretty woman as was ever seen,
Fresh as the Angel o'er a new inn door,
Or frontespiece of a new Magazine,
With all the fashions which the last
month wore,
Coloured, and silver paper leaved between
That and the title-page, for fear the Press
Should soil with parts of speech the parts
of dress.

(Lord Byron, BEPPO, 1818)

*[The town] is strongly fortified, but both fortifications and town suffered much in the Brazilian war. . The church is a curious ruin; it was used as a powder-*magazine, *and was struck by lightning in one of the ten thousand thunder-storms of the Rio Plata.*
(Charles Darwin, THE VOYAGE OF THE BEAGLE, 1839)

When a child decided to astound family and friends by producing a magazine, *often scurrilous in intent, the answer to the printing problem was a jellygraph, or hectograph. It was in essence a shallow metal tray filled with gelatine, smooth and firm enough to take the impression of a purple-inked sheet of paper. Other sheets could then be rubbed lightly on its surface and would take a reasonably legible copy. Many an 'alternative' school* magazine *was produced in this manner.*
(E. S. Turner, AN ABC OF NOSTALGIA, 1984)

When Robinson Crusoe was stranded on his island he made provision for himself by domesticating goats reasoning that '*the keeping up a breed of tame creatures thus at my hand would be a living* magazine *of flesh, milk, butter, and cheese for me as long as I lived in the place, if it were to be forty years. . .*' (Daniel Defoe, ROBINSON CRUSOE, 1719). Defoe is using the word in the original sense of 'storehouse'. The term is ultimately an Arabic one deriving from *khatzana*, 'to store up'. From this Arabic had *makhzan*, 'storehouse', but it is from the plural *makhāzin* that Italian derived its singular noun *magazzino*. This passed into Old French as *magazin*, still meaning 'storehouse', and from there into English in the second half of the sixteenth century. From here it was variously applied and developed a range of metaphorical meanings.

Sometimes *magazine* was applied not just to a storehouse but to its stock also, so that it came to mean 'a store of something'; this might be anything from body fat – which, according to Helkiah Crooke (A DESCRIPTION OF THE BODY OF MAN, 1615) was considered quite desirable by some, being '*a Stowage or* Magazine *of nourishment against a time of dearth*' – to the clothing which covered it.

Within a few years of its first appearance in English *magazine* had been pressed into military service to denote a 'store of arms and ammunition'. In the eighteenth century this particular use was extended to refer to a 'chamber on a gun' which held a supply of bullets. Both of these meanings are still current, the latter having been more recently further stretched to apply to the chamber in a camera that holds the roll of film.

On the literary front, from the 1630s onwards the word was purloined for the titles of reference books on specific subjects such as THE MARINER'S MAGAZINE (1669) or NEGOTIATOR'S MAGAZINE (1719), these volumes being figurative storehouses of facts or scholarship. The concept of a periodical carrying quality articles of less specialised, more general interest arose in the first half of the eighteenth century. THE GENTLEMAN'S MAGAZINE: or, MONTHLY INTELLIGENCER appeared in 1731, the title and the editors' stated aim, '*to promote a Monthly Collection to treasure up, as in a* Magazine, *the most remarkable Pieces on the Subjects above-mention'd*' showing an intention to provide the reader with a 'storehouse' of interest and information. Subsequent general periodicals followed suit and *magazine* gained a new dimension

The inevitable abbreviation *mag* is surprisingly old, dating from the early nineteenth century. The term *magazine* applied to radio and television programmes that contain miscellaneous items of general interest arose in the 1930s because of their similarity in content to printed periodicals.

magpie

1. a black and white bird of the crow family
2. a collector of bits and pieces

I never see magpies *myself without repeating the old rhyme: 'One for sorrow, Two for mirth, Three for a death, Four for a birth, Five, you will shortly be In great company.'*
(A C Benson, ALONG THE ROAD, 1913)

I wonder if it wasn't the biting cold that moved us to chatter like magpies.
(Emilie Carles, tr Avriel H Goldberg, A WILD HERB SOUP, 1991)

I pick at the Journal (this magpie *scholarship), struggle with the Origin, home in on the letters and the Autobiography.*
(Graham Swift, EVER AFTER, 1992)

You could almost write a book about the different types of bird present in art at the Nativity. . .Piero's magpie *probably features the bird in its usual symbolic role as a herald of good news. However, had Piero been Chinese he would have known that the* magpie *is a representation of a star, and that according to Chinese mythology the Milky Way is actually a bridge of* magpies.
(SUNDAY TIMES, 18 December 1994)

Guillaume Bélibaste, a fourteenth-century peasant from the village of Montaillou, not far from the French town of Albi, was seized with foreboding one day when he noticed a magpie cross his path three times. His companion laughed at him telling him to '*take no notice of signs of birds and other auguries of that kind*,' adding that, '*only old women bother about such things*' (Emmanuel Le Roi Ladurie, MONTAILLOU, 1978). Guillaume was not alone in his superstitions. Similar misgivings about the bird existed throughout Europe, where the magpie has long been looked upon as a bird of ill omen. In England people would bow, cross their fingers or raise their hats to the bird. In Staffordshire they would spit three times over their right shoulder and chant '*Devil, Devil, I defy thee*' to ward off any evil influence. In folklore the magpie is denounced for not appearing completely in black at the crucifixion and, in Scotland, is also charged with treasuring a droplet of the devil's blood under its tongue. But for all its sinister reputation, the bird's name has a surprisingly homely origin.

In past centuries the *magpie* was known as a *madge*, a *maggot-pie* or a *maggoty-pie*. Shakespeare writes:

Augurs and understood relations have
By maggot-pies *and choughs and rooks brought forth*
The secret'st man of blood.
(MACBETH, Act 3, scene 4, 1606)

Lexicographer Randle Cotgrave, writing at the same period, has *maggatapy*. *Magpie* is, therefore, a contraction of these which the OED dates from the beginning of the seventeenth century.

The word is of French origin and one authority, thinking of the bird's jabbering and antics, connects *magotpie* with *magot*, 'a Barbary ape'. Most authorities agree, however, that it comes from a combination in English of two separate Old French words, *margot* and *pie*, both meaning 'magpie'.

Margot is a diminutive form of the name *Marguerite*, which was used for a gossiping, garrulous woman and, by extension, for the *magpie* because of the bird's raucous chattering. The contemporary Larousse still lists it as occasionally used in both these senses today. *Margery*, *Madge*, *Magot*, *Maggoty* and *Mag* are diminutives of *Margaret*, the English equivalent of *Marguerite*, and were also associated with talkativeness.

Pie is a thirteenth-century borrowing of the Old French *pie*, from the Latin *pīca* 'a magpie'. It is the second element in *magpie*, but for several centuries it also stood alone as an English term for the bird, before losing ground to the more popular combined form *magpie*. *Pie* remains the modern French word for *magpie*.

◆ *Pie* is responsible for a number of words arising from the appearance of the magpie or its habits.

It is thought by some authorities, for instance, that the pastries that have been a mainstay of the English diet since medieval times were called *pies* as a joke, the various ingredients in the filling reminding the diners of the odd bits and pieces a magpie might have collected together.◆

On a more sombre note, the *pie* was also the name given to the service-book which laid down orders of divine service in pre-Reformation England. The suggestion is that the book, being boldly printed in black on white, brought to mind the colours of the pie's plumage. *Pica*, a printer's term for different sizes of print, is directly from the Latin for *magpie*.

Also from the magpie's plumage, *piebald* usually denotes black and white colouring. *Bald* derives from *balled* ('streaked'), which comes from the Welsh *bal*, meaning 'with a white streak on the forehead', a term applied to a horse.

It seems that the showy magpie has always been a bird to be noticed.

malaria

a fever transmitted by mosquito

When the American Government was facing near disaster in the building of the Panama Canal it was to Wellcome that they turned to resolve the crisis of malaria *that was decimating the workforce.*
(The Times, 24 January 1995)

When Jan's temperature rose alarmingly – only to plummet below normal – the nuns, who had never seen malaria, *accused her of rubbing the thermometer on the bedclothes.*
(The Times Magazine, 11 March 1995)

The death of Pope Alexander VI (father of the infamous Borgias of Renaissance Italy), which was probably brought about by a spot of political intrigue, is usually explained away as a case of malaria. This was a convincing story, as the often fatal disease, which was characterised by recurring bouts of fever, struck the city of Rome every summer. The Romans called the disease *mal'aria* (from *mala aria*, 'bad air') believing it to be a result of the fetid air rising from the marshes in the surrounding countryside. The term entered English in the first half of the eighteenth century, initially with reference to the conditions in Rome, as the word existing in English for the disease since the fourteenth century was *ague*. Horace Walpole wrote in 1740 of '*A horrid thing called the* mal'aria, *that comes to Rome every summer and kills one*'. Three-quarters of a century later, Joseph Forsyth, describing his travels in Italy, said that '*this* mal'aria *is an evil more active than the Romans, and continues to increase*'.

Only at the beginning of the twentieth century was it finally established that the disease was transmitted by the bite of female mosquitoes hosting the malarial parasite and not by the 'foul air' of marshes and swamps. The name remains unchanged, however, a testimony to earlier medical understanding.

For another illness with an Italian name, see **influenza**.

mall

a covered pedestrian area of shops

Alongside the mall's *hard sell tactics is an example of a 1990's phenomenon – corporate structures that care. Looking cheerful in their 'official'* Mall *Walkers' Club T-shirts a group of senoir citizens regularly use the* mall *as an all-weather exercise course; before most of the 12,000 employees begin their work day, this tracksuit-clad group circumnavigate the* mall's *pathways. Nobody minds their presence; the companies that own the* mall *are keen to project an image of community*

in the face of so much commerce, to the point of organising these clubs.
(Life, THE OBSERVER MAGAZINE, 27 November 1994)

There can be few towns now which do not have a shopping *mall*, at their centre or, increasingly, on the outskirts. These covered, heated precincts are built along American lines, but the history of the word *mall* originated in Italy and has close associations with London.

Pallamaglio was a popular game in sixteenth-century Italy. As its name implies, it was played with a hard ball – *palla* (a variant of *balla*) – and a mallet – *maglio* (from Latin *malleus*, 'hammer'). Play took place in a long alley over which a metal hoop was hung some way above the ground. Starting at one end of the alley the object was to hit one's ball through the ring using fewer strokes than one's opponents.

The game became popular in France, where it was known as *pallemaille*, and then in Scotland, where it was played by Mary Queen of Scots, who was connected to the French court through her parentage and her first marriage. It did not catch on in England until the seventeenth century, however, when it was introduced to the court by the Stuart kings and became known as *Pall Mall* or *Pell Mell*. Charles I is said to have enjoyed the game but it was most popular under Charles II, who played it in St James's Park. In his diary for April 2, 1661 Samuel Pepys records seeing for the very first time '*Pelemele*' played there by the Duke of York. Indeed so favoured was the royal sport that in that same year the traffic travelling between Charing Cross and St James's Palace was rerouted because dust from the carriage wheels reduced visibility down the new royal alley that had been constructed just inside the park wall. Every alley used for the game, like the game itself, was known as a *pall mall* (often shortened to *mall*), so the rerouted road, which ran along the old alley in St James's Field, continued to be referred to as *Pall Mall* rather than by its official title (Catherine Street, in honour of the Queen), and still is today.

The popularity of the game was not enduring, however, and when it waned Charles II's new tree-lined alley in St James's Park became a fashionable place to promenade. Those who frequented it called it *The Mall*. Other towns, too, had their *Malls* – shaded walks or pleasant streets that had originally been alleys. From here, in the eighteenth century, the term was widely applied to any pleasant walkway. It might have faded into obscurity, had it not been given a new lease of life in American English where, in the mid-twentieth century, it was dusted down and applied first to a pedestrian area lined with shops and then to a covered shopping precinct.

For another word with its origins in the history of royal London, see **mews**.

manure

dung used to fertilise soil

I parted company with several schools under what can only be described as a 'cloud'. My favourite departure was from the posh Riverdale Country Day School For Girls. The headmistress summoned my parents and said I had little academic aptitude and might do well at agricultural college. Had my parents taken this advice I might now be shifting manure *and rather more familiar with cows' backsides than is desirable. . . In the end I landed a career*

that needs no qualifications – TV. And my only agricultural link is that I meet a lot of TV executives who produce an awful lot of manure.
(GOOD HOUSEKEEPING, June 1994)

Manure, *once known by farmers as black gold, is the best mulch. It should always be at least three months old or it will burn your plants. Avoid chicken* manure, *which can scorch even after three years. In cities, you can obtain bagged* manure *by looking in the local papers, or even approaching city farms or stables.*
(SUNDAY TIMES, 6 November 1994)

When Oliver Goldsmith in his NATURAL HISTORY (1776) wrote of a man who '*is at the trouble neither of* manuring *his grounds, nor bringing in his harvests,*' he did not mean that he had neglected to spread fertiliser but that the ground had not been cultivated. *Manure* was originally a verb meaning 'to manage a property or land', more particularly with the sense 'to till and tend'. It originated in the Latin expression *manū operārī*, 'to work with the hand' (from *manus*, 'hand' and *operārī*, 'to work'). This passed into modern English by way of Medieval Latin *manūoperārī*, Old French *manovrer*, 'to till', Anglo-French *mainoverer*, and Middle English *manouren*.

Dung had long been used to feed the soil and various ingenious methods were devised to collect and spread it. A thirteenth-century verse extolling the usefulness of every part of the sheep claims '*Of the sheep is cast away nothing,*' adding that '*To the Lordes great profit goeth his entire dung.*' At night, apparently, the sheep would be gathered together on fields owned by the lord so that their dung could enrich the soil. Shepherds were even instructed to keep a look out for sparse places in the pasture and to entice the flock to assemble there by constructing a scratching post (Dorothy Hartley, FOOD IN ENGLAND, 1954). *Dung* is an old term of Germanic origin, the earliest written record appearing around the turn of the eleventh century. For centuries this basic, honest word served its down-to-earth purpose, and then, towards the mid-sixteenth century it was joined by a new noun, *manure*, derived from the verb *manure*, so that the term for 'to cultivate the land' also became the word for the 'dung' that was spread upon it to make that cultivation successful. Exactly why this happened is hard to say. Some suggest euphemism. Whatever the reason, this new noun influenced the old verb from which it sprang, so that, by the end of the sixteenth century, it had the additional sense of 'to spread fertiliser'.

◆ Old French *manovrer* became modern French *manoeuvrer*, which gradually lost its connection with farming, becoming instead a military term, 'to make strategic moves'. It was borrowed into English in this sense as *manoeuvre* in the eighteeth century. Other modern senses in French, and then in English, derive from this.

Latin *manus* gave the adjective *manuālis*, 'of the hand', source of English *manual* (15th cent). English *operate* (17th cent) derives from Latin *operārī*.◆

marathon

1. a race of 26 miles 385 yards
2. anything of long duration that calls for endurance

The rosemary and cardamom versions [biscuits] are recommended not only for teatime but also for serving with simple fruit dishes such as apple snow, fresh orange salad, baked apricots, and compote of forced rhubarb – the only sort of puddings most people feel able to face after the Christmas marathon.

(Philippa Davenport, WEEKEND FINANCIAL TIMES, 14 January 1995)

Dionizio Ceron did not get the world record he had spoken of earlier in the week but the Mexican, who yesterday became the first man to win the London Marathon *twice, demonstrated, particularly in the closing stages of the race, that he was an athlete of steady nerve, iron disposition and rare talent.*

(DAILY TELEGRAPH, 3 April 1995)

Marathon was a village in Attica, Greece, about twenty-six miles from Athens. In 490 BC it was the site of a celebrated victory by the Greeks over the invading Persians. According to the historian Herodotus, the sturdy messenger Pheidippides ran from Athens to Sparta and back again, a distance of 150 miles, in two days to warn of the impending battle and summon reinforcements. He might have spared himself the bother, however, for the Spartans were in a period of religious observance which prevented their speedy participation.

When the Olympic games were revived in Athens in 1896, a long-distance run from Marathon to the capital was included in the programme. The race, however, did not commemorate that heroic run almost a millennium and a half earlier, but was inspired by a less well-founded story which tells how a messenger ran from Marathon to Athens to announce the Persian defeat only to fall down dead when he had done so.

Curiously, races covering such taxing distances were never run in the Olympic Games of ancient Greece. Nor did the modern race remain a purely Olympic event for long. The following year saw the first *Boston marathon* and, since then, many capital cities have organised annual international marathons through their streets covering the prescribed distance of 42.195 kilometres (26 miles and 385 yards). The nonsensical distance dates back to the 1908 Olympic Games which were held in London. All Olympic marathons begin and end in the stadium and, on this occasion, it was deemed essential that the race should end in front of the royal box which effectively added an extra gruelling 385 yards.

It was not long before use of the word widened to embrace other endurance contests. THE DAILY CHRONICLE of 5 November, 1908 reported on a competition entitled '*The Murphy* Marathon', which involved the peeling of a quarter of a hundredweight of potatoes. Besides events such as these, the noun also denotes any kind of long-distance race (*a swimming marathon*) and, as an adjective, describes tasks of long duration which require sustained effort.

marmalade

a type of jam, usually made from oranges

QUINCE MARMALADE

A very old and delicious recipe.

Collect your quinces, and pare and chop up at least half of them, including the least ripe, just cover with water, and set to boil to pulp. When soft rub all through a sieve. To this golden red thickness now add the remainder of the quinces, pared, cored, and cut into neat sections. Set the pan back to simmer gently and steadily, till the whole quinces are almost soft, and the pulp pretty thick (stir well, or it will burn). Now add sugar, 3lb. to a quart of the pulp. When the sugar has dissolved, boil fast till it sets when tried. It should be very firm, and a dark bright-red colour. Slices cut from it make good garnishes for plain white 'creams' or it can be melted and used as a sauce over blancmanges.

(Dorothy Hartley, FOOD IN ENGLAND, 1954)

Publish a recipe that asks the cook to shred raw Seville orange skins, and a sackful of letters will arrive from chaps who make marmalade *by the peck and cook the fruit whole so that it is easier to cut up quickly. But propose boiling the oranges whole, and the fastidious fellows who like to see evenly cut slivers of peel suspended in a translucent goo, write to say that if the job is worth doing, it is worth doing properly.*

(WEEKEND TELEGRAPH, 21 January 1995)

The ancient Greeks had a fruit called the *melimēlon*, 'honey-apple' (from *meli*, 'honey' and *mēlon* 'apple'). It was produced by grafting an apple-tree on to a quince stock. The fruit might be preserved in a kind of jam, or it might be placed in a jar, covered with willow twigs and topped up with runny honey, the resulting syrup being known as *melomēli* (Brothwell, FOOD IN ANTIQUITY, 1969). The Romans, too, knew the honey-apple, which they called *melimēlum*, and its delicious honey syrup. Latin *melimēlum* was retained in Portuguese, where it became the word *marmelo*, 'quince'. The Portuguese made preserves from the fruit which they called *marmelada*. The preserves were successful on the Continent amongst the Spanish (*marmelada*), the Italians (*marmellata*) and the French (*marmelade*). French *marmelade* was spread still further, to Germany, the Netherlands, Scandinavia and, of course, England in the sixteenth century, where it had various spellings until it settled down as *marmalade* in the eighteenth century.

Until the eighteenth century, the confection was served as a dessert, rather like a syllabub. Marmalade was not just delicious to eat: it was regarded as an aphrodisiac (in the seventeenth century prostitutes were referred to as *marmalade madams*). It was also considered to be a useful stopper to the stomach after a heavy meal. John Lyly alludes to this in EUPHUES AND HIS ENGLAND (1580) when he writes: '*Therefore you must giue him leaue after euery meale to cloase his stomacke with Loue, as with* Marmalade.'

Fynes Moryson recommended the preserve to any queasy traveller eager for foreign parts. In his ITINERARY (1617) Moryson discusses the unpleasantness of sea-sickness. His reader is cautioned against restraining vomiting altogether, since *'that working of the Sea is very healthful'*. Instead he is to eat as normal '*and after eating, let him seal his stomach with* Marmalade.'

By the seventeenth century other English fruit confections were also called *marmalade*, so severing the unique connection with the quince. In the eighteenth century orange marmalade was produced from the finest, clearest Seville oranges, eventually to become the golden preserve of the English breakfast table.

See **treacle**.

maroon

1. to abandon on a wild coast as a punishment
2. to trap without means of escape

His voice sounded hoarse and awkward, like a rusty lock. 'I'm poor Ben Gunn, I am; and I haven't spoke with a Christian these three years. . .'

'Three years!' I cried. 'Were you shipwrecked?'
'Nay, mate,' said he; 'marooned.'
I had heard the word, and I knew it stood for a horrible kind of punishment common enough among the buccaneers, in which the offender is put ashore with a little powder and shot and left behind on some desolate and distant island.
(Robert Louis Stevenson, TREASURE ISLAND, 1883)

All hands went over the side, and there I was, marooned *on my own vessel.*
(Jack London, THE SEA WOLF, 1904)

There crowded upon her all the stories she had been told of Marooners' *Rock, so called because evil captains put sailors on it and leave them there to drown. They drown when the tide rises, for then it is submerged.*
(J M Barrie, PETER PAN, 1904)

Cimarrón was a term the Spanish applied in the sixteenth century to the black slaves in the West Indies and Guiana who, unable to tolerate the harsh conditions of colonialist rule, succeeded in fleeing to remote mountain and forest regions where they lived wild. (The adjective *cimarrón* is still current in American Spanish where, applied to animals or plants, it distinguishes the wild from the domesticated or cultivated.) The term is thought to derive from the Spanish *cima*, meaning 'summit, top' (from Latin *cȳma*, 'the sprout of a plant', from Greek *kyma*, 'a swollen thing, a young sprout') and therefore denotes 'living on mountain tops'. The French equivalent of the Spanish epithet was *marron*, an abbreviated borrowing of *cimarrón*. The French *marron* was borrowed into English in the seventeenth century to refer to the fugitive slaves and their descendants. Attitudes towards them can be gauged by John Davies's description in his HISTORY OF THE CARIBBY ISLES (1666):

They will run away and get into the Mountains and Forests, where they live like so many beasts; then they are call'd Marons, *that is to say Savages.*

In the 1720s the verb *maroon* appeared to describe the practices of pirates who would leave a man stranded on deserted islands or stretches of isolated coastline as a punishment, forcing them to scratch a living in the wild like the *maroons*. The modern development of sense removes the idea of punishment but retains the meaning of being trapped without hope of rescue. One can be *marooned* by a flood or in rural solitude.

mascot

a charm, animal or person that brings luck

Some of the places [souvenir stores] had a caged brown bear out front – the Cherokee mascot, *I gathered – and around each of these was a knot of small boys trying to provoke the animal into a show of ferocity, encouraged from a safe distance by their fathers.*
(Bill Bryson, THE LOST CONTINENT, 1989)

Jacob, a young Hungarian goose, flew into London from Budapest yesterday to take up its position as new regimental mascot *with the Coldstream Guards. . . According to the Coldstream regimental history, a goose saved its 2nd battalion during an attack by French settlers in Canada in the 1830s. The goose, later christened Jacob, alerted the troops and helped to see off the attackers by pursuing them, pecking at their heels. The camp was successfully defended. When the battalion returned to Britain they took Jacob with them as a* mascot. *Unfortunately, he was run over by a carriage in Portman Street, London, in 1846.*
(DAILY TELEGRAPH, 25 February 1995)

This word did not enter English until 1880 when Audran's comic opera LA MASCOTTE appeared. The French *mascotte* derives from a Provençal word *mascotto,* meaning 'charm or spell', which is a diminutive of *masco,* 'witch', 'sorcerer' (from Late Latin *masca,* 'witch'). According to Audran, the legend is one of a struggle between the powers of light and those of darkness. When the evil Agesago sends a band of malicious sprites to work their mischief among men, the Powers of Light dispatch a legion of *mascots* to frustrate their wickedness. Should a mascot marry a mortal rather than another of its own kind, then it forfeits its magic powers. These, however, reappear in children of the marriage, so that the mascots' powers become an hereditary supernatural blessing. From this story the word was transferred to an object which the superstitious carry with them to bring good fortune and ward off evil. In more extended contemporary uses, *mascots* can be found on the bonnets of cars as well as on the wrist or round the neck; *mascots* can be animals (ducks and goats have figured as regimental mascots); they can be people – football teams often choose a young supporter for this role.

masterpiece

an outstanding example of craftsmanship or artistry

American critics have compared Isler to Saul Bellow and Isaac Bashevis Singer. He could well reach that standard in future: this is only his first novel, though he is already in his sixties. There are some clumsy moments . . . there is some thematic fuzziness . . . but there is far more that is insightful and compelling, and the complex structure is wrought with dab-hand-skill. A masterpiece, *strictly, is the work by which a new artist shows his fitness to rank with the best. This is one of those.*
(INDEPENDENT WEEKEND, 28 January 1995)

The word is not of English origin but is probably a translation of either the German *Meisterstück* or the Dutch *meesterstuk.* Medieval guilds developed from religious societies, formed for the mutual assistance of their members, into trade associations which aimed to regulate the number of craftsmen engaged in a particular trade and to control the standard of workmanship produced. An apprentice would serve a period of several years under the guidance of a master craftsman before presenting a final piece of work, or *masterpiece,* to his guild. If this was recognised as quality craftsmanship, he would become a 'master' of the guild, enjoying all the benefits of such an association, and would be free to set up in trade himself. The word came into prominence to denote a 'product of great skill or outstanding artistic merit', a 'masterly achievement' in the early seventeenth century.

maudlin

1. intoxicated to the point of tears
2. mawkishly sentimental

Philip: Well, when I was talking to Celia this afternoon, she asked me why I wanted to get married, I mean, apart from wanting to marry her. It made me realize that she was right, that I did want to get married, that I was lonely, now that youthful hopes have . . . it's all right when you're with people, when there's someone there, as long as there are peop e there to fill the air with plausible sounds. It's when the silence comes. . . You know, I find it whistles and rings now, the older I am, the louder it seems to get, the silence. I'm sorry, I didn't mean to get maudlin.

Donald: No, go on. What is friendship, if not a chance to indulge in mutual self-pity?
(Christopher Hampton, THE PHILANTHROPIST, 1970)

The whisky bottle had emptied to the point at which Father Keogh turned maudlin.
(Roy Hattersley, THE MAKER'S MARK, 1990)

Magdala was a town which once stood on the western shore of the Sea of Galilee, probably on the site of the present day Khirbet Mejdel. Its name derived from the Hebrew *migdal*, meaning 'tower'. The town, or its immediate vicinity, was the home of a disciple of Jesus, *Mary Magdalene.* In ecclesiastical Latin Mary's name was *(Maria) Magdalēna.* This was taken into Old French as *Madelaine* and borrowed into Middle English as *Mawdlin*, becoming *Maudlin* by the early seventeenth century.

According to Luke's gospel (Chapter 8, verse 2) Mary became a follower of Jesus after he delivered her from seven demons. The Bible also tells us that she was present in Jerusalem for Christ's crucifixion and was one of the group of women who went to his empty tomb on the resurrection morning. The two angels inside question why she is weeping. Also, in Luke chapter 7 there is a portrait of a woman who, overwhelmed by her sin (said to be that of prostitution), washed Jesus' feet with her tears of repentance, wiped them with her hair and anointed them with costly ointment. The Bible gives no hint as to the woman's identity but the church has traditionally identifed her as Mary Magdalene. Not surprisingly, therefore, she has been shown in Christian art as a weeping figure, shedding tears of repentance. For this reason *maudlin* has always been associated with tears. From the early sixteenth century, for instance, *maudlin* was found in the expression *maudlin drunk*, which denoted the tearful stage of intoxication '*when a fellow wil weepe for kindnes in the midst of his Ale and kisse you*' (Thomas Nashe, THE APOLOGIE OF PIERCE PENNILESSE, 1592). The term is still current in this context. Nearly a century later, it was used first as a noun ('a tearfully repentant sinner'), then as an adjective ('weepy, lachrymose'). It was very soon pressed to serve in contexts far removed from Christian ones. By the 1630s it had come to mean 'effusively over-sentimental', this sense possibly influenced by *maudlin* when applied to drunkenness.

◆ There are *Magdalen* colleges at both Oxford and Cambridge universities. In spite of the spelling, the name is pronounced as *maudlin*.◆

For another word deriving from a corruption of a biblical name, see **bedlam**.

maverick

an independent, strong-willed individual

Composer or conductor, gay or straight, maestro or maverick *– who exactly was Leonard Bernstein?*
(INDEPENDENT, May 16, 1994)

At the beginning of the 1980s, it was assumed that politicians could navigate the world of ideas. . . Today horizons have shrunk. . . There are still a number of erudite mavericks *in Parliament, but their knowledge is far more likely to come from history and literature than from science or recent social science.*
(GUARDIAN, 14 January 1995)

Tony Secunda . . . was a maverick, *much given to intellectual pronouncements on youth culture or the beneficial properties of marijuana. . .*
(THE TIMES, 8 March 1995)

There are slightly varying accounts of how Samuel Augustus *Maverick* (1803–1870) gave his name to the lexicon of the English language. One has him leaving Massachusetts as a young man for a life of ranching in Texas. Another has him working in Texas as either a lawyer, a banker or civil engineer, and receiving a herd of cattle as payment for a debt. Possibly he disliked the practice of branding calves and, thus displaying a touching trust in his neighbours, he let his herds roam unmarked. Or alternatively he put his herd on to an island he had rented in the river Nueces, leaving them unbranded. In the winter, however, the flow of water diminished to such an extent that his cows were able to wade across to the fields at the river's edge.

There may be doubt as to exactly how Sam Maverick's animals got to be wandering about unbranded, but from this point on all agree that the stock-men thereabouts recognised a good thing when they saw one: they would round up an unbranded calf and stamp it with their own brand. A *maverick* became a local term for a stray calf or yearling that had no mark of ownership and by the 1860s it was widespread. By the 1880s its use had been extended to refer to a dissenter or person of independent mind, with no particular attachment to a place or group – an application recognised in British usage in the following decade. Since then, any person rejecting the standard orthodoxies of society, church or state might be termed a *maverick. Mavericks* in politics (see the quotation above), who will not toe the party line, are fairly common and enliven a bland political landscape. Such are, in recent British politics, Tony Benn, Enoch Powell and Dennis Skinner. An older example from 1930s America is Congressman Maury Maverick, who had a formidable reputation for fierce individualism. Appropriately enough, he was a descendant of Samuel Maverick.

There is a certain cachet attached to the term. A television series was named after the hero, Maverick. A major car manufacturer thought the word had the right positive associations to call one of its products a Maverick.

mews

a small street of houses and flats in converted stabling

Our route was certainly a singular one. Holmes's knowledge of the byways of London was extraordinary, and on this occasion he passed rapidly and with an assured step through a network of mews *and stables, the very existence of which I had never known.*
(Sir Arthur Conan Doyle, THE RETURN OF SHERLOCK HOLMES, 1905)

Mews addresses are now considered very chic. At one time, however, they were only appreciated by hawks. A *mew* was a cage used to confine hawks, especially while they were moulting. The word was borrowed into English in the fourteenth century from Old French *mue* (from *muer*, 'to moult, to change', from Latin *mutare*, 'to change').

In medieval times the *Royal Mews* was sited at Charing Cross, London and housed not only the hawks but the king's falcons and falconers as well. By the reign of Henry VII the buildings had been converted into stabling although they continued to be known as the *mews*.

Even when the buildings burnt down in 1534 and purpose-built stables were erected on the site during the reign of Elizabeth, the name *Royal Mews* remained. Things royal invariably set a fashion and in the seventeenth century the term was applied to other alleys or courtyards containing stabling. When horses no longer had need of them the stables were given over to human habitation. Records of mews housing date back to the early nineteenth century.

For another hawking term see **haggard**, and for another word with its origins in the history of royal London, see **mall**.

milliner

a maker of hats for women

Herbert Johnson, the oldest milliners *in London, caters for a sartorially distinguished clientele – Joan Collins and the Princess of Wales included. Alternatively, all over the country you will find excellent, if less established,* milliners *such as Katharine Goodison. . .A bespoke hat will usually involve three or more visits to the milliners. 'The aim is to come up with something which suits the wearer's personality as well as their outfit' Ms Goodison says.*
(THE TIMES WEEKEND, 18 March 1995)

Today Milan is one of the fashion capitals of the world. It is not a new reputation, it seems, for the origins of the word *milliner* lie with those decorative Milanese finishes and touches that make an outfit really special. Originally *Milaner* simply denoted an inhabitant of Milan but, in the sixteenth century, the city became known for its production of ribbons and fancy cloth and for its prettily trimmed capes, gloves and bonnets. Soon a *milaner* (also found in a variety of other spellings, including the one that became standard) was no longer necessarily Italian but a vendor of such luxury items made in Milan and by the nineteenth century someone who made, and decorated, just women's hats. A good *milliner* needed more than nimble fingers, however. He or she also needed an appreciative eye. According to the humourist John Gay, in an article for that short-lived periodical THE GUARDIAN (1713): *The* milliner *must be thoroughly versed in physiognomy; in the choice of ribbons she must have a particular regard to the complexion.*

miniature

1. a small, detailed picture, usually of a person
2. tiny, very small

The joke was too obscure for Derek. . . There was a miniature, *embarrassed silence between them.*
(Jeremy Vine, THE WHOLE WORLD IN MY HANDS, 1995)

Another smart small town dog is the schnauzer. . . They're very sparky and full of personality. So are their owners, judging by the miniature *schnauzer puppy that was discovered in a stolen handbag at Oxford Circus recently, and returned to its owner because it was recognised by a London vet who identified it by its yellow jumper and miniature Barbour.*
(GOOD HOUSEKEEPING, April, 1995)

A unique collection of hand-made doll's house furniture. . .is to be sold at auction later this month. The miniature *furniture was made in the early years of the century by scores of children in the village of West Acre, near King's Lynn. . .*
(DAILY TELEGRAPH, 16 March, 1995)

A reasonable supposition might be that *miniature*, with its sense of 'reduced size', belongs to a class of words deriving from Latin *min-*, 'less', along with *minimum, minute, mini, diminish* and *diminutive*, for instance. Surprisingly the origin of the word has nothing to do with smallness at all but is found in a red pigment that was used to rubricate initial letters or titles in handwritten manuscripts. The pigment, red lead or cinnabar, was known as *minium* in Latin, which gave the medieval Latin verb *miniāre* meaning 'to colour with red lead' and, by extension, 'to illuminate a manuscript'. This became *miniare* in Italian, whose derivative *miniatura* denoted 'the process of rubricating' and then an 'adornment or picture on the illuminated page'.

Miniature was borrowed into English in the sixteenth century. John Evelyn in his diary for 2 September 1680 remarked upon some brevaries which had '*a great deal of* miniature *and monkish painting and gilding.*' The diminutive size of these illustrations, together with an apparent similarity to that class of Latin words mentioned earlier, was responsible for the term's later application to small-scale portraits or to representations which were much reduced in size.

Miniature has been used as an adjective since the early eighteenth century and in modern English denotes anything which is smaller than one might expect, from golf games to railways and from poodles to the bottles of spirits given out on aircraft.

minion

1. a subordinate
2. a sycophant, a slavish follower

I could not but observe that my young minion *was as much spruced out as could be expected from one in his condition: a desire of pleasing that could not be indifferent to me, since it prov'd that I pleased him; which, I assure you, was now a point I was not above having in view.*
(John Cleland, FANNY HILL, 1749)

When the French gush and exclaim over an attractive toddler or a cuddly toy, the adjective *mignon* readily springs to their lips. The English equivalent is 'sweet' or 'darling'. *Mignon* (from Old French *mignot*, through Gaulish, related to Old High German *minna*, 'love') originally came into English around the turn of the sixteenth century to denote 'a darling or favourite'. This might be a lady-love, for instance, or the favourite of a sovereign or other leading figure. Before the century was out, however, it had become a term of contempt, denoting a 'mistress' or a 'sycophant'. The mistress has slipped into obscurity but the sycophant is alive and well in modern usage. He and his kind have also spawned a new breed of *minion* lower down the pecking order: the 'dependent underdog', the subordinate who performs menial or routine tasks. The tone is now jocular rather than contemptuous.

mint

the place where legal currency is coined

*The trouble now is that jargon, both the thing and the word, have become a kind of battle ground. There are nasty people (a pox on their house) who use fresh-*minted *language not simply or even primarily to communicate with their peers, but to repel boarders; just as prep-school boys use cabalisms to confuse rival Football teams.*
(NEW SCIENTIST, 1983)

Enterprising students at California's Stanford University are making a mint

Homonyms

A homonym is a word identical with another in spelling and pronunciation, but different in meaning and origin. *Mint* as recorded in the entry in this book, for instance, is different from the herb that shares the same form. *Bank* (of a river) and *bank* (a financial institution) and *bat* (as in cricket) and *bat* (a flying nocturnal mammal) are amongst many other homonyms. A looser definition of homonym – that the words in question should merely sound the same, that they should be 'homophones' – in many instances makes the different roots clearer. It is easier to see that *foul* and *fowl* and *peace* and *piece* come from separate sources.

from high technology by designing and marketing computer hardware and software. With Silicon Valley on their doorstep, the students are running small but growing computer companies from their dormitories and houses.
(New Scientist, 1983)

When I and my family were leaving the airport at Iguaçu and had to pay the $3 airport tax . . . we were told we would not be allowed on the plane if we could not find nine clean dollars.

There has been speculation recently that counterfeit $100 notes are circulating and some countries – including Argentina – have been demanding that tourists spend mint-*condition notes.*
(Weekend Telegraph, 4 March 1995)

The Roman goddess Juno, queen of heaven, was especially honoured for her protection of women. Some of her other duties are reflected in her title *Juno Moneta:* she was to warn people of danger – Latin *monēre* means 'to warn'. Indeed her temple on the Capitoline hill was built by a grateful subject after her warning of an imminent invasion by the Gauls in 344 BC. But, besides these responsibilities, under the name *Juno Moneta* she shared with Saturn the guardianship of financial affairs. Her temple in Rome contained the *mint,* and her name *monēta* was applied both to this and to the money it produced. *Monēta* made its way into English along two different routes.

Borrowed into primitive West Germanic, probably as *munita,* it reached Old English as *mynet* where, from at least the eighth century, it meant 'a coin' or 'money'. In the fifteenth century the Middle English form *mynt* (Modern English *mint*) began to denote a place where legal currency was coined, the chief officer there being known as the *Maister of the Mynte*.

Monēta in its Latin sense 'money' was also borrowed into the Romance languages. In Old French it became *monoie* (Modern French has *monnaie* for 'loose change') and this was taken into Middle English in the fourteenth century as *moneye,* 'money'.

For other words concerning temples, see **anathema** and **fanatic**.

mob

1. a disorderly crowd out for trouble
2. the common people, the plebs
3. to attack in a crowd

There was an eddy in the mass of human bodies, and the woman with helmeted head

and tawny cheeks rushed out to the very brink of the stream. She put out her hands, shouted something, and all that wild mob *took up the shout in a roaring chorus of articulated, rapid, breathless utterance.*
(Joseph Conrad, THE HEART OF DARKNESS, 1902)

The Latin term *mōbile vulgus* literally means the 'moveable crowd', moveable being understood in the sense of 'fickle, easily influenced, excitable'. It is found as '*the moeuable poeple*' in Chaucer's translation of BOETHIUS (c. 1374). At the beginning of the seventeenth century the Latin term was used to denote the 'common people', the 'rabble'. It was not often used in full but was abbreviated to *mobile*, pronounced in three syllables as in Latin:

Tho' the mobile *baul*
Like the devil and all,
For religion, property, justice and laws.
(N. ROWE, SONG OF AN ORANGE, STATE POEMS, 1716)

By the late 1680s the term was being further shortened to *mob*. This trend had considerable momentum, as Nares points out. In the preface to DON SEBASTIAN (1690), Dryden uses the word *mobile* but, two years later, in the preface to CLEOMENES he writes:

Yet, to gratify the barbarous part of my audience, I gave them a short rabble-scene, because the mob *(as they call them) are represented by Plutarch and Polybius, with the same character of baseness and cowardice, which are here described.*

The brackets indicate Dryden's hesitation over the acceptability of the term. His trepidation was perhaps justifiable for other men of letters deplored the adoption of abbreviations as new words. The British essayist Sir Richard Steele (1672–1729), writing for his periodical THE TATLER, was among them:

I have done my utmost for some years past to stop the progress of 'mob' *. . . but have been plainly borne down by numbers, and betrayed by those who promised to assist me'.*

However, he was not let down by his friend Joseph Addison who, in an article for Steele's SPECTATOR (1711), wrote:

It is perhaps this Humour of speaking no more than we needs must which has so miserably curtailed some of our Words . . . as in mob. *rep. pos. incog. and the like.'*

But the rage for abbreviation continued and was later ridiculed by Swift. In his POLITE CONVERSATION (published 1738), a satire upon the conversation of fashionable society of the period, he wrote of '*Abbreviations exquisitely refined; As Pozz for Positively,* Mobb *for* Mobile.'

Just under two decades later Dr Johnson capitulated by making room for *mob* in his DICTIONARY along with the longer *mobile*. It would seem that, once the fickle *mōbile vulgus* has decided, it will have its way and there is nothing the purist with his pen can do to stop it.

muscle

tissue that stretches and relaxes to bring about movement in animals

. . . the male form demonstrated the musculature *of the human frame in ways the female did not. The female body was smothered with fat, smoothed into curves, and especially after childbirth obscured the underlying structure which the artist sought to grasp . . . the greater challenge to the artist lay in the male body.*

Study anatomy, commanded Alberti in De Pictura in 1435, and Pollaiuolo, for one, began to dissect corpses to analyse how

the muscles *lay beneath the skin and gave volumetric form to it. Even when you paint the clothed figure, added Alberti, you must draw the nude first, so that underlying form was clear.*
(DAILY TELEGRAPH, 16 January 1995)

The Romans, doubtless gazing at the firm and finely tuned bodies of their athletes, conceived the fanciful notion that, when the main muscles in the upper arm and leg were flexed, their shape and movement resembled that of a mouse. The Latin word for muscle was therefore *mūsculus*, a diminutive form of *mūs*, meaning 'mouse'. The word was taken into all the Romance languages and the modern Germanic ones, coming into English in the sixteenth century by way of the French *muscle*.

In spite of its different spelling, *mussel* also derives from *mūsculus*. The Romans were very fond of eating shellfish which they smothered in fancy sauces. They ate mussels fried or boiled with a sauce based on oil, herbs and honey or oil and wine. To the Roman eye the colour and form of this small delicacy also suggested a little mouse, hence *mūsculus*. Or, some say, the likeness was with a *muscle*. Either way, it needed a particularly vivid Roman imagination to see the connection. As for the spelling of the word in English, there is scope for confusion. For several hundred years after its arrival into Old English, our contemporary word *mussel* was spelt *muscle*. It was only from about Shakespeare's time onwards that it started to be written *mussel*. Dr Johnson in his dictionary of 1755, under the entry for 'muscle', deals with both *muscle* and *mussel*. He does, however, also provide a separate entry for *mussel*. The change to the spelling *mussel* came about for two reasons. First, it was only from the sixteenth century, with the introduction of *muscle* in the sense of 'muscle', that there was a cause for confusion. Before that, there hadn't been a need for differentiation. Second, there was a ready alternative spelling to hand: German had *mussel*, Dutch *mosscele*. Both stemmed from late Latin *mūscula*, a variant of *mūsculus*. These spellings probably influenced the developing English orthography.

This obsessive likening of things to mice was not unique to the Romans, however. *Musk*, which was widely used as a perfume base and for medicinal purposes, derives from Sanskrit *muska*. This term was generally used to mean 'testicle' but was also applied to the scrotum-shaped pouch of the musk deer and to the pungent oil secreted by the gland. Originally, however, it meant 'little mouse', being a diminutive of Sanskrit *mūs*, 'mouse'. *Muska* was borrowed into Persian as *mushk*, into Greek as *moskhhos* and into Late Latin as *muscus*. It came into Middle English as *muske* in the fourteenth century by way of Old French *musc*.

The mouse is not the only animal to be associated with *muscle*. Americans see a connection with horses. Old nags suffer from sweeny (the atrophying of shoulder muscles) and stiffness. Athletes, too, can suffer similar muscle strains. Since the latter part of the nineteenth century, sportsmen (particularly baseball players) who suffered the tearing apart of the fibres of the muscle through overstrain, with a subsequent hard muscle knot and swelling, are described as being affected with a *Charley horse*.

Imagined likenesses and connections provide the etymology for **hearse, lizard** and **vanilla**.

nasty

unpleasant, offensive

You are deceiv'd, if you think Don Carlo more chaste than I; only duller, and more a Miser, one that fears his Flesh more, and loves his Money better. Then to be condemn'd to lie with him – oh, who would not rejoice to meet a Woollen-Waistcoat, and knit Night-Cap without a Lining, a Shirt so nasty, *a cleanly Ghost would not appear in't at the latter Day? then the compound of* nasty *Smells about him, stinking Breath, Mustachoes stuft with villainous snush, Tobacco, and hollow Teeth: thus prepar'd for Delight, you meet in Bed, where you may lie and sigh whole Nights away, he snores it out till Morning, and then rises to his sordid business.*

(Aphra Behn, THE ROVER; OR THE BANISH'D CAVALIERS, Part II, 1677)

But my knee was bothering me terribly. As well as I could make out, the kneecap seemed turned up on edge in the midst of the swelling. As I sat in my bunk examining it, Henderson took a passing glance at it.

'Looks nasty,*' he commented. 'Tie a rag around it, and it'll be all right.' That was all. And on the land I should have been lying on the broad of my back, with a surgeon attending me, and with strict injunctions to do nothing but rest.*

(Jack London, THE SEA WOLF, 1904)

Even the non-violent protests are A1 news stories: visual, dramatic, confrontational. And as one cameraman recently confided to me in an unguarded moment: 'It's a bit like motor racing really. There's always the possibility that something might get seriously nasty.*'*

(WEEKEND TELEGRAPH, 11 February 1995)

'It's a foul bird that defiles its own nest', runs an old European proverb which dates back at least a thousand years. Such a bird might once have been described as *nasty*. The origins of the word are rather obscure but there is a probable connection with Dutch *nestig* (Middle Dutch *nistich*), which certainly meant 'foul' but may have originally meant 'defiled like the nest of a dirty bird'. There is also a suggested link between the Middle English form *naxty* and a Swedish dialectal word *naskug*, 'dirty', 'foul'.

In the fifteenth century, *nasty* was a very forceful adjective to be used with the greatest care. It meant 'exceptionally filthy', 'offensively foul'. Pity the Lady Margaret then whom Edward Hall describes in his chronicle (c. 1548) as having a 'nasty *complexion and euill sauored breathe*' – she was obviously no peach. Shakespeare, too, uses the word in a similar strong sense:

Hamlet: Nay, but to live
In the rank sweat of an enseamed bed,
Stew'd in corruption, honeying and making love
Over the nasty *sty!*

(Shakespeare, HAMLET, 1601)

Around the turn of the seventeenth century *nasty* gained a moral dimension when it came to mean 'indecent, obscene' and was applied to conduct, language, lewd jokes and the like. The English are always on the look out for an adjective to express their heartfelt feelings about the weather and, by the 1630s, *nasty* was a vitriolic way of complaining about driving rain. This use was probably the downfall of the word, however, for it began to lose some of its forcefulness – although, even today, it is not an adjective to apply lightly to a person or his conduct. By the early eighteenth century the adjective had weakened to 'very unpleasant, objectionable'. The meanings 'spiteful' and 'dangerous' (as in a *nasty temper* or a *nasty bend in the road*) both date from the nineteenth century.

naughty

1. badly behaved
2. mildly wrong
3. suggestive, indecent

I have heard many cry out against sin in the pulpit, who yet can abide it well enough in the heart, house, and conversation. Joseph's mistress cried out with a loud voice, as if she had been very holy; but she would willingly, notwithstanding that, have committed uncleanness with him. Some cry out against sin even as the mother cries out against her child in her lap, when she calleth it slut and naughty *girl, and then falls to hugging and kissing it.*
(John Bunyan, THE PILGRIM'S PROGRESS, 1678)

Every night my prayers I say,
And get my dinner every day;
And every day that I've been good,
I get an orange after food.
The child that is not clean and neat,
With lots of toys and things to eat,
He is a naughty *child, I'm sure–*
Or else his dear papa is poor.
(Robert Louis Stevenson, A CHILD'S GARDEN OF VERSES, 1885)

(Marie picks up the sandal and slings it at Harry. He ducks and it vanishes in the sand. Harry looks briefly, resumes his strip. Slowly he unbuckles his belt and dangles it suggestively before Marie. She giggles and makes a grab for it.)
Harry: Naughty *! You'll be outa the club.*
Marie: You should be in the clubs.
(Harry lowers his jeans to his knees, waggles his pelvis. The girls look away, embarrassed, then look back, giggling.)
(E. A. Whitehead, THE FOURSOME, 1972)

A month later a seven-year-old boy came in with a worm in his nose. . . Little Raja listened attentively when I told him how I proposed to get out that nasty old worm. 'It won't hurt a bit – just a little tickle in the back of your throat and – poof! – we'll be done, and you'll be rid of that naughty *worm and on your way home as happy as can be.'*
(Thomas Hale, ON THE FAR SIDE OF LIGLIG MOUNTAIN, 1989)

'Naughty but nice' whispers the advertising slogan tempting dieters to sink their teeth into a cream-filled eclair. In Modern English the adjective *naughty* is largely confined to the censure of such petty sins or to the bad behaviour of young children. It was not always so. The word derives from Old English *nāwhit*, 'nothing' (from *nā*, 'no' and *whit*, 'creature', 'thing'). This was often contracted to *naht* and became *naught* in Middle English. At the time of King Alfred in the ninth century *naught* had the dual senses of 'nothing' and 'good for nothing, wicked, evil'. The suffix *-y*, meaning 'having the qualities of', was added to the word to form *naughty* in the fourteenth century. Initially this meant 'having naught, poor', but in the sixteenth century the old sense of 'worthless, evil' was picked up. People described as *naughty* were 'morally bankrupt' and *naughty* behaviour was 'wicked'. The adjective was first applied in the modern sense to a child's misbehaviour in the seventeenth century. George Herbert records an early use in his collection of proverbs JACULA PRUDENTUM (1633): *'A* naughty *child is better sick than whole.'* The playful or mildly disapproving tone of *naughty* to denote questionable adult behaviour dates from the eighteenth century and is obviously an extension of this sense.

The 1520s saw a further extension of *naughty* in its meaning of 'worthless', when it also came to mean 'inferior, substandard'. The Puritan pamphleteer Philip Stubbes, uncovering dishonest practices in the spinning industry denounces those who '*put in* naughty *wool, and cause it to be spun and drawne into a very small thred*' (ANATOMIE OF ABUSES, 1583). Bad food or drink might also be described as *naughty*. In Miles Coverdale's translation of the Bible (1535), as well as the King James Authorised Version of 1611, the bad figs in Jeremiah's vision were described as 'naughtie *figes*' because they were inedible (Jeremiah 24:2). Bad health and inclement weather might also fit this use of the adjective. This particular sense is now obsolete but makes amusing reading in the light of modern usage.

There are many shifts of meaning in the history of words. A common one is the narrowing of a general sense (*naughty* meaning 'morally bankrupt') to a restricted sense (*naughty* meaning 'sexually suggestive'). This latter fairly new meaning has undoubtedly been influenced by the last decade of the nineteenth century. Prim Victorian standards were loosening, to such an extent that the period became known as the *naughty nineties*. Nowadays the word can signify 'smutty, slightly indecent', and suggest a similar ambivalence of 'naughty but nice' that the advertisers play on in other contexts.

nectar

1. a sweet, delicious drink
2. a sugary fluid produced by plants

'Holy Virgin!' said Gurth, setting down the cup, 'what nectar *these unbelieving dogs drink, while true Christians are fain to quaff ale as muddy and thick as the draft we give to hogs!'*
(Sir Walter Scot, IVANHOE, 1819)

Large red clover has such deep corolla tubes that the tongues of ordinary honeybees are too short to reach the nectar *readily. . . Bumblebees, which have long tongues, can easily get* nectar *from even the largest red clover blossoms and a profitable partnership exists between them and this plan. . . Bumblebees are becoming scarcer with the extension of cultivation and the destruction of their nesting places, and scientists are trying to solve the problem of red clover fertilization by developing honeybees with longer tongues and red clover with shorter flowers.*
(George Stimpson, INFORMATION ROUNDUP, 1948)

Yet another survey has pointed out that wine by the glass, being served in most pubs and bars in Britain today, is execrable, undrinkable and not fit to put in trifle or stew. There is a huge mark-up on the roughest kind of plonk that makes Liebfraumilch or Soave seem like nectar. *If you want a glass of white wine, the simple choice is usually sweet or medium dry. It's likely to be tepid and come out of a box or one of those giant bottles with screw tops frequently seen littering the streets of London around carousing alcoholic dossers.*
(DAILY MAIL, 4 January 1995)

In classical mythology where *ambrosia* was the food of the gods, *nectar* was the heavenly drink. The word possibly derives from the Greek *neo-*, 'death' and *tar*, 'conquering', signifying its ability to impart immortality. One wonders whether the Australian beer which describes itself as the 'amber nectar' can do the same, or whether it simply pickles those who drink it.

Ambrosia and *nectar* share a lot in common. Both mean 'rendering immortal', both were regularly on the gods' menu, both were first used in English in the sixteenth century, both on occasion could take the meaning of the other (nectar was used for food, ambrosia for drink), both have figurative uses. Nowadays ambrosia can be applied to anything delicious to eat, nectar to anything particularly pleasant to drink. By extension, nectar is the sweet liquid secreted by certain flowering plants which hummingbirds sip and from which bees make honey – see the quotation above. The sweet *nectarine* fruit gets its name from the same source. *Nectarine* was an adjective, found from the early seventeenth to the nineteenth century, meaning 'nectar-like'. It has been used as a noun from the same date to refer to the fruit, possibly a shortening of *nectarine peach.*

◆ The Greek origin for *nectar* given here is disputed; assuming it is right, then the term is related to a good number of compounds beginning with *necro-* (from *necrós*, 'corpse'): *necromancy, necrophilia, necropolis, necrobiosis.* Still further back, the root of the Greek *nec* is the postulated Indo-European *nek-*, meaning 'kill'. This by another route gave rise to the Latin *nocere*, 'to harm'. From this comes our *innocent*, 'not doing any harm to'. So one might say that a type of peach and a blameless person are distantly related!◆

See **ambrosia**.

nepotism

favouritism and preferment towards family and friends

NEPOTISM, . Appointing your grandmother : office for the good of the party. (Ambrose Bierce, THE DEVIL'S DICTIONARY, 1911)

Stories about the corruption and loose morality of many of the popes are legion. Along with their other sins, they were notorious for their preferment of family members for high office. Perhaps the most notorious of all was Alexander VI (1492–1503). This Spanish pope, born as Rodrigo de Borja y Borja (Borgia in Italian), invariably let family interests dictate his policies. He took special interest in elevating his four illegitimate offspring by Vannozza Catanei – Juan, Cesare, Lucrezia and Goffredo. Juan was accordingly married to a Spanish princess and was given part of papal holdings at Benevento. Cesare, who was made Archbishop of Valencia by the age of eighteen and cardinal at nineteen, was used to strengthen the papal empire, while Lucrezia made three advantageous marriages to the same end.

Alexander VI openly acknowledged his children, but other popes sometimes referred to their illegitimate sons as 'nephews' before promoting them. So besetting was this sin that Italian coined the word *nepotismo* (from Italian *nepote*, and Latin *nepōs*, 'nephew') to denote the practice, with particular reference to the sixteenth-century popes. The word came into English in the 1660s by way of French *népotisme.* Initially it was with reference to the preferment of papal nephews, then more broadly to that of the relations of other ecclesiastics, and finally, in the nineteenth century, to anyone who bestowed unfair advancement upon a relative.

In July 1691 Innocent XII was crowned and this devout, charitable man issued a decree stating that no pope should freely grant land or offices to his relatives. A single relative might be considered for cardinal but only if he were particularly suitable and agreed to a modest income. Naturally this met with certain resistance amongst a number of cardinals with an eye to the future, but was eventually signed by all.

news

information on noteworthy, topical events

Oliver: Good Monsieur Charles! What's the new news *at the new court?*
Charles: There's no news *at the court, sir, but the old* news*; that is, the old Duke is banished by his younger brother the new Duke; and three or four loving lords have put themselves into voluntary exile with him, whose lands and revenues enrich the new Duke; therefore he gives them good leave to wander.*
(Shakespeare, AS YOU LIKE IT, Act 1, scene 1, 1601)

[Jones] went AWOL late in December. . . A native of Jamestown, N.Dak., Jones was brought up to respect authority, and he wanted to straighten things out with the Army. So his American civilian lawyer arranged for Jones to surrende . . . Says Karen Jones: 'The captain called me later and said, "I have good news *and bad* news. *The good* news *is that your husband has turned himself in; the bad* news *is that he's in Saudi Arabia. And he looked like he was in shock."'*
(PEOPLE WEEKLY, 4 February 1991)

A popular folk etymology has it that the word is made up of the initials of the four points of the compass: N(orth) E(ast) W(est) S(outh). Apparently these were used to make up a cross-shaped figure which was displayed at the head of some of the early news-sheets to indicate that the information had been gleaned from every corner. However, instances of *news* in its present-day sense have been found in texts dating back to the beginning of the fifteenth century, whereas the earliest English newspaper was not printed until 1620.

There are probably two main strands in the development of *news.* Old English had a phrase *hwæt newis*, meaning 'what news?' In subsequent centuries Old French *noveles* and medieval Latin *nova* – both plural, meaning 'new things, news' – were influential in the development of the word. Used in the plural and with the sense 'novelties', *news* was found in English from the fourteenth to sixteenth centuries, before becoming obsolete. Also in the plural, meaning 'tidings, news of events', *news* continued to be used up to the nineteenth century: *There are bad* news *from Palermo* (Shelley, ESSAYS AND LETTERS, 1821).

The singular form has continued to be found from the sixteenth century; John Florio, for example, in his WORLD OF WORDS of 1597 has *Novella, a tale, a newes.* The writings of two kings show this move to the singular as the predominant form in English. When James 1 of Scotland wrote in about 1423, he used the plural: *Awak . . . I bring The [thee]* newis *glad, that blisfull ben.* His descendant James VI of Scotland and I of England had changed by 1616 to the singular in the first recorded use of *No news is good news*:

Lett none living knowe of this, and if it take goode effect, move him to sende in haste for the commissioners, to give thaime satisfaction, but if he remaine obstinate, I desyre not that ye shoulde trouble me with an ansoure, for it is to no ende, and no newis *is bettir then evill* newis.

Although *news* is now singular in English, the present-day French *les nouvelles* retains the plural.

nice

1. pleasant, agreeable
2. discriminating, refined
3. precise, exact

. . . I can't remember when I wasn't a republican. The mechanics aren't difficult.

You need a national greeter, someone with manners, presence, political shrewdness, but no power drive, also a humanising sense of humour . . . you want someone naturally liked and agreeable, dare I say it, someone nice*?*
(THE GUARDIAN, 14 January 1995)

I like the luxury accommodation and it's nice *not to risk your health by eating local grub.*
(INDEPENDENT WEEKEND, 28 January 1995)

. . . the dictionary was first published as A NEW ENGLISH DICTIONARY ON HISTORICAL PRINCIPLES . . . (the adjective New here is nicely *ambiguous; the 19th-century philologists, using a calque from their German confrères, used New English to describe the language from about 1450 – anything before was either Middle or, before about 1150, Old English or Old English).*
(THE SPECTATOR, 11 February 1995)

Our bed has proper linen sheets and satin-edged blankets. Very nice.
(WEEKEND TELEGRAPH, 4 March 1995)

This now unexciting little word has undergone a revolution in sense since it was first recorded in the thirteenth century and has passed through so many shades of meaning that only the main threads can be discussed here. *Nice* originally meant 'foolish, stupid', being a direct borrowing from Old French where it meant 'silly' or 'simple' (from Latin *nescius*, 'ignorant', and *nescire*, 'to be ignorant': from *ne-*, 'not' and *scire*, 'to know'). Indeed, in the fourteenth and fifteenth centuries it was occasionally used as a noun to mean 'a foolish person', 'a simpleton'.

During the fourteenth century *nice* also came to mean 'lascivious', the connection perhaps being that a person so described was foolish and careless of the consequences. This description of wanton Youth, who was simply out for a good time, comes from Chaucer's ROMAUNT DE LA ROSE (c. 1366):

And after daunced, as I gesse,
Youthe, fulfild of lustinesse,
That nas not yit twelve yeer of age,
Wigh herte wilde, and thought volage;
Nyce *she was, but she mente*
Noone harme ne slight in hir entente,
But oonely lust & jolitee.
For yonge folk, wel witen ye,
Have litel thought but on hir play.

Surprisingly, by the fifteenth century a completely opposite meaning was developing, that of 'shy, coy, overly modest and reluctant'. This remained current until at least the late seventeenth century. It was the sense that Dryden intended when he wrote in his heroic play AURENG-ZEBE (1675) that *Virtue is* nice *to take what's not her own.*

Meanwhile, the sixteenth century saw the emergence of one of the current meanings of *nice*, that of 'careful, particular, refined', especially with regard to food, taste or manners. In an edition of his periodical THE RAMBLER (1751), Dr Johnson speaks of minds that become 'nice *and fastidious, and like a vitiated palate*'. A related meaning, that of 'demanding special care or precision', developed at the same time. When the seventeenth-century Irish-born physicist and chemist Robert Boyle spoke of '*nice experiments*', he meant those requiring a high degree of precision. Equally problems requiring particularly careful thought and attention were also described as *nice*, and still are. *Nice* as a synonym for 'exact' or 'fine' is related to these senses.

The second half of the eighteenth century saw the downfall of *nice* from its place of precision to its current position as a workhorse word; an overused expression of pleasure that comes readily to mind when a more exact adjective would have served better. In modern English *nice* can be used to give a stamp of approval to anything at all from a stunning landscape to a birthday card, so that it is now nothing more than a bland little word – perhaps that is the inevitable fate of a word with such a long and chequered history. Its status has fallen so low that a careful writer, as in the quotation from the GUARDIAN above, almost has to apologise for using it.

For other words that have undergone a complete change in meaning, see **buxom** and **silly**.

nightmare

1. a bad dream
2. an awful experience

My feet seemed positively racked with pain, yet I could not move them. They seemed to be numbed. There was an icy feeling at the back of my neck and all down my spine, and my ears, like my feet, were dead yet in torment; but there was in my breast a sense of warmth which was by comparison delicious. It was as a nightmare*–a physical* nightmare, *if one may use such an expression; for some heavy weight on my chest made it difficult for me to breathe.*
(Bram Stoker, DRACULA'S GUEST, 1914)

Canon Yeats stopped to look at her. He had never liked her. Her big handsomeness always reminded him of those dreadful bossy voluntary army women who had made his wartime army chaplaincy such a nightmare.
(Joanna Trollope, THE CHOIR, 1988)

. . . if you know you are dreaming, you can take charge of the dream action, become the director of your own interior movie. Nightmare *sufferers can learn to confront their dream monster, turning a raging lion into a mild-mannered tabby cat, or reclaim a dream as they're waking up in time to impose a different ending.*
(GOOD HOUSEKEEPING, May 1994)

Amongst the Germanic peoples of the eighth century and earlier, someone suffering from terrifying dreams and feelings of suffocation in the chest was said to be having a visitation from the *Mara* or *Mera*, a spirit or demon which settled upon the breast of a sleeper to torment his rest. According to Walsh, a knife bound in a cloth and swung three times around the body while incantations were repeated would banish the spirit. Mistletoe was also deemed efficacious.

By the thirteenth century the *Mare* was often also known by the compound *nightmare.* But it was not until the sixteenth century that *Mare* and *nightmare* were also applied to the terrifying dream itself. According to Turner (HERBAL, 1568) the *nyght mare* was a strangling sensation, and in his METHOD OF PHYSICK (1624), Barrough concurred:

Of the mare. – Ephialtes *in Greeke, in Latine* incubus *and* incubo. *It is a disease, where as one thinketh himselfe in the night to be oppresssed with a great weight, and beleeveth that something cometh upon him, and the patient thinketh himselfe strangled in this disease. It is called in English the* mare.

From medieval times the *incubus* (Late Latin, from Latin *incubare*, 'to lie down upon') and its counterpart the *succubus* (from Late Latin *succuba*, from Latin *succumbere*, 'to lie under') both denoted evil spirits that induced nightmares and were thus alternative terms to *mare.* The *incubus* was a devil which assumed the form of a man in order to have intercourse with a sleeping woman, while the *succubus* took a female form and lay with men. In the Middle Ages their existence was recognised by the judicial systems of church and state. Italian retains the word *incubo* for nightmare but Old French borrowed the Germanic term *mare* which it compounded with the Old French verb *cauchier*, 'to trample upon' so that modern French has the word *cauchemar*, 'nightmare'.

Modern English has extended the fearful quality of a dream during sleep to any bad experience, even during waking hours. It is now quite possible to talk of having had 'a nightmare day at work' without incongruity.

Although *mare*, meaning 'female horse' and 'demon', both look identical and both go back to Old English, in fact they have different roots, and are not connected. The apparent similarity has prompted wild speculation that attempts to link horses to bad dreams.

oaf

a clumsy, loutish person

She talked to me even though I was almost oblivious in that small death which follows loving. We must have looked so incongruous, a delicious colourful bird with dazzling lustrous hair, sitting kneeling in a lost orchard with her elegant new dress crumpled, nursing a slumbering dishevelled oaf *who wasn't paying the slightest heed to a word she was saying.*
(Jonathan Gash, THE GONDOLA SCAM, 1984)

Recent scientific research has brought us into a new understanding of why children are born deformed or retarded. In past centuries, more credulous than our own, the tragedy was given a supernatural explanation. It was said that the infant was an *oaf*, 'a changeling, an elf or goblin child', left in the cradle by the fairies as a substitute for the human child that they had stolen. In his DESCRIPTION OF THE ISLE OF MAN (1731) George Waldron gives an account of the appearance and habits of such a changeling. According to Waldron's witnesses the child never spoke or cried '*but if anyone called him a Fairy-Elf he would frown, and fix his eyes earnestly on those who said it, as though he would look them through. . .*' Neighbours often found the child laughing alone and '*this made them judge that he was not without Company more pleasing to him than any mortal's could be. . .*' To this was added the further evidence that if he was left dirty he reappeared clean.

Oaf is a variant of the earlier *aufe* which came from an Old Norse word, *alfr*, meaning 'elf' or 'goblin'. The word was freely applied to the slow-witted or deformed, with the implication that they were changelings. Over time belief in the fairies waned but the term lingered to denote any 'clumsy, awkward or stupid person'.

odd

1. not even (of a numeral)
2. out of the ordinary
3. strange, peculiar

Besides his sleeping-room and bath, there was a large room, formerly a painter's studio, which he used as a study and office. It was furnished with the cast-off possessions of his bachelor days and with odd *things which he sheltered for friends of his who followed itinerant and more or less artistic callings.*
(Willa Cather, ALEXANDER'S BRIDGE, 1912)

I realised instantly that something odd *had happened. Neither of them greeted me, they simply stared, not smiling, and yet*

with a certain retaining solicitude. I closed the door. For a wild moment I imagined that they were going to tell me that they had changed their minds about getting married.
(Iris Murdoch, A SEVERED HEAD, 1961)

She wore a rather ordinary tweed skirt and dark-green knitted jumper. Her shoes, however, were a little odd*; low-heeled, but a bit fancy; they didn't seem to go with the rest. There was something else out of place, too, though I did not fix it at the moment. Only afterwards did I realize that it must have been the way her fair hair was dressed – very becoming to her, but the style was a bit off the beam.*
(John Wyndham, THE SEEDS OF TIME, 1956)

Prepare to feel dwarfed; here [in the Serengeti National Park] humans are the odd *ones out, and the animals know it full well and treat you with a healthy irreverence.*
(GOOD HOUSEKEEPING, April 1995)

Odd is a strange word. Its sense 'not even' derives from Old Norse *oddi* which means 'point, triangle', the concept arising from the image of a triangle which rests upon two base angles with a solitary third thrusting upwards. A number of related words in Germanic languages carry meanings such as 'point, origin, triangle of land, tip of a weapon, etc', but only Old Norse developed the notion of oddness. *Oddi* appeared in several Old Norse combinations to this effect. The expression *standask ī odda*, for instance, meant 'to be at odds, to be in dispute'. *Oddamdr* was an 'unpaired' and therefore 'odd' member who gave a casting vote. Examples of this usage in English have been recorded since the fourteenth century. William Tyndale, for instance, wrote of a seventh man as being *'the* odd *man and umpire'* (1530). *Oddatala* signified an 'odd number'. Again written records of this sense of *odd* in English date back to the fourteenth century. A manuscript entitled ART OF NOMBRYNGE (c. 1430) instructs the reader to '*compt the nombre of the figures, and wete yf it be* ode *or even*'.

Other uses of *odd* emerge from this basic notion of 'unpaired'. The sense 'remainder' (*a hundred and odd,* for example) dates back to the fourteenth century; it was well established by the time of Aphra Behn:

The King of Coramantien was himself a man of an hundred and odd *years old, and had no son, though he had many beautiful black wives: for most certainly there are beauties that can charm of that colour.*
(Aphra Behn, OROONOKO: OR, THE ROYAL SLAVE,1688)

Lewis Carroll's vision of the world of Alice is perhaps the best literary example of *odd* meaning 'strange, different in appearance or behaviour from the rest'. It is a logical development of earlier senses, and it arose in the second half of the sixteenth century. Carroll uses the term extensively:

Tweedledee smiled gently, and began again:
'The sun was shining on the sea,
Shining with all his might:
He did his very best to make
The billows smooth and bright –
And this was odd, *because it was*
The middle of the night.
...
But four young oysters hurried up,
All eager for the treat:
Their coats were brushed, their faces washed,
Their shoes were clean and neat –
And this was odd, *because, you know,*
They hadn't any feet.'
(Lewis Carroll, ALICE'S ADVENTURES IN WONDERLAND, 1865)

The shop was very dark towards the end. 'The egg seems to get further away the more I walk towards it. Let me see, is this a chair?

Why, it's got branches, I declare! How very odd *to find trees growing here! And actually here's a little brook! Well, this is the very queerest shop I ever saw!'*
(Lewis Carroll, THROUGH THE LOOKING GLASS AND WHAT ALICE FOUND THERE, 1871)

omelette

beaten eggs, fried in a round flat pancake shape

It was a wonderful little dinner. There was watercress soup, and sole, and a delightful omelette *stuffed with mushrooms and truffles, and two small rare ducklings, and artichokes,and a dry yellow Rhone wine.*
(Willa Cather, ALEXANDER'S BRIDGE, 1912)

This quick, simple, straightforward dish has a long, complicated and quirky etymology. It begins not in France but in ancient Rome where the Latin word *lāmella* (a diminutive of *lāmina*, 'plate, layer') meant 'a thin metal plate'. When this passed into Old French as *lemelle* it also denoted a 'thin blade' such as that of a knife or sword. So far, so good – but here comes the first quirk. The word and its definite article, *la lemelle*, was often erroneously written as *l'alemelle* which is identical in pronunciation. In this way the term gained an initial vowel. A slight change in the medial vowel then produced *alumelle*, 'thin plate, a blade'. Next, this corrupted form was given the diminutive suffix *-ette* to produce *alumette*. By now a mixture of beaten eggs cooked until they resembled a thin flat plate was common fare, its appearance suggesting the name *alumette*. By yet another linguistic quirk the *l* and *m* sounds were reversed so that the word changed from *alumette* to *amelette* during the fifteenth century. Other forms followed as speakers and writers tussled with the initial syllable; *aumelette*, *omelette* and even *oeufmolette* (in an attempt to reconcile the word to *oeuf*, the French word for 'egg').

English too struggled with the word which it borrowed from French in the seventeenth century. During the seventeenth and eighteenth centuries *omelet*, *aumelet*, *amulet*, and *aumulet* are all found. The well-known eighteenth-century cookery writer, Mrs Hannah Glasse, favoured *aumlet*.

During the nineteenth century both *omelet* and *omelette* were current but the twentieth century saw a parting of the ways between American and British English; American English retained the old form *omelet* while British English plumped for the modern French spelling *omelette*.

onion

a very common vegetable with a strong-smelling and tasting bulb

Lucy-amma was cutting onions. *Bombay* onions. *The beards sliced off each* onion *were heaped on one side. She worked the knife like a stern goddesss – a devatara – slicing translucent, perfect semicircles. She was always cutting* onions.
(Romesh Gunesekera, REEF, 1994)

Onions were widely grown in Roman times; upper-class citizens enjoyed their flavour in sauces or dressings while the lower classes ate them as vegetables as part of an economical diet. And pickled onions are not exclusive to the British chip shop. As long ago as the 1st century AD Junius Moderatus Columella, a writer on farming and agriculture, suggested preserving onions in brine and vinegar (Brothwell, FOOD IN ANTIQUITY, 1969).

The source of the word is Latin *uniō* (stem *ūniōn-*), a rustic dialectal term for a kind of onion. It is very possible that this is the same word as Latin *ūniō*, which derived from *ūnus*, 'one'. *Ūniō* had two meanings, either of which would satisfactorily explain its metaphorical application to an onion. Firstly it meant 'unity' – the allusion here would clearly be to the united layers of the vegetable. Secondly it meant a 'large, perfect and (according to Pliny) unique pearl' – the comparison obviously being between such a jewel and a perfect translucent pearly onion.

Onion made its way from Latin into Middle English in the fourteenth century as *unyon* (or *oynoun*) through Anglo-French and Old French *oignon*.

◆ Latin *ūnus*, 'one', is also ultimately responsible for:

union (15th cent) by way of French *union* and Latin *ūniō*, 'number one, unity'

unique (17th cent) through French *unique* and Latin *ūnicus*, 'only, single'

The prefix *ūni-* is derived from *ūnus* and is combined in a large number of words such as:

unicorn (13th cent) Middle English, from Old French, from Latin *ūnicornis*, from *ūni-* and *cornū*, 'horn'

uniform (16th cent) from French *uniforme*, from Latin *ūniformis*, 'of one form', from *ūni-* and *forma*, 'form'. Uniform was first used as a noun to denote 'an outfit worn by every member of a group' in the eighteenth century

unison (16th cent) through Old French *unison* and Latin *ūnisonus* (from *ūnus*, 'one' and *sonus*, 'sound'.

universe (14th cent) through Old French *univers* and Latin *ūniversum* 'the whole world', from *ūniversus* 'entire, turned into one' (from *ūni-* and *versus*, from *vertere*, 'to turn'). Coined to translate the Greek *to holon*, 'the whole'.

Ūnus itself goes back to the unattested Indo-European form *oinos*. From this came the Old Germanic form *ainaz* which is ultimately responsible for English *one*.◆

opportunity

chance, occasion

What Lady Chalker should have done was seize the opportunity *to deliver a lecture on the benefits of democracy. Among her audience. . .were some greedy, dictatorial scoundrels whom she could and should have set squirming.*
(THE TIMES, 13 March 1995)

Just north of Jasper we ran into our first wildlife jam. Cars and camper vans slewed off the road. People everywhere. . . A signal for any knowing tourist to screech to a halt for a photo opportunity. . . *There, unconcernedly browsing the verge, and occasionally raising its headgear in classic Landseer pose, stood a tremendous elk.*
(THE TIMES WEEKEND, 11 March 1995)

In the days of sailing ships few things could have been more dispiriting to a crew than to have their progress towards port impeded by contrary winds or arrested by calms. The Latin sailors coined an adjective *opportūnus*, 'blowing in the direction of the harbour' (from *ob-*, 'to' and *portus*, 'harbour') to describe favourable winds which arose at just the right time. Soon this particular application broadened out to give the general sense 'seasonable, timely, convenient'. From this Old French took *opportun* which passed into English as *opportune* in the early fifteenth century.

Some fifty years earlier, the Latin noun *opportūnitās*, derived from the adjective *opportūnus*, was taken into Middle English as *opportunite* by way of Old French.

In Modern English, the adjective retains the sense of 'timely, just at the right moment'; the noun used to have this sense but now the emphasis is on the chance, the possibilities, that a favourable set of circumstances offers.

◆ Latin *portus* was borrowed into Old English as port, 'harbour'. The original meaning of the derived Latin verb *portāre* was probably 'to bring [a cargo] into port' before it achieved the more general sense 'to carry'. (See also **arrive** and **starboard**). It is evident in a number of English words, such as: *deport*, *export*, *import*, *transport*, *portable*.◆

For another word deriving from good sailing weather, see **bonanza**.

oscillate

1. to swing rhythmically backwards and forwards
2. to be undecided, to vacillate

The second handling-machine was now completed, and was busied in serving one of the novel contrivances the big machine had brought. This was a body resembling a milk can in its general form, above which oscillated *a pear-shaped receptacle, and from which a stream of white powder flowed into a circular basin below.*

(H G Wells, The War of the Worlds, 1898)

According to mythology the god Bacchus taught man how to cultivate the vine and prepare wine from its fruit. Roman viniculturists hoping for a good harvest would hang a little mask of the god from a tree in their vineyard to swing about in the breeze. The charm was known as an *ōscillium*, literally a 'little face', being a diminutive of *ōs*, a term which meant 'mouth' but which was also sometimes applied to the whole face. In time *ōscillium* came to mean 'a swing' and as such was the source of the verb *ōscillāre*, 'to swing'. This was taken into English in the 1720s as *oscillate*, initially a scientific term to describe the regular movement of a pendulum.

◆ In Latin *ōs* was the nominative and *ōr-* was the stem of the other cases. Both forms are present in English words.

osculate (17th cent) which strictly means 'to kiss' but which has particular meanings in biology and geometry, from *ōsculārī* from *ōsculum*, 'little mouth, kiss'

oscitancy (17th cent), 'yawning, drowsiness resulting from indolence', from *ōscitāre*, 'to gape', from *ōs* and *citāre*, 'to move'.

The stem *ōr-* is evident in:

orifice (16th cent), 'an aperture, an opening, a mouth', from *ōr-* and *facere*, 'to make'.

oral (17th cent)

oracy (1960s) a recent coinage modelled on literacy.

Quite a number of words go back to Latin *ōrāre*, 'to beg, to pray, to tell', itself from *ōr-*:

adore (early 14th cent)

oracle (14th cent)

orator (14th cent)

oratory (14th cent),'a small chapel' – from *ōrātōrium templum*, 'a place for prayer' *oratory* (16th cent), 'public speaking' – from *ōrātōria ars*, 'the art of public speaking'

oration (14th cent)

orate (16th cent) A back formation of a verb from a noun

The original root is less obvious in:

usher (14th cent) Middle English from Anglo-French *usser*, from Old French *ussier*, from Medieval Latin *ūstiārius*, variant of Latin *ōstiārius*, 'doorkeeper', from *ostium*, 'entrance, door', from *ōs*.

inexorable (16th cent), 'relentless' – from *inexōrābilis*, 'not capable of being pleaded with'.

ostracise

to exclude someone from social contact, to blackball

BRITISH CINEMA AT THE LONDON FILM FESTIVAL
Director Antonia Bird, became a convert to Jimmy McGovern's PRIEST *'a story about a Liverpudlian priest who must deny his love for another man' because of the humanity and humour of the script. 'During filming, I was most saddened by how ungenerous and inhumane people are. People don't accept faults in others. Instead, they* ostracise.*'*
(OBSERVER, 30 October 1994)

The word comes from the Greek verb *ostrakizein*, 'to ostracise', which is derived from *ostrakon*, meaning a 'potsherd'. Every year the citizens of Athens had the right to gather together and vote for the *ostrakismos*, or 'banishment', of anyone whose power and authority threatened the equilibrium of the democratic state. People recorded their votes by writing a name on a fragment of pottery known as an *ostrakon*. A total of 6000 votes had to be cast before the poll was declared valid. If a majority of these denounced one particular person he was ostracised, initially for ten years and later for five, although he did not relinquish any property he might own. Very few citizens were cast out by this vote and there were no more ballots after the 5th century BC.

In English sixteenth-century uses of the noun *ostracism* were confined to a discussion of the classical practice. Figurative use of both the noun and the derived verb dates from the first half of the seventeenth century.

◆ The Indo-European root *ost-* meant 'bone' and was responsible for several Greek words which denoted objects of a similar texture. *Ostrakon* was one of these. *Osteon*, 'bone', was a second. Its stem *osteo-* is found in a number of largely medical terms to do with the bones such as *osteoarthritis, osteology, osteoid, osteopathy, osteoporosis*, etc. A third derivative was *ostreon*, which meant 'oyster'. This came into Middle English as *oystre* in the mid-fourteenth century by way of Old French *oistre* and Latin *ostrea*.◆

palaver

1. a trouble, a fuss, a hassle
2. chatter, talk

. . . I consoled myself with the thought of how educational the whole caboodle would be. Both my daughter, who'd just started school, and her 10-year-old half-sister would learn so much . . . what did it matter that cleaning the filter each day (no soap) was completely beyond either of them? Or that I had to carry out a complete gallon-plus water change every three days (rainwater or treated tap-water only, plus a mugful of pond algae)? It took ages. . . At last we tipped nearly a

hundred little frogs with tails into the pond . . . soon they'd hop away and start hunting. But the palaver *was by no means over. 'Watch where you're walking, keep off that grass,' became my catchphrase. . .*
(WEEKEND TELEGRAPH, 14 May 1994)

In Portuguese *palavra* (from Late Latin *parabola*) means 'word, talk' and was the term used by traders of that nation when they wanted to meet for a parley or negotiation with the natives of the African coast. Here the term was picked up by British sailors. This piece of seafaring slang appeared in written English as *palaver* in the first half of the eighteenth century and was soon absorbed into colloquial speech to denote 'empty, idle chatter' or 'coaxing, cajoling talk' – a little of each doubtless characterised the original *palavras*. Although these meanings are still current amongst some speakers, the term is more commonly used in its twentieth-century extended sense, to refer to 'a fuss' or 'a wearisome, involved task or process'.

◆ Latin *parabola* gave Medieval Latin *parabolāre*, 'to talk'. From this Old French derived *parler*, 'to talk'. The past participle *parlée* was borrowed into sixteenth century English as *parley*, originally 'talk, debate', then 'negotiation'.◆

For words from the same origin, see **parlour** and **parole**.

pamphlet

1. a tract, a treatise
2. a leaflet

He would drive back to Crampsford; he would complain to Mr. and Mrs. Allaby; he didn't mean to have married Christina; he hadn't married her; it was all a hideous dream; he would – But a voice kept ringing in his ears which said: 'You CAN'T, CAN'T, CAN'T.'

'CAN'T I?' screamed the unhappy creature to himself.

'No,' said the remorseless voice, 'YOU CAN'T. YOU ARE A MARRIED MAN.'

He rolled back in his corner of the carriage and for the first time felt how iniquitous were the marriage laws of England. But he would buy Milton's prose works and read his pamphlet *on divorce. He might perhaps be able to get them at Newmarket.*
(Samuel Butler, THE WAY OF ALL FLESH, 1903)

Towards the end of the twelfth century an erotic comic poem, written in Latin and of unknown authorship, gained great popularity in northern Europe. The bawdy content of PAMPHILUS SEU DE AMORE (Pamphilus or About Love) so tickled the fancy of students at the University of Paris that they were officially admonished for neglecting their studies to read it. At that time it was common for brief works to be referred to by the addition of the diminutive *-et*. Cato's couplets, for instance, became *Catonet* and Aesop's fables *Esopet*. The same convention was applied to Pamphilus which became *Panflet* in Dutch and *Pamfilet* in French.

The love poem was certainly known in England as both Chaucer and Gower mention it. It is therefore not unreasonable to assume that, here too, it was called by a diminutive such as *Panflet* or *Pamfilet* and that the term was then transferred to other short texts. Indeed this must have happened before 1344, for in PHILOBIBLON, the English scholar and bibliophile Richard de Bury says he would rather have a pamphlet to read than a plump horse to ride.

pandemonium

hubbub, uproar, chaos

We gave our youngest a hamster. Come Christmas morning he opens the parcel ever so excited and the cage is empty. The little bleeder escaped, and I know what happened, the husband's had it out on the kitchen table the night before – he'd had a few – and I just know it's got into the turkey. Which has been on mark 6 for three hours. Well, you can imagine, there's tears and five shades of pandemonium *and whiskies all round, and I chucked the turkey in next door's bin, chipolatas, tin, the lot. And then Rosemary shouts, 'Mum, mum, I've found the hamster.' It got in the sprouts not the turkey. And the youngest goes hooray, and Rosemary says, 'Not so fast, they've been boiling for an hour.'*
(THE SUNDAY TIMES, 18 December 1994)

This word springs from the imagination of John Milton. In PARADISE LOST, Book 1 (1667), Milton tells us that *Pandemonium* is the capital of Hell where Satan presides over his council of Evil Spirits:

> *A solemn Councel forthwith to be held*
> *At* Pandaemonium, *the high Capital*
> *Of Satan and his Peers*

Later in the poem *Pandemonium* is described as the '*citie and proud seate of Lucifer*'. Milton coined his word from two Greek words; *pan-*, meaning 'all', and *daimōn*, 'spirit'.

In the earliest written references *Pandemonium* is simply used as a name for hell. Then, in the second half of the eighteenth century, writers began to describe any place of wickedness and lawlessness as a *pandemonium*. The term was finally applied to the chaos and commotion itself in the second half of the nineteenth century.

pander

to satisfy, indulge another's wishes

There are men who are misers, and also spendthrifts; but they are rare. There are men sensual and also ascetic; but they are rare. But if this mass of mad contradictions really existed, quakerish and bloodthirsty, too gorgeous and too thread-bare, austere, yet pandering *preposterously to the lust of the eye, the enemy of women and their foolish refuge, a solemn pessimist and a silly optimist, if this evil existed, then there was in this evil something quite supreme and unique.*
(G K Chesterton, ORTHODOXY, 1909)

Pandarus was a proper name which was borne by two ancient characters. THE AENEID tells of *Pandaros*, a companion of Aeneas, while THE ILIAD describes *Pandarus*, a distinguished archer in the Trojan army at the siege of Troy. The tone had changed by the time the name was popularised in English through Chaucer's celebrated poem TROILUS AND CRISEYDE (c. 1385). Here *Pandarus*, or *Pandare*, was the character who acted as a go-between on Troilus's behalf to secure Criseyde's affections. Chaucer's story was based in part on Boccaccio's FILOSTRATO where the same character, *Pandaro*, appears.

In the sixteenth century, then, a *pander* was initially 'one who arranged illicit love affairs', and then 'a pimp'. *Pander* was used as a verb from the beginning of the seventeenth century, with the dual senses 'to act as a pander' and 'to serve the baser designs of others'.

Pander to, with the weaker meaning 'to gratify or indulge another's whims', arose in the second half of the nineteenth century.

parlour

1. a room in a house for entertaining, a sitting room
2. a salon, a shop, equipped for a particular purpose

'Just on your way?' he asked.

His question was almost justified by Winifred's proximity to the hat stand.

'I was. But now you're here, I'll stay for a bit. It seems ages since I saw you. Come into the parlour *and sit down.'*

Frederick could not imagine any other woman inviting him into his own parlour.
(Roy Hattersley, THE MAKER'S MARK, 1990)

. . . despite many letters from Riponians to the people of their twin town and though the framed document proclaiming undying friendship had pride of place in the mayor's parlour, *nothing of significance ever came back.*
(DAILY TELEGRAPH, 8 March 1995)

Etymologically a *parlour* is 'a place for talking'. Middle English borrowed the term from Old French *parleur*, a derivative of the verb *parler*, 'to speak'. The *parlour* was a room in a medieval monastery or convent which could be used for private conversation or the reception of visitors. The earliest written record comes from the ANCRENE RIWLE (c. 1225), a devotional manual which offered guidance for the organisation and government of monastic communities. In time, however, the word escaped from the cloisters. Medieval houses featured a hall which was originally used for all domestic activities. It was a busy area filled with smoke, heat and noisy bustle. Privacy was limited. By the second half of the fourteenth century the *parlour* was becoming a feature of domestic households, a quiet room where private conversation could be held (as in a monastery) and genteel pastimes pursued. This gradually evolved into the family sitting-room, still with the name *parlour*.

The word is today dialectally used in this sense but mainly survives in a number of compounds such as *parlour game, ice-cream parlour, beauty parlour, parlour politics* and *milking parlour*.

For words of the same origin, see **palaver** and **parole**.

parole

1. word of honour
2. supervised early release from prison, on condition of good behaviour

Until recently 'life' sentences were usually terminated by parole *after a maximum of nine or ten years' incarceration, because it was realized that longer periods of confinement made it unlikely that the prisoner, when released, would be able to cope with life outside.*
(Anthony Storr, SOLITUDE, 1988)

Six prisoners, all Cuban and all serving life without parole, *used kitchen spoons to shovel away the soft wet soil at the Glades Correctional Institution, close to Lake Okeechobee in Florida, to dig a 60 foot tunnel to freedom.*
(DAILY TELEGRAPH, 5 January 1995)

The term is short for *parole of honour*, a translation of the French *parole d'honneur*, 'word of honour'. It was taken into English in the seventeenth century with special reference to the solemn undertaking of a prisoner of war to abide by certain conditions in exchange for privileges. He might, for instance, be granted his freedom if he agreed not to fight again for the duration of the war. The word was later applied to the early release of prisoners on condition of continued good behaviour.

French *parole*, 'word of honour', is from unattested Vulgar Latin *paraula*, a derivative of Late Latin *parabola*, 'word, speech'.

For words from the same origin see **palaver** and **parlour**.

pedigree

line of descent, ancestry

There are some trees, Watson, which grow to a certain height, and then suddenly develop some unsightly eccentricity. You will see it often in humans. I have a theory that the individual represents in his development the whole procession of his ancestors, and that such a sudden turn to good or evil stands for some strong influence which came into the line of his pedigree. *The person becomes, as it were, the epitome of the history of his own family.*
(Sir Arthur Conan Doyle, THE RETURN OF SHERLOCK HOLMES, 1905)

Our next problem is finding a suitable mate. . . Fate intervened and we spotted an advertisement for a Pig Workshop at the Rare Breeds Centre . . . we discovered that the trust has a Berkshire boar. He has a very grand pedigree *name but is known to his frends as Sid, and we have arranged that, in the next few weeks, Naomi and Doris will be going a-calling.*
(THE TIMES WEEKEND, 18 March 1995)

A *pedigree* dog is a purebred animal with no trace of mongrel in him. Indeed, his line of descent will have been carefully recorded to prove it. The documentation is similarly available for the lineage of royalty and nobility. When medieval genealogists charted the ancestry of powerful families they used a three-lined mark to indicate the line of succession. This claw-like symbol reminded people of a crane's foot and so, in Old French it was called the *pie de grue* (pie, from Latin *pēs*, 'foot'; *grue*, from Latin *grūs*, 'crane'). This became *pedegru* in Middle English. The spelling did not settle down as *pedigree* until the eighteenth century.

perfume

1. a liquid that gives off an agreeable odour
2. any pleasant scent

Perfume rose up from her, and when I moved in to spoon the potatoes on to her plate it seemed the scent was stronger. It rose up from below her throat down inside her flapping dress. She had her elbows on the table; her body was concave. She must have smeared the perfume *with her fingers, rubbing it in like honey paste to enrich the skin.*
(Romesh Gunesekera, REEF, 1994)

The Midi is the only waterway basking in a decent Mediterranean climate, with vineyards on the very banks, cicadas chirping from leafy lairs and perfumes *borne by morning breezes.*
(THE GUARDIAN, 14 January 1995)

The source of this word is an early Italian verb, *perfumare* (ultimately derived from Latin *per-*, 'through' and *fūmāre*, 'to smoke'), which meant 'to permeate with smoke'. The derived noun was *perfumo*. These were borrowed into French as *parfumer* and *parfum* in the fifteenth century and passed from there into English in the first half of the sixteenth century. As the etymology of the word suggests, *perfume* did not originally denote the delicate scent of a rose or a dab of fragrant oil but 'odoriferous smoke emitted by burning a substance'; this might be from incense or an oil warmed to make a room smell sweet, or it might be from herbs burnt for medicinal purposes or to disinfect a house after an infectious illness. Soon the word was applied to any agreeable fragrances, such as that emitted by flowers, and then to scents designed to be worn rather than burnt.

◆ Latin *fūmāre* derives from *fūmus*, 'smoke', which is ultimately responsible for English *fume* (15th cent) and *fumigate* (16th cent).◆

pirate

1. a sea robber
2. someone who steals another's rights, copies another's work without permission
3. an unauthorised broadcasting station

Sometimes of a morning, as I've sat in bed sucking down the early cup of tea and watched Jeeves flitting about the room and putting out the raiment for the day, I've wondered what the deuce I should do if the fellow ever took it into his head to leave me. . .. Young Reggie Foljambe to my certain knowledge offered him double what I was giving him, and Alistair Bingham-Reeves, who's got a valet who had been known to press his trousers sideways, used to look at him, when he came to see me, with a kind of glittering, hungry eye which disturbed me deucedly. Bally pirates*!*
(P G Wodehouse, Carry On, Jeeves, 1925)

Gina's husband leaves her. In her distress she becomes an emotional pirate, *snatching at love wherever she can find it.*
(Good Housekeeping, April, 1995)

Peiratēs was a Greek term for a 'marauder'. It derived from the verb *peiran*, 'to attempt, to attack' and the noun *peira*, 'an attempt'. After it was borrowed into Latin as *pīrāta*, it came to mean 'one who plunders on the sea' and in this sense it was taken into English in the fifteenth century.

The figurative application of *pirate* for 'one who reproduces the work of another for his own gain' arose in the second half of the seventeenth century. In those days it was the written word which was snatched for profit; in modern times piracy extends to design, film and video games. With the invention of radio, pirates roved the sound waves rather than the ocean waves, the term being applied to 'one who broadcasts programmes illicitly' in the early twentieth century.

placebo

1. a remedy designed to please rather than cure
2. an inactive substance given to a control group in an experiment

In medieval Europe herbal remedies for ageing were associated with witchcraft as they were often administered by old women muttering incantations and sometimes using special rites. The placebo *effect of spells could be compared with the faith we have in modern science and all its incantations – as mystifying as magical spells to most of us.*
(New Zealand Woman's Weekly, 14 January 1991)

In the Latin rite the first anthem for Vespers in the Office for the Dead begins with the line '*Placēbo Dominō in rēgiōne vivōrum.*' It comes from Psalm 114:9 and translates as 'I shall please the Lord in the land of the living.' Since at least the thirteenth century the service has been known by the first word of this anthem *Placēbo*, 'I shall please' (from Latin *placēre*, 'to please').

From the fourteenth to the seventeenth centuries the word was used in a number of idioms such as to *play placebo*, or *to be at the school of placebo.* These drew on the sense 'I shall please' for they meant 'to flatter, to curry favour' so that *placebo* became synonymous with 'sycophant'.

By the eighteenth century this idiomatic sense was virtually obsolete but during the 1780s the word was given a new lease of life when it was applied to a medicine which was designed to please; the value of the remedy might be in question but taking it humoured the patient and might prove of some psychological help. Copper bracelets worn by sufferers from rheumatism probably work on this principle although those who sell them say the metal draws acid from the body. Modern medicine has extended the use of *placebo* to refer to a harmless substance which is used as a control in an experiment.

For a similarly derived word, see **dirge**.

plaudit

acclaim, approval

Not in the clamour of the crowded street,
Not in the shouts and plaudits *of the throng,*
But in ourselves, are triumph and defeat.
(Henry Wadsworth Longfellow, THE POETS AND POETRY OF EUROPE, 1845)

Being a middle-aged woman in the nineties is a time-consuming business . . . we rise at dawn to drag the children out of bed and harry them to practise their instruments. . . While they breakfast, we feed the cat, let the dog out, slap on anti-ageing moisturiser and make packed lunches. By 8 am we are out of the house and ready to start the real working day, into which we must remember to incorporate 20 minutes of vigorous excercise (to ward off osteoporosis and middle-age spread). After school it's ballet, riding, skating, football, homework, cooking, mending. . . While the rest of the household sleeps, we dedicate an hour to our creams – neck cream, eye cream, hand cream – destined to refresh the parts that nature's juices, alas, no longer reach.

Now, just when we thought we might win plaudits *for the daily clock-beating, gravity-defying miracle that defines our existence, along comes someone to chide us.*
(WEEKEND TELEGRAPH, 22 October 1994)

'*Valete et plaudite*' ('Farewell and give us your applause'), Terence urges his audience at the end of his play EUNUCHUS (161 BC). The words were not only Terence's but were the closing exhortation of many performances as Quintilian confirms in his DE INSTITUTIONE ORATORIA (c. AD 80): *Quo veteres tragoediae comoediaeque clauduntur, Plodite.* (The phrase with which old tragedies and comedies used to end, *'Friends, give us your applause'*).

The cry *plaudite*, 'applaud' was the plural imperative of the Latin verb *plaudere*, 'to applaud'. The word first appears in English in the sixteenth century through the renewed interest in classical studies that characterised the period. In its earliest uses it appears, not as an imperative, but as a three syllable noun meaning 'applause'. During the seventeenth century the final *e* became mute and was dropped giving *plaudit*. Through the nineteenth century the word still meant 'applause' or some other audible form of praise or appreciation. Today, however, *plaudit* is usually a 'written or verbal expression of critical acclaim'.

◆ The Latin verb *plaudere*, 'to clap', is the source of other words which entered English in the sixteenth century.

Applause, for instance, derives from the Latin *ad-*, 'to' and *plaudere*, while *plausible* comes from the related Latin adjective *plausibilis* meaning 'deserving applause'. *Plausible* was originally used in the sense of 'worthy of praise or approval'. The modern meaning 'seemingly reasonable or valid', as in a *plausible argument*, also dates from the sixteenth century.◆

For another word from the same Latin source, see **explode**.

precocious

significantly more developed or advanced than the norm

She was a very good baby and a precocious *child who could read perfectly before she was four. My mother was horrified when Antonia picked up* THE TIMES *and started reading the leader article out loud. She accused me of teaching Antonia to read it parrot-fashion. I said, 'She's never seen it before, and of course she doesn't understand any of it. Who does?'*
(Lady Longford about her daughter, Lady Antonia Fraser, in THE SUNDAY TIMES MAGAZINE, 18 December 1994)

Beyond its elemental appeal as a uniquely sacred artefact, the papyrus may have much to tell us about early Christianity. Dr Thiede's dating suggests that the new religion was highly precocious, *that it spread quickly and that its early scribes were capable of a literate Greek.*
(THE TIMES, 24 December 1994)

Beetroots bake in their own skin to a precocious *sweetness that has more in common with a fruit than a vegetable.*
(THE INDEPENDENT, 18 January 1995)

When Sir Thomas Browne in his VULGAR ERRORS (1650) spoke of 'precocious trees ', he was using the word in a particular botanical sense. He goes on to explain that such plants '*have their spring in the winter.*' A *precocious* plant then is one which fruits or flowers early or which, like the forsythia or the apple, flowers or sets its fruit before it comes into leaf. The word first came into English in the mid-seventeenth century from the Latin adjective *praecox*, 'ripening prematurely', which derived from the verb *praecoquere*, 'to cook, to ripen beforehand' (from *prae-*, 'before', and *coquere*, 'to cook', 'to ripen'). By the last quarter of the century *precocious* was figuratively applied to people who, in one respect or another, had come into early maturity. Thus a *precocious* child is one who has flowered before his time.

For another word from the same source, see **apricot**.

prestige

renown, status, admiration

Archie: Inspector, my patronage is not extensive, but it is select. I can offer prestige, *the respect of your peers and almost unlimited credit among the local shopkeepers – in short, the chair of divinity is yours for the asking.*
(Tom Stoppard, JUMPERS, 1972)

Whatever the shape of the table, subjects suffer almost without exception from what [Grayling] calls 'host or hostess deprivation'. . . The obvious way of having

no head of the table–the circular shape–does not work because of the prestige *factor. . . The solution [Grayling] finds the most feasible at present is to have a circular table with a hole in the middle. . . Then everybody is the same distance from the person he considers 'top guy'.*
(NEW SCIENTIST, 1983)

David Baddeil and Frank Skinner write for the Sunday Mirror. Ben Elton, Alexei Sayle and Stephen Fry have all been columnists, too. Comics have come to occupy a particular prestigious *place in our cultural landscape – one they never had before. Who ever read the Peter Sellers or Tony Hancock column or knew what Sid James thought about world events?*
(SUNDAY TIMES, 19 March 1995)

This word's origins lie with the skilful tricks and illusions of the juggler. These were known by the plural word *praestigiae* in Latin. This was an altered form of unattested *praestrigiae,* which derived from the verb *praestringere,* 'to bind fast', 'to blindfold' (from *prae-*, 'before', and *stringere,* 'to bind'). The sense was that the audience was blinded by the conjuror's skill. From this, sixteenth-century French had *prestige,* meaning 'illusion', 'trick', 'deceit', a word which, like its Latin ancestor, was often used in the plural. It was borrowed directly into English in the second half of the seventeenth century, again regularly in the plural.

In the early nineteenth century the word appears to have been borrowed from French once more, this time in the singular to denote 'dazzling success or reputation arising from past achievements or wealth'. This sense possibly alludes to the blinding, almost magical, aura of success. Skeat quotes the comment that *prestige* is one of the rare examples of a bad word turned good. Nevertheless some people cannot shake off the suspicion that the glory invariably masks the true facts, just as the conjuror's sleight of hand hides the deceit. The Victorian historian Edward Augustus Freeman was certainly of this cynical, or realistic, opinion: Prestige, *you know, I always like to have a pop at; I take it it has never lost its first meaning of conjuring tricks.* (1881). Perhaps he is right to suggest that *prestige* is a mask that covers a baser reality.

For an example of a good word turned bad, see **villain**.

protocol

1. a code of etiquette for formal occasions
2. a preliminary draft of a treaty, convention, etc
3. annexes to a treaty, etc

May I remind you that the first protocol *of the European Convention of Human Rights declares that the State must respect the right of all parents to ensure that the education and training of their children conforms to their own religious and philosophical convictions.*
(Joanna Trollope, THE CHOIR, 1988)

Fergie broke completely with royal protocol *and said something brave and, more surprisingly, relevant when she admitted to having been tested at least twice for HIV. Perhaps it will help to prevent the victimisation that goes on against others who have the good sense to do likewise.*
(THE SUNDAY TIMES, 18 December 1994)

[Stanley Matthews is] just an ordinary man who, despite his fierce pride at the honour, blushes whenever protocol *demands that he be presented unto us as 'Sir Stanley'.*
(DAILY TELEGRAPH, 23 January 1995)

The Late Greek compound *prōtokollon* meant 'glued on at the beginning' (from *prōt-*, 'first' and *kolla*, 'glue'). In the Byzantine Empire it denoted the first leaf glued on to a roll of papyrus which bore details of the manuscript's provenance and content. When the word came into English in the sixteenth century via medieval Latin *protocollum* and Old French *prothocole*, it no longer referred to a fly-leaf but to the outline of an agreement or negotiation that formed the basis of a subsequent legal document. In the seventeenth century the word was specifically used in diplomatic contexts to denote the minutes or first draft made at a conference from which the final treaty or agreement was drawn up.

In the late nineteenth century, French preoccupation with etiquette led them to apply *protocol* to the ceremonial procedures and formalities that surrounded such dipomatic negotiations and conferences. There was even a *Director of the Protocol*, an official in charge of a department of that name which was hidden away in the French Ministry of Foreign Affairs. This insistence on etiquette paved the way for the adoption in English, at the very end of the nineteenth century, of the modern sense of the word, that of 'a strict code of conduct proper in a formal situation'. The extension of the word into scientific contexts to mean a 'detailed record of correct experimental procedure and results' dates from the same time.

For another word signifying a code of behaviour, see **etiquette**.

puny

weak, physically small

Peter Wright's NUTCRACKER *for Birmingham Royal Ballet is more solemnly 'adult'. It has arrived at the Coliseum for its first London visit bedecked with praise – and when you see the Transformation Scene you understand why. Every production pulls out the stops to show Clara shrinking to doll-size, but Tchaikovsky's music to the scene is on so cosmic a scale that it makes most stagings look* puny. *Not BRB's, though. Sheer wizardry.*
(DAILY TELEGRAPH, 28 December 1995)

Some of our early lambs were puny *things: unborn twins always seemed to be muddled, limbs wrapped around each other in a politically correct but obstetrically lethal embrace that had to be unravelled before they could enter the world. . . It always seems to lead to weakly lambs.*
(THE TIMES WEEKEND, 18 March 1995)

Old French had the word *puisne* to denote a 'younger child'. It was a compound of *puis*, 'after' (from Vulgar Latin *postius*, comparative of *post*, 'after') and *ne*, 'born' (from Latin *nātus*, past participle of *nāscī*, 'to be born'). Modern French has *puîné* with the same meaning. *Puny* was a phonetic rendering of *puisne* which arose in English in the sixteenth century. Both *puisne* and *puny* were current and described someone who was either junior in age or, by extension, in rank. In the seventeenth century *puisne* in particular was applied to an associate judge and remains part of legal vocabulary in Modern English. *Puny*, on the other hand, was rarely used in this way but developed instead a sense of 'small', 'weak' and 'inferior' and, with it, overtones of contempt.

quarantine

a period of separation and isolation

Shelley's cremation [was] stage-managed by his friend of only six months, Trelawny. . . Mary did not attend and, according to

Trelawny's account, the others could hardly face it; Byron swimming off to his boat and Hunt remaining in his carriage. Trelawny observed that Shelley's heart was not consumed in the fire and rescued it, burning his hand and risking quarantine *in the process.*
(THE GUARDIAN, 18 January 1995)

The Commons Select Committeee on Agriculture has called for all dogs and cats to be microchipped and has recommended replacing quarantine *controls with universal vaccination for rabies, enforced through microchipping and 'pet passports'.*
(DAILY TELEGRAPH, 8 March 1995)

In the fourteenth century, as sea trade between Venice and eastern Mediterranean countries increased, so did the incidence of plague which was borne on returning ships. The Venetian authorities, therefore, adopted a system in which ships were isolated for a period, to give time for disease and infection to develop or dissipate. Since detention was for forty days the period was known as *quarantina,* a word derived from Italian *quaranta,* 'forty' (from Latin *quadrāgintā*). This sensible system was copied by other countries. In the sixteenth century the frustrations of *quarantine* were eased by the introduction of an international system of bills of health. These consisted of a declaration that the vessel's last port of call had been free of disease. This, together with a consul's visa from the country of arrival, exempted the ship from *quarantine.* As world trade expanded, the list of diseases covered by quarantine grew. Yellow fever, for instance, was added to the list as a result of trade with America.

Over time the required period of *quarantine* varied but the term remained. Present British regulations for the isolation of imported animals, for example, stipulate a quarantine of six months.

The earliest recorded use of the word in English occurs in Pepys' diary in the entry for 26 November 1663. It is particularly interesting in that Pepys was obviously aware of the origin of the term. Few would be today.

Making of all ships coming from thence.. to perform their 'quarantine *for thirty days', as Sir Richard Browne expressed it . . . contrary to the import of the word (though, in the general acceptation, it signifies now the thing, not the time spent in doing it).*

quarry

1. a site from which stone is extracted
2. the target of a hunt, prey

A moment before I had been safe of all men's respect, wealthy, beloved . . . and now I was the common quarry *of mankind, hunted, houseless, a known murderer, thrall to the gallows.*
(Robert Louis Stevenson, THE STRANGE CASE OF DR JEKYLL AND MR HYDE, 1886)

But it is to Rano Raraku that the visitor should go. This volcanic cone, dormant for at least 3000 years, provides the prized yellow rock from which the moais *were carved. Outside and in, the rock face has been transformed into a* quarry *for giant busts. They lie, as dormant as their volcano, stacked up ledge upon ledge. With every move the visitor transfers from one ear to another, steps over the roughed out eye-socket of a sleeping figure, or dodges round a protruding nose.*
(NEW SCIENTIST, 1983)

Etymologically Old French *quarriere* is a 'place from which square blocks of stone are obtained'. The ultimate source of the word is Latin *quadrus,* meaning 'square' but, in order to trace the development of the word, it is necessary to supply a missing link. Although there is no written evidence, it is assumed that Old French once had the word *quarre*, derived from *quadrus*, to denote a 'square stone' and that *quarriere* was then formed from this unattested term. Middle English borrowed the word as *quarrer* (variant *quarey*) in the fourteenth century.

Quarry meaning 'game' is derived from a totally different source. In medieval times a reward was customarily offered to the hounds at the end of a successful hunt. It consisted of a share of the dead animal's entrails spread out upon its hide. Similar titbits were also presented to hawks after a kill. The word came into Middle English as *querre* or *quirre* by way of Anglo-French and Old French *cuirée*. This was a variant of *couree*, 'intestines' (from Vulgar Latin *corāta*, from Latin *cor*, 'heart'), perhaps influenced by *cuir*, the French for 'skin' or 'hide'. Later the word was applied to the *quarry* while it was still on the hoof or wing, so that it came to mean the 'animal pursued' rather than bits of it dead.

quick

1. swift, rapid, speedy
2. living, alive

At the door, Logan gave Melissa a quick *kiss on the forehead and said he'd call her on Tuesday. And, of course, on Tuesday, he called, just as he'd said he would.*
(COSMOPOLITAN, April 1991)

Keen observation, coupled with a confident, amazingly quick *hand, formed the solid foundation of Church's art, and he honed his skills with constant practice, often under difficult conditions. . . Using thin paint, he* quickly *brushed in the zones of foreground, distance, and sky. . . He managed to make his brushstrokes 'read' immediately as indicators of the shape and texture of foliage, rocks, and distant hills. This was one of the keys to the speed with which he was able to work.*
(AMERICAN ARTIST, January 1994)

Thinking seriously about what to do about the country's problems (which young people are quick *to define, rightly, as failing schools and diminishing economic opportunity) is, in fact, all too rare.*
(WASHINGTON MONTHLY, Jan–Feb 1995)

Originally *quick* meant 'alive', coming from Old English *cwic(u)* and the unattested Germanic form *kwikwoz*, 'lively'. This is related to the still older, unattested *gwiwo-*, 'living', itself the root of Latin *vivus*, 'alive' and Greek *bios*, 'life'.

From the earliest uses of *quick* (dating back over a millennium), there has often been an implied contrast with the inanimate. A man's estate, for instance, might be divided into *quick* and *dead* goods, the *quick* being livestock. The contrast still lingers in the expression *the quick and the dead*, made familiar through older versions of the bible. Again, *quick flesh* was 'living' flesh. Used as a noun since the sixteenth century, the *quick* denoted the 'most tender flesh' of the body, that which was most alive to pain – hence the idiom to be *cut to the quick*. Vigour, energy and, particularly, rapid movement are evidence of life and it is from these concepts that subsequent senses of *quick* emerged, including the present day sense of 'swift,' which started to develop in the late thirteenth century.

American evangelist Billy Graham tells a story that brings together the old and new senses of *quick*. To the question, *What types of people are there in New York?* the answer is: *Just two – the quick and the dead.*

quixotic

excessively idealistic and unrealistic

When you fell in love at first sight, how long, let me ask, did it take you to become ready to fling every other consideration to the winds except that of obtaining possession of the loved one? . . . suppose your nature was Quixotic, *impulsive, altruistic, guileless . . . how long under these circumstances do you think you would reflect before you would decide on embracing what chance had thrown in your way?*
(Samuel Butler, THE WAY OF ALL FLESH, 1903)

In 1605 the Spanish author Cervantes published his novel DON QUIXOTE DE LA MANCHA, EL INGENIOSO HIDALGO, a satire on chivalric literature which was popular at the time. The story tells of the exploits of a poor knight who is so caught up in the idealism of the chivalric romances he reads that he feels impelled to roam the countryside righting wrongs. Don Quixote's overactive imagination totally transforms reality. He sees a flock of sheep as an army, for instance, and, in a particularly well-known episode, attacks windmills with his lance, thinking they are giants.

Others attempted to cash in on the book's popularity by continuing the knight's adventures, and this goaded Cervantes into writing a second volume which appeared in 1615. English translations appeared in 1612 and 1620 and the work also appeared in various languages. Within a few years references to the work started to appear in English literature. The line '*Thy head is full of windmills*', for instance, occurs in Massinger and Dekker's THE VIRGIN MARTYR as early as 1622. The English idioms *to have windmills in one's head* and *to tilt at windmills* both originate in the story.

Since then a variety of words have been derived from the gentle knight's name to express 'fervent but impractical idealism'. *Quixotism* appeared in the 1680s to be followed by *quixotry* and *quixoticism*. These are now defunct but the early nineteenth century adjective *quixotic*, applied first to the hopelessly idealistic knight and subsequently to people or actions with similar characteristics, is current in modern English.

For another word originating in foreign literature, see **gargantuan**.

recipe

a list of ingredients and instructions for making a dish

David makes a great fuss over his sauce for the spare ribs, a potent mixture of dark-brown sugar, soy sauce, wine vinegar, mustard and tomato purée. 'It's an age old secret recipe *handed down to the youngest son at Brookfield for six generations, ever since great-great grandad Archer came back from the Spanish Main,' he says, and Jill says, 'What he means is he got it off the back of a* recipe *card in Tesco's.'*
(Caroline Bone, THE AMBRIDGE BOOK OF COUNTRY COOKING, 1986)

Clinton had better study Harry Truman's advice: If you can't stand the heat, get out of the kitchen. Or, at least, find yourself some new recipes.
(THE PROGRESSIVE, January 1994)

Diamond combines strong bonds with simple stable structure: this recipe *accounts for its remarkable strength as a cutting tool, and its resistance to extremes of temperatures and pressure.*
(NEW SCIENTIST, 1983)

Recipe is the singular imperative form of the Latin verb *recipere*, 'to receive'. In the Middle Ages lists of the ingredients required to make up a medicinal compound were usually written in Latin and were invariably headed by the command *Recipe*, 'Take'. Even when lists were written in English, they were usually prefaced by the Latin imperative. The same convention was then applied to other similarly instructive lists, notably in cookery.

By the 1580s *recipe* was being applied to the prescription (itself the modern successor to *recipe* in a medical sense), and sometimes to the medicine prepared from it. The word gained its culinary extension towards the mid-eighteenth century. A study of the recipe for *Genoua-Bisket* in the entry for **biscuit** shows how the imperative *take* is much used in these contexts; the repetition shows how easy it was for the Latin *recipe* to develop the senses it did in earlier English.

regatta

a meeting, social as well as competitive, for yachting and rowing races

They were progressing famously, and John Bunsby was in high hope. He several times assured Mr. Fogg that they would reach Shanghai in time; to which that gentleman responded that he counted upon it. The crew set to work in good earnest, inspired by the reward to be gained. There was not a sheet which was not tightened; not a sail which was not vigorously hoisted; not a lurch could be charged to the man at the helm. They worked as desperately as if they were contesting in a Royal yacht regatta.
(Jules Verne, AROUND THE WORLD IN EIGHTY DAYS, 1873)

English travellers to Venice in the seventeenth century were sometimes fortunate enough to be present at a *regatta*, colourful gondola races along the Grand Canal. One report of the period called the *regatta* 'a costly and ostentatious triumph'. The word itself is from the Venetian dialect and probably derives from a Middle Italian verb *rigattare*, 'to contend', 'to struggle'.

Not to be outdone, other countries also started to hold *regattas*. The first in England was held on the Thames on 23 June 1775 and caused great excitement in polite society. The PUBLIC ADVERTISER, 24 May, predicted that the Regatta would '*keep at home many of our Nobility and wealthy Commoners*'.

rehearse

to practise in advance of performance

One day they got a special call for five o'clock, and there they learnt a thing which pleased Pauline, and made Petrova take an entirely different view of rehearsals. *They were to fly—*
(Noel Streatfeild, BALLET SHOES, 1936)

A quite opposite book is Elisabeth Valentine's Conceptual Issues in Psychology. Without so much as one cartoon, Valentine offers a brisk introduction to such perennials as the role of introspection, free will, the relation of psychology to physiology and some newer 'big questions', such as the role of humanistic psychology and computers in studying behaviour. She rehearses *the outlines of arguments efficiently and is not frightened of forcing students to grapple with tough material.*
(NEW SCIENTIST, 1983)

The first-night party was in the cupboard flat of Sergei Vlasov, one of Russia's leading actors. I spoke to his colleague Pyotr Semak. . . His mightiest part was the lead in The Possessed, an eight-hour event which took three years to rehearse.
(DAILY TELEGRAPH, 2 January 1995)

Old French *herce*, 'a harrow', 'a large rake', yielded the verb *hercer*, 'to harrow'. Sometimes lumpy ground would need harrowing again, and the term for this was *rehercer*. Over time this verb also developed the sense 'to repeat'. It was borrowed into Middle English as *rehercen* and meant 'to recite, to repeat aloud'. By the 1580s the verb had become *rehearse* and was being used in theatrical contexts with the modern sense 'to practise a performance'. Early uses of *rehearse* and *rehersal* (the spelling was not yet quite fixed) occur in Shakespeare's A MIDSUMMER NIGHT'S DREAM (1590) when Quince, Snug, Bottom, Flute, Snout and Starveling are busy preparing their 'comedy' PYRAMUS AND THISBY (Act III, scene 1):

Pat, pat; and here's a marvellous convenient place for our rehersal. *This green plot shall be our stage, this hawthorn brake our tiring-house; and we will do it in action, as we will do it before the Duke.*

Come sit down, every mother's son, and rehearse *your parts. Pyramus, you begin; when you have spoken your speech, enter into that brake; and so every one according to his cue.*

For another word from the same source, see **hearse**.

remorse

deep regret at a wrong action

So there you have the posish, and you can see why, as I left the dock a free man, remorse *gnawed at my vitals. In his twenty-fifth year, with life opening out before him and all that sort of thing, Oliver Randolph Sipperley had become a jail-bird, and it was all my fault. It was I who had dragged that fine spirit down into the mire, so to speak, and the question now arose, What could I do to atone?*

(P G Wodehouse, CARRY ON, JEEVES, 1925)

Remorse is very descriptive of the pangs of shame which continuously gnaw at the guilty conscience, for the word literally means 'a biting back'. The Latin verb *remordēre* primarily meant 'to bite again' (from *re-*, 'again' and *mordēre*, 'to bite'), though it was mostly used in poetical contexts in its figurative sense 'to torment', 'to vex'. Medieval Latin derived the noun *remorsus* from the past participle of this verb and coined the phrase *remorsus conscientiae*, 'anguish of conscience'. This was borrowed into Old French as *remors de conscience* and from there, still as a phrase, into English in the fourteenth century. The earliest record is in Chaucer's TROILUS AND CRISEYDE (c. 1385). The expression lingered until the early 1800s although, by the turn of the fifteenth century, *remorse* was already being used independently to convey exactly the same meaning.

rigmarole

1. a complicated, wandering statement
2. an unnecessarily complex set of procedures

At 10 a.m. went on the box of Miss Newton's brougham to the reopening of Mansel Grange Church after a good restoration. More than 25 clergy in surplices. The Bishop preached in the morning, the Archdeacon, Lord Saye and Sele, in the afternoon. It was difficult to say which was the worse sermon. The former was a screed, the latter a rigmarole, *but the* rigmarole *was more appropriate and more to the purpose than the screed.*

(Francis Kilvert, DIARY, 26 February 1878)

Six of the nine cuts on this LP are run-of-the-mill synth-pop pap. . . They are characterised by robotic drum-machine programming, occasional dramatic pauses and an absence of noteworthy instrumental solos. Cetera's usually expressive vocals are emtombed in electronic rigmarole. *This LP, like many others on the charts now, is a computer programmer's dream, a music lover's nightmare.*
(Mary Shaughnessy, PEOPLE'S WEEKLY, 11 August 1986)

Ragman was a game that was popular in the thirteenth century. It consisted of a set of character outlines, both good and bad, written in verse and inscribed on a scroll or *ragman roll*. A string and seal was fastened to each verse. When the scroll was rolled up, players would choose one of the strings and then read aloud the character description that chance had allotted to them, often occasioning great hilarity.

The source of the word *ragman* is obscure. It may be of French origin; the earliest English form is *rageman* (pronounced as three syllables with a hard *g*) and *Rageman le bon*, 'Rageman the good', is the first character to appear in a series of French verses dating from 1290. There is, however, an earlier recorded appearance of *Rageman* in English. In 1276 it was given as a nickname to a statute of Edward I by which commissions of enquiry were set up to investigate complaints of injustice. The juries' returns were written on parchment and bore pendent seals. Their appearance either suggested a 'ragged man' or a game of 'ragman roll'. Which came first – the statute or the game? The word was subsequently applied to other documents of similar appearance, in particular to a charter of 1291 in which the Scottish nobility pledged allegiance to Edward I.

Whatever the origins, it is considered that the game with its list of characters influenced the figurative application from the fourteenth century of both *Ragman* and *Ragman roll* to any sort of inventory or catalogue, especially a long register of names. And by the early sixteenth century Scottish English records the use of *ragman* for a 'long unintelligible discourse', an application apparently arising from the dislocated nature of a long list. A similar use was developing in English. Here, well over a century after it had ceased to be used for 'a list', *ragman roll* reappeared in the first half of the eighteenth century as *rig-my-role, riggmonrowle, rig-me-role* and finally *rigmarole* to describe 'a disconnected, long-winded discourse', 'an elaborate, contrived story' or, more generally, rhetoric of this kind:

Alfonso paused a minute – then begun
Some strange excuses for his late proceeding:
He would not justify what he had done,
To say the best, it was extreme ill-breeding;
But there were ample reasons for it, none
Of which he specified in this his pleading:
His speech was a fine sample, on the whole,
Of rhetoric, which the learn'd call 'rigmarole'.
(Lord Byron, DON JUAN, 1818)

The history of *rigmarole* has developed still further in more modern times, for in the middle of the twentieth century its use was extended to apply to 'a long, complicated procedure', 'a palaver'.

For other words originating in games, see **handicap** and **hazard**. For a word with similar meaning, see **palaver**.

rival

a competitor, an opponent

. . . there has survived in writing only the strange story that Thessalian women beat a rival *to death with wooden tortoises in a shrine to Aphrodite.*
(Colin Thubron, THE HILLS OF ADONIS, 1968)

We moored 200 metres off the coast of Little English Island, populated by noisy, busy sea lions preparing for mating with displays of rivalry *and pomp.*
(THE GUARDIAN, 14 January 1995)

I'll tell you what the nicest thing is about being the mother of a single parent – you're the only grandmother. You have no rival.
(GOOD HOUSEKEEPING, April 1995)

Rival is a watery word, its ultimate source being the Latin noun *rīvus*, meaning 'a stream', 'a brook'. From this came the adjective *rīvālis* which meant 'belonging to a brook'. This term was applied to those who 'belonged' to the brook in the sense that they lived near it and used it for their water supply. Before long *rīvālis* was used as a noun to mean 'one who shares a stretch of water with another', 'a near neighbour'. It is not difficult to imagine the kind of dispute that arose over use of the stream – rerouting it for irrigation, accusations of pollution, and the like. This notion of neighbours struggling bitterly against each other was taken up by playwrights and poets who applied it figuratively in the context of love, so that *rīvālis* came to mean 'a competitor in love, one who pursues the same mistress as another'. *Rival* was taken into French, initially with this Latin meaning, in the fifteenth century and into English in the last quarter of the sixteenth century.

◆ *Derive* and *rival* have *rīvus* in common. *Derive* comes from Latin *derīvāre*, 'to conduct water from its source', (from *de-*, 'away' and *rīvus*, 'brook') and hence the figurative applications with the general sense 'to draw, obtain or receive from a source'. The word entered Middle English as *deriven* by way of Old French *deriver*.◆

For other words connected with the river, see **river** itself and **arrive**.

river

1. a large stream of water flowing ultimately to the sea
2. any large flow, of blood, drink, lava, etc

She by the River *sate, and sitting there,*
She wept, and made it deeper by a teare.
(Robert Herrick, 1591–1674)

Never in his life had he seen a river *before – this sleek, sinuous, full-bodied animal, chasing and chuckling, gripping things with a gurgle and leaving them with a laugh. . . All was a-shake and a-shiver – glints and gleams and sparkles, rustle and swirl, chatter and bubble.*
(Kenneth Graham, THE WIND IN THE WILLOWS, 1908)

From *rīpa*, meaning 'riverbank', Latin derived the adjective *rīpārius* 'belonging to a bank' to describe land or a dwelling place beside a river. It is assumed that in time the Vulgar Latin noun *rīpāria* evolved to denote land thus situated. The Spanish, Portuguese and Italian words that derived from this noun, *ribera*, *ribeira* and *riviera* respectively, all mean 'strand' or 'shore'. Initially the Old French term *rivière* had the same meaning, but this was then extended to refer to the water course as well. When Middle English borrowed the word in the second half of the thirteenth century, it absorbed this dual meaning, although *river* ceased to refer to the 'bank' after the fifteenth century. In Modern English riverside buildings – castles and houses, pubs and tea-rooms – are described as being *on* the river, a throwback to the time when a river was also a shore.

See **arrive**, and also **rival** for those who lived on the river bank.

robot

1. an automaton, a machine that automatically carries out the tasks of a human
2. a person who behaves coldly, unthinkingly, mechanically

They may be slower and less exciting than Astaire and Rogers, but two robots *being developed in The Telford Institute at Salford University are light on their wheels. Already Fred and Ginger, as they are nick-named, can pick up and carry around objects, while avoiding obstacles. All the mini-*robots *have potentially valuable applications, so outside companies are keenly interested in the Salford research, which has a £220,000 grant from the Engineering and Physical Sciences Research Council.*
(THE TIMES, 18 October 1994)

. . . my attempts to move economically round the kitchen produced a curious tottering gait reminiscent of the robot *in Woody Allen's film* SLEEPER. . .
(WEEKEND TELEGRAPH, 22 October 1994)

The modern nightmare of mechanical beings that gradually develop reasoning and emotions before destroying their creators was originally the theme of a play. R. U. R. (ROSSUM'S UNIVERSAL ROBOTS), written in 1920 by the Czeck playwright Karel Čapek, was performed in London and New York in 1923. Čapek derived his word *robot* from a Czech word *robota* which means 'forced labour, drudgery'. '*You see,*' Čapek wrote in his play, '*the* robots *have no interest in life. They have no enjoyments.*' In his play, the robots move towards becoming humans by developing emotions and ultimately overthrowing their masters. The word also came to be used in the converse direction: Čapek's description is seen to be just as true of people who spend their waking hours at repetitive tasks on a production line, with the result that figuratively the word was equally applicable to them. So in modern English a *robot* is a passionless, dehumanised human, as well as a highly sophisticated automaton that can be programmed to perform routine repetitive chores normally carried out by a human being.

The science of the design, building and application of such robots is known as *robotics* and was the coinage in the early 1940s of another writer altogether, the American immigrant scientist Isaac Asimov, a well-known author of popular science and science fiction. Asimov was also responsible for *robotical*, the adjective *robotic* and the noun *roboticist*, meaning 'an expert in the science of robotics.'

robust

strong, resilient, forceful

I am better... but I intend to take care of myself... My mother often tells me I go at things too hard. Besides, I don't really get

enough air and exercise – without which one can never be truly robust.
(Anthony Powell, A BUYER'S MARKET, 1952)

Good robust *friends and therapists don't probe and analyse endlessly, ignoring your instinct for privacy. . . They're happy to be life belts and happy when you swim away on your own. You'll know them when you meet them.*
(Libby Purves in GOOD HOUSEKEEPING, November 1994)

It is also wrong to assume that new, reproduction pieces are more robust *than antiques. Often antiques are better built (they would not have survived otherwise), dowelled, not glued, and in well-seasoned timber. This goes especially for Tudor and Jacobean furniture, made of solid oak.*
(WEEKEND TELEGRAPH, 21 January 1995)

The unattested Indo-European root *reudh*, meaning 'red' is the ultimate source of *rōbus*, an old Latin word for a type of oak tree with very hard, reddish coloured wood. The mighty tree suggested great power and so *rōbus* (later *rōbur*) was also used to mean 'strength'. Etymologically, therefore, the adjective *rōbustus*, which is derived from it, meant 'strong and solid as an oak'. The word was borrowed into English, possibly by way of French *robuste*, in the sixteenth century to describe a person who was 'vigorous and hardy', being 'of a sturdy constitution'.

◆ *Rōborāre*, a Latin derivative of *rōbur* meant 'to strengthen'. When the intensive *com-* was added it yielded *corrōborāre*, 'to strengthen, to invigorate', which was borrowed into English as *corroborate* in the sixteenth century. The sense 'to strengthen an opinion or argument' dates from the early eighteenth century.

rostrum

a dais, a platform or stand for public speaking, conducting, auctioneering, etc.

As I feared the big Yank collared me as I climbed down from the rostrum.
'Excuse me, sir.'
'Eh?'
The rotund weatherbeaten face of an outdoor man gazed reproachfully down at me. He was the size of a bus.
'You missed seeing my bid, sir. For Lord Nelson's father's letter. I've come a long way—'
(Jonathan Gash, FIREFLY GADROON, 1982)

Rōstrum in Latin meant 'beak', being derived from the verb *rodere*, 'to gnaw'. Metaphorically, it was applied to the prow of a ship since the shape was considered reminiscent of a bird's bill.

The Romans had a colony at Antium (now Anzio on the west coast of Italy), a place notorious for its piracy. When it revolted, the Romans returned in force to re-establish the colony in 338 BC. Antium was deprived of all its ships and their 'beaks' were taken to the Forum in Rome where they were used to decorate the orators' platform. For this reason the stand, and the area in the Forum where it was situated, was known as the *rōstra* (the plural of *rōstrum*). *Rostra* is found in English from the sixteenth century onwards in classical translations or with specific reference to the platform in Rome, but not until the second half of the eighteenth century was the singular form, *rostrum*, adopted into English to denote a 'church pulpit' or a 'dais set up for public speaking'.

◆ *Rōdere*, 'to gnaw' is evident in *corrode* and *erode*, both meaning 'to gnaw away', and also in *rodent*, a nineteenth century zoological coinage (from New Latin *Rodentia*, from the stem *rodent*).◆

sack

1. a large bag of coarse material
2. to plunder, to spoil
3. to dismiss

'. . . he spoilt a spade plate.'

'And he were sacked *for that? For one spade plate?'*

'Not on its own. He tried to pass it off for good. And he argued with Mister Hattersley.'

'It's still not much to get the sack *for.'*

(Roy Hattersley, THE MAKER'S MARK, 1990)

Some postworkers take a handful of dog biscuits with them on their round; others adjust the postal sack *so that it covers vital organs before opening the garden gate.*

(WEEKEND TELEGRAPH, 25 February 1995)

This word is Semitic in origin and has made its way into all the languages of eastern and western Europe from the Hebrew *saq*, meaning 'sackcloth'.

The sackcloth of the Old Testament was made of animal hair, especially that of a goat. It was usually black in colour and always coarse in texture. This cheap, hardwearing cloth was worn by herdsmen but was also used to make grain bags with so that *saq* also meant 'sack': the word is used in this sense in Genesis 42, for instance, where Joseph tests his brothers by placing a gold cup in one of their sacks of grain.

The term was taken into Greek as *sakkos* and then into Latin as *saccus*, still meaning both 'sackcloth' and 'sack'. From here it was extensively borrowed into other languages. Old English had *sacc* which became *sak* or *sack* in Middle English.

Sack with the sense 'pillage', 'spoil', dates from around the mid sixteenth century and derives from French *sac*, which in turn comes from Italian *sacco*, 'plunder'. Many authorities consider that this Italian word and *sacco* meaning 'bag' (from Latin *saccus*) are one and the same and suggest that its use in this context arose through the stuffing of spoil into sacks in order to cart it away. In support of this contention, the Italian and French phrases *mettere a sacco* and *mettre à sac* both mean 'to plunder' and have the literal sense 'to put in a bag'. The sixteenth-century English equivalent, a direct borrowing of the French, was *to put to sack* or *to put to/onto the sack*. The verb *to sack* also dates from the sixteenth century.

Sack in the sense of 'dismissal from one's occupation' has been current in English in the idiomatic phrases *to give someone the sack* or *to get the sack* since the nineteenth century but *den zac krijen*, 'to get the sack', already existed in Middle Dutch and it was known in French from the seventeenth century. The usual explanation offered for the expression is that workmen would leave their tools in a bag at their place of work. If a master wanted to dismiss a bad workman, he would hand over his sack of tools to show that he shouldn't come back.

◆ Latin *saccelus*, a diminutive of *saccus*, gave Old French *sachel*, 'a small bag'. This was borrowed into Middle English, becoming *satchel* around the turn of the seventeenth century.

Sachet is a French diminutive of *sac*, 'bag, sack', which was borrowed into English in the nineteenth century.◆

salad

a dish mainly of green vegetables

Then he [father] rushed into the room, donned his skullcap and found the place in the prayer book.

'Is the food spoilt?'

'Is it ever? Isn't it always gefüllte fish on Shabbas?'

'I wonder who started that particular tradition? Do you suppose Moses' wife inflicted cold fried fish cakes on him every Friday evening?' Father lifted the lid off a tureen and peered inside. 'And salad*!'*

'Now don't start grumbling. You'll put the children off. I've made it in a dressing just how you like it, especially for you;'

'I don't like salad *eith. . .'*

David was silenced by one of my mother's terrible stares.

(Michele Guinness, CHILD OF THE COVENANT, 1985)

Salad *vegetables are not all equal when it comes to the calorie count. Runner beans, mushrooms, peppers, radish and tomatoes are five calories or less per ounce. But pulses such as kidney beans, chickpeas and sweetcorn are more than 30 calories per ounce.*

(DAILY MAIL, 23 April 1994)

She was suddenly homesick for the salads *back home, a few petals of soft green lettuce, and a hard-boiled egg with buttercup centre, a sliver of home-cured ham and a sprig of scallion.*

(Clare Boylan, LOVE WITH A GENTLEMAN, in GOOD HOUSEKEEPING, April 1995)

The salad *is the glory of every French dinner and the disgrace of most in England* (Richard Ford, GATHERINGS FROM SPAIN, 1846). It seems that the English cannot get anything right when it comes to appetising food, not even dishes where no cooking is required. The secret must lie in the dressing. The Romans ate raw vegetables which they flavoured with salty dressings. Cato enjoyed cabbage served in this way and the Emperor Tiberius had a passion for cucumbers. Apicius, a fourth-century cookery writer, gives a recipe for cucumber salad with a dressing of pepper, pennyroyal, honey, liquamen (a type of salty fish sauce rather like anchovy essence) and vinegar. Roman fondness for salads extended into the winter months. For instance, Columella, who wrote on agricultural matters in the first century, preserved lettuce leaves by pickling them in brine and vinegar (Brothwell, FOOD IN ANTIQUITY, 1969).

The Vulgar Latin for the salad dishes over which the Romans drooled was *salāta* (a shortening of *herba salāta*, 'salted greens', from the unattested verb *salāre*, 'to salt', from *sāl*, 'salt'). This became *salada* in Provençal and *salade* in Old French and then Middle English. An early recipe from FORME OF CURY (1390) runs:

> Salat. *Take persel. sawge, garlec . . . waische hem clene . . . and myng hem wel with rawe oile, lay on vyneger and salt, and serue it forth.*

The word, then, entered the language but not, by popular repute, the culinary flair – although Sidney Smith (1771–1845) seemed to know what he was doing:

SIDNEY SMITH'S RECIPE FOR SALAD*:*
To make this condiment, your poet begs
The pounded yellow of two hard-boiled eggs;
Two boiled potatoes, passed through
kitchen-seive,
Smoothness and softness to the salad give;
Let onion atoms lurk within the bowl,
And, scarce-suspected, animate the whole.
Of mordant mustard add a single spoon,
Distrust the condiment that bites so soon;

But deem it not, thou man of herbs, a fault,
To add a double quantity of salt.
And, lastly, o'er the flavoured compound toss
A magic soup-spoon of anchovy sauce.
Oh, green and glorious! Oh, herbaceous treat!
'Twould tempt the dying anchorite to eat;
Back to the world he'd turn his fleeting soul,
And plunge his fingers in the salad bowl!
Serenely full, the epicure would say,
Fate cannot harm me, I have dined today.

◆ Other salty culinary terms deriving from Latin *sāl*, 'salt', are:

salami (Italian plural of *salame*, 'salted pork', from *salare*, 'to salt', from unattested Vulgar Latin *sālare*, 'to salt')

sauce (Middle English through Old French from Latin *salsa*, feminine of *salsus*, 'salted')

sausage (Middle English *sausige*, through Old Norman French *saussiche*, from Late Latin *salsīcia*, from Latin *salsīcius*, 'prepared by salting', from *salsus*, 'salted') ◆

See also **salary**.

salary

remuneration for work, a wage, usually paid monthly

The Pope is offering a bouncing perk. Vatican staff, who include 3,400 lay persons, 250 of them lay female persons, may apply for a baby bonus. Not to be sneezed at, equivalent to two thirds of a month's salary *for each pregnancy, but any priests or nuns applying will doubtless be viewed with suspicion.*
(GUARDIAN, 2 February 1994)

In the Queen's Ballroom every night there are 12 'Gentlemen Hosts' employed by Cunard to act as dancing partners for the single: silver-haired retired American men for the most part, who receive bed and board but no salary *for their efforts.*
(WEEKEND TELEGRAPH, 11 February 1995)

These days salt is plentiful and cheap and therefore taken for granted. In ancient times, however, this was not the case. Salt, which was essential to enhance the flavour of food and to preserve it, was a luxury and had to be imported into many regions of the Roman empire. At one time Roman soldiers were given a *salārium* (from Latin *sāl*, 'salt'), an allowance with which to buy salt. The word was then applied to the soldier's pay and later extended into civilian use. The related expression *to be worth one's salt* (that is, one's wages) derives from this ancient practice but, curiously, only appears to date back to the early nineteenth century. *Salary* came into English in the fourteenth century from Anglo-French *salarie*.

For other words derived from *sāl*, see **salad**.

sandwich

two slices of bread with a filling between

At the restaurant, sitting on a high stool before a pine counter, he choked over an egg sandwich *made with thick crumby slices of a bread that had no personality to it.*
(Sinclair Lewis, OUR MR. WRENN, THE ROMANTIC ADVENTURES OF A GENTLE MAN, 1914)

What else would a true Englishman put in his sandwich but cold roast beef? According to Grosley (LONDRES, 1770), who supplied an account of the origin of the word, this traditional fare, wedged between slices of toast, was offered to John Montagu, 4th Earl of

Sandwich (1718–92), a compulsive gambler who spent entire days at the tables without stopping for food or rest. Grosley was in London in 1765 when he first came across the word, but it is recorded earlier in the journal of the writer Edward Gibbon. After a visit to the Cocoa Tree, one of London's fashionable clubs where men of society could gamble for very high stakes, Gibbon wrote in his Journal:

I dined at the Cocoa Tree... That respectable body ... affords every evening a sight truly English. Twenty or thirty ... of the first men in the kingdom, ... supping at little tables ... upon a bit of cold meat, or a Sandwich.
(24 November 1762)

To trace the word back still further, the estimable Earl took his title from *Sandwich,* a town in Kent and one of the medieval Cinq Ports which defended the south-east coast. Situated about two miles up river, Sandwich ceased to be a port in the sixteenth century when the harbour silted up. Its name derives from Old English *Sandwic,* meaning 'sand-village'.

For a game played at the Cocoa Tree, see **hazard**. For the early history of the club, see **chocolate**.

sarcasm

sharp, wounding, bitter comment

The blatant soldier often convulsed whole files by his biting sarcasms *aimed at the tall one.*
(Steven Crane, THE RED BADGE OF COURAGE, 1895)

Sarcastic humour or comment is intended to wound. This is evident from the savage etymology of the word *sarcasm.* The ancient Greeks had a verb *sarcazein* (from *sarx,* 'flesh'), which meant 'to tear flesh like dogs'. When they applied the term figuratively it had the sense 'to bite the lips in fury', 'to sneer'. From this came the noun *sarkasmos* which meant 'a barbed comment', 'a biting taunt'. Late Latin had *sarcasmus* which was taken directly into English in the second half of the sixteenth century as a personification of a cutting, scoffing spirit, 'a figure called Sarcasmus'. In his ANATOMY OF MELANCHOLY (1621), for instance, Robert Burton writes: *Many are of so petulant a spleene, and haue that figure Sarcasmus so often in their mouths...*

In the first quarter of the seventeenth century English borrowed the word again, this time from French as *sarcasme.* It meant 'a biting remark' and it was often found in the plural as *sarcasmes* or *sarcasms. Sarcasm* as a general noun dates from the second half of the nineteenth century.

For a word from the same stem, see **sarcophagus**. For a word with a similar meaning, see **sardonic**.

sarcophagus

an ornate stone coffin or tomb

A grand piano stood massively in a corner; with dark gleams on the flat surfaces like a sombre and polished sarcophagus.
(Joseph Conrad, THE HEART OF DARKNESS, 1902)

This is a word to make your flesh creep: Greek corpses were encased in stone coffins which had the reputation of devouring the contents.

Sarkophagos was the name the Greeks gave to a type of limestone which they cut from quarries near Assus, a city in Troas, Asia Minor. The name is a compound derived from *sark-,* stem of *sarx,* 'flesh' and *-phagos*, from *phagein*, 'to eat', and means, quite literally, 'flesh-eating'.

In Philemon Holland's translation of Pliny's NATURAL HISTORY (1601) we discover the reputed properties of the stone. It seems that '*within the space of forty daies it is knowne for certaine to consume the bodies of the dead which are bestowed therein*'. Those laid to rest in a *sarkophagos* could therefore expect a speedy decomposition. The word, promoted by Holland's translation, came into English in the seventeenth century by way of Latin *sarcophagus*. The first references are to the stone only, subsequently to the coffin.

◆ The Greek stem *sark-* is also evident in words such as *sarcoma*, *sarcoplasm* and *sarcasm*.◆

For a word sharing the same root, see **sarcasm**.

sardonic

cynically mocking, scornful

She laughed sardonically. *'Father Payne, recognised at last. Whatever next?'*
(Roy Hattersley, THE MAKER'S MARK, 1990)

What of the superstar? Eliminating practically all of the Ron Moody Jewish caricature, Pryce plays Fagin cleverly as a piratical swashbuckler long gone raddled, sozzled and rancid; his sardonic *veneer and Tommy Cooper conjuring tricks thinly disguising his self-loathing.*
(THE TIMES, 9 December 1994)

A little bit of classical confusion surrounds this word. The ancient world was familiar with a poisonous herb which grew on the island of Sardinia. If eaten, it was supposed to cause facial spasms and contortions which looked like a bout of hideous laughter. Dryden's verse translation of Virgil (1697) refers to the horrible spectacle thus:

May I become. . .
Rough as a Burr, deform'd like him who chaws
Sardinian Herbage to contract his Jaws.

The Greeks called the plant *Sardonios*, meaning 'Sardinian'. Greek already had a word *sardanios* which meant 'bitter' or 'scornful'. However, the similarity in sound and the association of a scornful expression with the leer of a person under the influence of the Sardinian herb brought about a substitution of *sardonios* for *sardanios* in late Greek. From this came the Latin expression *Sardonius risus*, 'bitter laugh'.

The first English uses in the sixteenth century refer to *Sardonian laughter* and *Sardonian smiles*, a translation of the Latin through French. Robert Green, for instance, in his romance MENAPHON (1589) has the lines:

Haue you fatted me so long with Sardenian smiles, *that. . . I might perish in your wiles?*

During the sixteenth century the French *sardonien* became *sardonique* (from the unattested Latin adjective *sardonicus*, instead of *sardonius*) which influenced the seventeenth-century English forms *Sardonick* and *Sardanique*. The modern spelling *sardonic* emerged from these in the early eighteenth century, discarding at the same time the capital letter that properly denotes an adjective of place in English.

The Latin *risus Sardonicus* has been retained as a medical expression to denote the involuntary and rather disagreeable grin worn, for instance, by sufferers of tetanus where the facial muscles are in spasm.

scandal

1. a public outrage, disgrace
2. malicious gossip

This morning [name rubbed out] came privately to church at 10.30 with [name rubbed out] to be churched after the birth of her son, which took place three months after her wedding. This has been a great scandal *and grief to us.*
(Francis Kilvert, DIARY, Sunday, 5 October 1873)

One should never make one's debut with a scandal. *One should reserve that to give an interest to one's old age.*
(Oscar Wilde, THE PICTURE OF DORIAN GRAY, 1891)

After the whole sad story had been recounted and a decent silence had been allowed for those who had fallen in the great scandal, *Nicholas said, with his usual fairness, 'One feeds sorry for the Minister. It was the lying, of course. I don't suppose anyone cares who the fellow jumped into bed with.'*
(John Mortimer, PARADISE POSTPONED, 1985)

One man's scandal *is another man's burning conviction.*
(Arts and Books, DAILY TELEGRAPH, 4 March 1995)

*In the New Testament, we find that people were offended by Jesus. He is described as the rock of '*skandalon*' – He's a real, solid* skandaliser *(Romans. 9:33)! He* skandalised *the Pharisees, everybody in His home town and some of His disciples so much that they left Him (Matthew 13:57; 15:12; John 6:61,66). He* skandalised *even His closest disciples (Matthew 26:31) . . . If Jesus could offend so many, how much more will imperfect humans accomplish!*
(Duncan Watkinson, FRONTLINE INTERNATIONAL, March/April 1995)

Greek had an old word, *skandalon*, 'trap', which was figuratively applied to mean 'a moral snare or stumbling block'. Late Latin borrowed it as *scandalum* and used it in ecclesiastical contexts to denote 'that which causes one to fall into sin', a meaning it retained when it was taken into Old French as *escandle*. From there the word followed two routes into English, one arriving at *scandal* and the other at *slander*.

On the first it was borrowed into early Middle English as *scandle* with the ecclesiastical sense of 'dishonour brought to the Christian faith by the unseemly conduct of its adherents'. Its appearance was brief, however, and exclusive to the ANCREN RIWLE (c. 1225), a devotional manual for religious recluses. Then, in the second half of the sixteenth century, it was re-adopted either directly from Latin or through a revised French form *scandale*.

Scandale had been introduced into French as a specifically religious term because the Old French *escandle* had gone astray – it had developed variants, *escandre* and *esclandre*, and the additional sense of 'calumny, malicious falsehood'. These variants also started to appear in Middle English from the late thirteenth century as *sclaundre* and *slaundre* and similary denoted 'false reports maliciously spoken to injure a person's reputation' – in other words, *slander*.

scapegoat

1. a sacrifice that bears the sin of the people
2. someone who singlehandedly is made to take shared blame

. . . Mr Sproat's hopes of keeping a low profile were wrecked by the fiasco over the D-Day celebrations. A former officer in the Royal Green Jackets, he had led the way in persuading Mr Major to make it an occasion of national celebration. Though he stressed his intention to mobilise the nation

to pay tribute to the heroism and sacrifice of D-Day, his enthusiasm for the celebrations helped to draw accusations of 'frivolity'. In the Whitehall buck-passing exercise Mr Sproat is being lined up as the scapegoat. (TELEGRAPH, 22 April 1994)

But what makes long-range shooting a unique sport is the role of the coach. In no other sport is the partnership between coach and athlete so crucial to immediate success. The coach is sage, guru, weather cock, servant and scapegoat *rolled into one.* (DAILY TELEGRAPH, 11 October 1994)

The most solemn day of the Jewish religious calendar is that of Yom Kippur, the Day of Atonement when, in the Judaism of the Old Testament, animal sacrifices were offered to atone for sin and reconcile the people to God. On this day alone was the high priest permitted to bring the blood of sacrifice into the holy of holies, directly into the Lord's presence. First a bullock was sacrificed as a sin-offering for the priest and his house. Next two goats were presented before the Lord and lots were cast to determine which of them should be slaughtered as the sin-offering for the people. When this sacrifice was complete the high priest laid his hands upon the remaining goat and confessed all the sins of the people over it before finally casting the creature out into the desert, where it ran off, symbolically taking the sins of the people away with it.

This goat has been called the *scapegoat* since Tyndale's translation of the Pentateuch in 1530, *scape* being an archaic variant of *escape*, the unstressed initial vowel having been omitted. The term arises from Tyndale's rendering of a particular word, *Azazel*. This is found only in the directions given for the Day of Atonement in Leviticus 16, where it occurs in verses 8, 10 and 26. Tyndale, along with other translators before him, understood *Azazel* as meaning 'the goat that goes away', from 'ēz, 'goat' and '*azal*, 'departs' or 'escapes', hence *scapegoat*: *And Aaron cast lottes ouer the.ii. gootes: one lotte for the Lorde, and another for a* scape-goote (verse 8).

This is not the only interpretation, however. Other scholars have deliberated long over *Azazel* and have come up with various of alternative explanations. Some point to similarities with the Arabic verb *'azala*, 'to remove', and say it is an infinitive with the sense 'in order to remove'. Others suggest it means 'a lonely place' or 'a precipice'. The translators of the New English Bible have taken this view. Their rendition of verse 8, for instance, reads: He shall cast lots over the two goats, one to be for the Lord and the other for the Precipice. The majority considers that *Azazel* derives from '*āzaz* 'to be strong' and '*ēl*, 'God' and is the name of a demon which prowled the wilderness. They point out in support of their theory that wherever it is used the name counterbalances that of the Lord. The Revised Standard Version of the Bible is deemed correct in its translation of verse 8: *Aaron shall cast lots upon the two goats; one lot for the Lord and the other lot for* Azazel.

While none of the interpretations of *Azazel* changes the essential import of the passage in Leviticus at all, they do cast into doubt the correctness of the translation *scapegoat*, although, interestingly enough, the term has been chosen for the widely acclaimed New International Version.

In English early uses of the word were strictly confined to religious comment. Not until the first half of the nineteenth century was it applied in secular contexts to denote one who, like the biblical scapegoat, shoulders all the blame for the misdeeds of others. Today, the word frequently appears in the press as the plaintive cry of politicians reprimanded or dismissed because of unpopular government policies.

For other words concerning sacrifices and offerings, see **anathema** and **holocaust**.

scavenger

a human or animal that searches through what others have discarded for useful items or food

The following list completes, I believe, the terrestrial fauna: a fly (Olfersia) living on the booby, and a tick which must have come here as a parasite on the birds; a small brown moth, belonging to a genus that feeds on feathers; a beetle (Quedius) and a woodlouse from beneath the dung; and lastly, numerous spiders, which I suppose prey on these small attendants and scavengers *of the water-fowl.*
(Charles Darwin, THE VOYAGE OF THE BEAGLE, 1839)

In the Middle Ages the governing authorities of London, and many other English towns, protected their own merchants by imposing a tax upon goods offered for sale within their boundaries by any trader coming from outside. The tax was called the *scavage*, derived from Anglo-French *scawage* which in turn came from Old Northern French *escawage*, 'inspection', and *escauwer*, 'to inspect' (whose Germanic origins were also responsible for English 'show').

In Middle English the officers who collected the levy were known as *scavagers* but, in the sixteenth century, the variant form *scavenger* appeared and took precedence. (This insertion of an *n* in words ending in *-ger* occurred in other words in late Middle English: *messenger*, *harbinger* and *passenger* among them.) During the sixteenth century the *scavengers* were also given the extra responsibility of keeping the streets clean and, when the tax was no longer levied, they remained as street cleaners. The term for one who did this unappealing but necessary work was soon more widely applied to any person or creature who lived by what others discard.

scruple

a moral hesitation over a course of action

While it was in progress, some of the Spaniards observed what appeared to be a door recently plastered over. It was a common rumour that Montezuma still kept the treasures of his father, King Axayacatl, in this ancient palace. The Spaniards, acquainted with this fact, felt no scruple *in gratifying their curiosity by removing the plaster. As was anticipated, it concealed a door. On forcing this, they found the rumour was no exaggeration. They beheld a large hall filled with rich and beautiful stuffs, articles of curious workmanship of various kinds, gold and silver in bars and in the ore, and many jewels of value. It was the private hoard of Montezuma.*
(William Hickling Prescott, THE HISTORY OF THE CONQUEST OF MEXICO, 1843)

'A Scruple *is a great trouble of mind proceeding from a little motive*,' wrote Jeremy Taylor in DUCTOR DUBITANTIUM (1660), his book of guidance on questions of morality and conscience. In Latin a *scrūpulus* was 'a tiny pebble', the word being a diminutive of *scrūpus*, 'a rough stone'. When the smallest pebble falls into a person's shoe it is the cause of great discomfort, just as a seed of doubt or uncertainty over an ethical point brings mental torment. The word was used in this figurative way in Latin and, as such, came into English through French in the sixteenth century.

Back-formations

English commonly makes a verb from an existing noun. One of the ways this happens is by back-formation: a new word is created from another by the removal of what is perceived to be an affix.

For example, *burglar* was not formed, as one might suppose, from the verb *burgle* and the agent suffix *-ar*. On the contrary the verb, which only appeared in the second half of the nineteenth century, is a back-formation of *burglar*, a noun in use since the fifteenth century. The verb was simply created by the removal of the assumed suffix *-ar*. In the same way the verb *scavenge*, which dates back principally to the nineteenth century, is a back-formation of the late sixteenth-century noun *scavenger*. Other examples of a similar kind are:

eavesdrop (17th cent) from *eavesdropper* (15th cent)
peddle (mid-17th cent) from *pedlar* (14th cent)
swindle (18th cent) from *swindler* (18th cent)
edit (late 18th cent) from *editor* (mid-17th cent)
stage-manage (1870s) from *stage-manager* (early 19th cent)

Many verbs are back-formations of other kinds of nouns: *injury* (14th cent) yielded *injure* (16th cent) and *enthuse* is a nineteenth-century American back-formation from *enthusiasm* (16th cent). To take a modern example, most people would guess correctly that *televise* was derived from *television*. It is a back-formation modelled on verbs like *revise* which end in *-(v)ise* and whose related nouns end in *-ision*, like *revision*.

Although most of the words which are formed in this way are verbs, nouns and adjectives are also created:

greed (17th cent) from *greedy* (10th cent)
haze (18th cent) from *hazy* (17th cent)
gullible (19th cent) from *gullibility* (18th cent)

Other languages increase their stock of words in a similar fashion. English *democrat* is a borrowing from French *democrate*. This in turn is a back-formation of the adjective *democratique*, 'democratic'. Indeed, the word was modelled on the earlier *aristocrate*, a popular back-formation of *aristocratique* at the time of the French Revolution.

Occasionally old, forgotten words are resurrected as back-formations. Today the negative forms only are familiar for *uncouth, unkempt, unruly*. For humorous effect, some authors resuscitate by a process of back-formation the Old English and Middle English adjectives *couth, kempt* and *ruly*. See entries for **uncouth, unkempt, unruly** and **Negative Prefixes** (page 254).

serendipity

1. the gift of making fortunate discoveries
2. the happy find itself

THE LAWS OF SERENDIPITY
1 In order to discover anything, you must be looking for something
2 If you wish to make an improved product, you must already be engaged in making an inferior one.
(ANON)

SOME UNEXPECTED DISCOVERIES
Just over two hundred years ago, in 1754 to be precise, Horace Walpole coined the word 'serendipity' *which has now come to be accepted into our language. The word, which is derived from the ancient name for Ceylon, is defined as 'the faculty of making happy and unexpected discoveries by accident'. Before I go on to discuss the work of translating the Gospels I feel I must mention some of the 'happy and unexpected discoveries' which I made in the translation of the Epistles. . . There are naturally many more happy and unexpected discoveries which I made over the years, some of them perhaps merely revealing how superficial must have been my previous knowledge of the New Testament Letters. But since this is a personal testimony, I have felt it right to mention some of the things which came to me with fresh and startling clarity.*
(J B Phillips, RING OF TRUTH, A TRANSLATOR'S TESTIMONY, 1967)

In all scientific research, the researcher may or may not find what he is looking for – indeed his hypothesis may be demolished – but he is certain to learn something new, which may be and often is more important than what he had hoped to learn. This is the principle of serendipity. *It is so invariant that it can be considered to be an empirically established Natural Law.*
(Richard Boyle quoting Robert Heinlein in his report before the House Select Committee on Aging, from SERENDIB, July–August 1991)

On that magical morning, as we descended towards the tiny airstrip in the middle of the Serengeti, a hot-air balloon was drifting into the distance and below us a zebra lay unpeturbed beneath a black and white windsock fluttering in the breeze – serendipity *I think they call it.*
(GOOD HOUSEKEEPING, April 1995)

This happy coinage to describe 'the knack of making fortunate and surprising discoveries' was from the pen of Horace Walpole. In a letter to Horace Mann, written on 28 January 1754, Walpole described how he came to invent the word and what exactly he meant by it, explaining that Mann would 'understand it better by the derivation than by the definition':

I once read a silly fairy tale, called The Three Princes of Serendip*; as their highnesses travelled, they were always making discoveries, by accidents and sagacity, of things which they were not in quest of: for instance, one of them discovered that a mule blind of the right eye had travelled the same road lately, because the grass was eaten only on the left side, where it was worse than on the right – now do you understand* Serendipity?

The fairytale itself dates back to the mid-sixteenth century. It was written by an Italian, Christoforo Armeno and was included in a collection of stories based on travel.

Serendip, on the other hand, has an ancient history. Around the year AD150, Graeco-Egyptian mathematician and geographer Ptolemy (c. AD100–170) charted the first map of the island of Sri Lanka, which he called *Sila-Diva*. Ptolemy's work was extensively referred to in the Islamic world and his maps greatly assisted Arabic seafarers plying the trade route to China. These sailors came to refer to the island as *Sarandib*, which became *Serendip*, or *Serendib*.

Serendipity was not much used until the twentieth century when it became a favourite title of compilers of anthologies inviting their readers to take a literary lucky-dip. Ivor Brown mentions a *Serendipity* bookshop in Bloomsbury, London, a name that invites sagacious browsing.

Even so, the sense in modern English often deviates from that intended by Walpole, so that *serendipity* is seen not so much as a gift for discovery but the unexpected discovery itself. The derived adjective is *serendipitous*.

Precise timing

It is unusual to be able to date very precisely the first use of a new word. Sometimes it can be done, however. *Sputnik* entered the English language (and many other languages throughout the world) on the day it was launched in 1957.

TIME magazine is innovatory in its use of language and amongst the many words that have first seen light of day on a specific occasion and subsequently survived some twenty years are: *heightism* (1971), *televangelist* (1973), *roadies* (1973), *petropolitics* (1973), *chillout* (1973). *megadisaster* (1976), *superbug* (1977)

Of course TIME magazine is not the only experimenter with language. Many others have done the same and some of their neologisms have gained acceptance. The poet Browning, for instance, seems to have been the first to use *artistry* in THE RING AND THE BOOK (1868–9). See also **serendipity**.

There is a nice story about the word *quiz* that dates its origin to one twenty-four hour period. A certain Mr Daly, the manager of a Dublin theatre, bet that he could get the whole city talking about an unknown word within one day. He won his bet by having the letters *quiz* written on walls throughout the city, so provoking everyone into asking what it meant.

It may be a nice story but, sad to say, it is probably not true. The only corroborating evidence dates it to 1791 – some 12 years after the first recorded use of the word.

Shrovetide

the three days before Ash Wednesday

After Christmas, festivities continued with Plough Monday, Candlemas and St Valentine's Day. Shrovetide *was a three-day orgy of football, violent without teams or rules, cock-threshing, and bingeing on rich foods forbidden in Lent. 'A day of great gluttony, surfeiting and drunkenness,' was how one disapproving Protestant preacher described it in 1570. Worn out and hungover, the revellers returned to the very straight and narrow path of Lent on Ash Wednesday, having their heads daubed with ashes and water.*
(Ronald Hutton, THE RISE AND FALL OF MERRY ENGLAND, 1994)

With its emphasis on the Church service which follows the race, Olney's lenten tradition is considerably more civilised than those of other parts of Britain. The competition in Jedburgh, Roxburgh, where

its Shrovetide *football game, originally played with the severed heads of English border raiders, is waged through the boarded up streets; another in Atherstone, near the Warwickshire border with Leicestershire, originated during the reign of King John in a fierce struggle for a bag of gold.*
(INDEPENDENT, 16 February 1994)

In England the carnival season before Lent was known as *Shrovetide* and remains so. *Shrove* is the past tense of the verb *shrive*, meaning 'to hear confession and impose penance', so *Shrovetide* was a period of spiritual preparation for Lent which corresponded to the continental carnival season. The word became current, against competition from other terms such as *Fastens-eve* and *Fastingong*, in the early fifteenth century.

Spiritual preparation it may have been, but it was also a time of unruly festivities: city youths in the twelfth century played football (a violent and undisciplined game in those days) and held cock-fights; fifteenth century children indulged in rowdy behaviour at school; satirical plays mocked ecclesiastical and other authorities; and pancakes were eaten to use up reserves of butter and eggs, which were amongst foods forbidden during Lent. Tradition has it that in 1445 a woman in Olney, Buckinghamshire, was still busy making pancakes when the shriving bell rang. Anxious not to be late, she rushed into the church still clasping her pan. The annual pancake race, open only to women, is still run in Olney every Shrove Tuesday to commemorate the tardy housewife. The quotation from THE INDEPENDENT above illustrates some contemporary customs.

See **carnival** and **Lent**.

silhouette

the outline of an object or person, filled with a uniform colour

A widening band of light fell across us. I turned my manacled body and saw a sapphire blue vista through an opening door. There, silhouetted *in grotesque outline was a slender, pinched body, short bandy legs, bulging ears on a head depressed between thick shoulders.*
(H G Wells, THE FIRST MEN IN THE MOON, 1901)

As usual in Wales, the rain poured down. Musician friends played folk and rock, and Pauline's guests bopped the night away, looking out on to the yard festooned with fairy lights and sheep silhouetted *on the damp blue hills.*
(COUNTRY LIVING, November 1991)

There are only three other contemporary delineations of Jane Austen's features. . . One is a profile in silhouette *attributed to Mrs Collins.*
(Arts and Books, TELEGRAPH, 4 March 1995)

In 1759 the new French Controller General of finances, Étienne de *Silhouette*, proposed a number of petty fiscal reforms aimed at reviving the French economy, which was suffering the strain of the Seven Years War. The nation's table plate, for instance, was handed over to the mint and the purses of the nobility were squeezed when their pensions and privileges were reduced. Soon the phrase *à la silhouette*, meaning 'on the cheap', had been coined, a satirical stab at the minister's perceived penny-pinching. Another story says that this same phrase was used of men's suits – cut without pockets in order to ridicule his stinginess.

Coincidentally, the mid-eighteenth

Days of the week

Monday for wealth,
Tuesday for health,
Wednesday the best day of all.
Thursday for crosses,
Friday for losses,
Saturday no day at all.

It is not known which ancient people first divided days into groups of seven giving each of the days the name of one of the planets in the solar system, but it was through the Romans that this reckoning spread to Europe. For the Romans most of the names of the days of the week not only represented the planets but honoured their deities as well. Most of the Romance languages absorbed the Latin titles for weekdays but renamed those of the weekend for Christian religious observance. The Germanic tribes, however, translated the titles, substituting wherever necessary the names of those of their own deities who most closely resembled the particular Roman gods.

Latin	Romance (eg Italian)	Old English
diēs sōlis (day of the sun)	*domenica* (Lord's day)	*sunnandæg* (day of the sun)
lūnae diēs (day of the moon)	*lunedì* (day of the moon)	*monandæg* (moon's day)
Martis diēs (day of Mars, god of war)	*martedì* (day of Mars)	*tiwesdæg* (day of Tiu, god of war)
Mercurii diēs (Mercury's day)	*mercoledì* (Mercury's day)	*wodnesdæg* (day of Woden, or Odin – eloquent and swift, like Mercury)
Jovis diēs (Jove's, or Jupiter's day, god of the sky)	*giovedì* (Jove's day)	*thuresdæg* (day of Thor's, god of Thunder)
Veneris diēs (day of Venus, goddess of love)	*venerdì* (day of Venus)	*frīgedæg* (day of Frig, wife of Woden and goddess of married love)
Sāturnī diēs (Saturn's day)	*sabato* (sabbath day)	*sæterdæg,* contracted form of *sæternesdæg* (Saturn's day)

century saw the growth of interest in outline portraiture, an art which had been widespread in seventeenth century Europe. The simplicity of these unadorned portraits inspired society wags to refer to them as *silhouettes*, a reference to the minister's parsimony. Littré, the compiler of the DICTIONNAIRE DE LA LANGUE FRANÇAISE (1877), claims that the term arose because Silhouette himself made a hobby of the art. If so, one can imagine the barbed jokes at his expense: that the portraits were as cheap as the Controller's economies; that, adorning the walls of his chateau at Bry-sur-Marne, they saved him the expense of purchasing more costly works of art. The unpopular minister resigned his post within nine months and would doubtless have sunk into obscurity had his name not become the rather attractive term for an outline. Its first recorded use in England is in 1798.

silly

foolish, without judgement

'Please,' called Sam. 'Could Scales tell the story today? He's got a very interesting family.'

'If Scales can tell a story, yes,' said Miss Green. 'I want to tidy my cupboard, but remember, although I shall be on the other side of the room with my back to you, I shall be listening, and if anyone's silly. . .'

'No one will be silly *with me!' said Scales. . .*

(June Counsel, A DRAGON IN CLASS 4, 1984)

Bulloch's is rather proud of its quick-lunch routine and leaves nothing to chance. As the waitress takes your order, she puts an hour-glass on your table and turns it over with a flourish. It's a nice touch. It's also a damn silly *touch. And it plays straight into the hands of people of a humorous disposition.. Waiting till 20 minutes had passed, and the waitress was out of view, I turned the hour-glass over again. . .*

(WEEKEND TELEGRAPH, 11 February 1995)

Christina, my 17-year-old dance partner, was sorry that the traditions she had grown up with were eroding so quickly. But when I asked her why she wasn't wearing traditional dress herself, she laughed: 'Because it looks silly.'

(WEEKEND TELEGRAPH, 4 March 1995)

Through its long history *silly* has undergone a startling change of meaning. Ultimately it derives from *sœli*, an unattested Germanic word meaning 'luck, happiness'. This came into Old English as *gesœlig*, 'happy', and into Middle English as *seely* in the thirteenth century, where it meant 'blissfully happy, fortunate' and therefore 'blessed by God'. Whether or not it is the nature of the fortunate or blessed to be innocent and artless, *seely* soon began to develop a further sense, that of 'harmless and defenceless' and hence 'deserving compassion'. The latter sense became common from the fifteenth century, typically now with the spelling *silly*. Until the second half of the seventeenth century, then, *silly* variously came to mean 'meriting sympathy', 'innocent', 'weak and helpless' and finally 'humble, unsophisticated and ignorant'. In these senses it was particularly applied to children, women, dumb animals (especially sheep), the sick and common, untutored people, especially country folk. Since all of these were generally deemed deficient in wisdom or commonsense, the word also started to develop a sense of 'foolish' during the last quarter of the sixteenth century and this prevailed to become the current modern meaning.

For another word that has undergone a complete change in meaning, see **nice**.

sirloin

a choice cut of beef

The features expressed nothing of monastic austerity, or of ascetic privations; on the contrary, it was a bold bluff countenance, with broad black eyebrows, a well-turned forehead, and cheeks as round and vermilion as those of a trumpeter, from which descended a long and curly black beard. Such a visage, joined to the brawny form of the holy man, spoke rather of sirloins *and haunches, than of pease and pulse.*
(Sir Walter Scott, IVANHOE,1819)

Lunch was in the nursery during the week but on Sundays we would be cleaned up and brought down to the dining room for lunch, which was always the same. Two sirloins *would be produced (one for the staff and one for the dining room) and we would each get a cut of meat, a nice globule of yellow fat and a piece of proper Yorkshire pudding, followed by Mrs Barker's plum pudding speciality. It really was a very good life.*
(Lord Hailsham, DAILY MAIL, 23 April 1994)

In his CHURCH HISTORY OF ENGLAND (1655), Thomas Fuller repeats the tradition that Henry VIII coined *sirloin* when he knighted a loin of beef. The ATHENIAN MERCURY (6 March 1694) also provides a detailed account:

King Henry VIII, dining with the Abbot of Redding, and feeding heartily on a Loyn of Beef, as it was then called, the Abbot told the King he would give a thousand marks for such a Stomack, which the King procured him by keeping him shut in the Tower, got his thousand marks, and knighted the Beef for its good behaviour.

Another tradition accredits James I with the jest. Swift refers to it in POLITE CONVERSATION (1738):

Miss Notable: But pray, why is it called a sirloin?

Lord Smart: Why you must know, that our king James I., who loved good eating, being invited to dinner by one of his nobles, and seeing a large loin of beef at his table, he drew out his sword, and in a frolic knighted it.

The good monarch must have thought it a particularly witty act for he evidently repeated it. Both Blackburn in Lancashire and Chingford in Essex have houses where the extempore ceremony is said to have taken place. John Roby in his TRADITIONS OF LANCASHIRE (1829–31) gives a detailed account of the first of these at Houghton Tower in 1617.

Not to be outdone, Charles II also has his champions, doubtless because he is styled 'the merry monarch'. Under the heading *Sir-Loin of Beef*, the COOK'S ORACLE (1822) states:

This joint is said to owe its name to King Charles the Second, who dining upon a Loin of Beef, . . . said for its merit it should be knighted, and henceforth called Sir-Loin.

The witticism is obviously an old seventeenth-century joke centring on a play on words. In the sixteenth century English had *surloyn*, a borrowing from the postulated Old French *surloigne*, a variant of *surlonge* (from *sur*, 'above' and *longe*, 'loin'; from Latin *super*, 'above' and *lumbus*, 'loin'), the joint being cut from the upper part of the rump. Records of the variant spelling *sirloin* date back to the 1630s. Subsequently Addison spells it thus in the SPECTATOR of 1712, and the lexicographer Samuel Johnson enters it in his dictionary under this spelling in 1755. Although *sirloin* is now the only accepted orthography, the word was still commonly spelt with a *u* in the last quarter of the nineteenth century and this form was robustly defended by Skeat, who calls *sirloin* 'an inferior spelling of *surloin*'. The old tradition that the joint was knighted by one of our monarchs may be untrue, but it has certainly been influential in the demise of *surloin* and the rise of *sirloin.*

◆ Also from Latin *lumbus* are *lumbar, loin* and a few technical words. *Loin* is related to *sirloin* in that from the fourteenth century it too could refer to a joint of meat from an animal used for food. Its uses as a plural noun are much wider: since the fourteenth century it has referred to a part of the human anatomy, and has been the figurative seat of power and procreation since the sixteenth.

Certain words in modern English reflect the Old French prefix *sur,* 'over, above, excessive': *surfeit, surplice, surplus, surround, survive.* A large number of English words begin with Latin *super-*, source of the Old French *sur. Super-* is less obviously the root prefix in: *sojourn, sovereign, sum.*◆

slippery

1. difficult to stand upright on or grasp
2. not to be trusted

The cigar-makers, with seven of them in full evening-dress and two in dinner-coats, were already dancing on the waxy floor of Melpomene Hall. . . [Mr. Wrenn] felt very light and insecure in his new gun-metal-finish pumps now that he had taken off his rubbers and essayed the slippery *floor.*
(Sinclair Lewis, OUR MR. WRENN, THE ROMANTIC ADVENTURES OF A GENTLE MAN, 1914)

Middle English probably took its verb *slip* from Middle Low German *slippen,* itself from the Germanic base *slip-*. This same base was responsible for an earlier Old English adjective *slipper* which meant 'smooth and slippery'. By the close of the sixteenth century, however, *slipper* was all but redundant, having been replaced by a smart new coinage, *slippery.* The earliest written record of this word dates back to Miles Coverdale's translation of the Bible into English in 1535 where Psalm 34:6 reads: *Let their waye be darcke and slippery.* Coverdale's translation was not from original texts but from the Vulgate and Luther's Zurich Bible. In Luther's rendering of this same verse the German word *schlipfferig,* 'slippery', is used. It seems likely that Coverdale, influenced by this term, used it to rework the existing English adjective *slipper.* Any word that refers to the ease of falling over is likely to be productive figuratively. Certainly it came to be applied in a wide variety of contexts: a *slippery* character, the *slippery* ladder of ambition, a *slippery* slope, a *slippery* subject and so on.

Slipper as a noun to describe a light indoor shoe that was easy to slide on and off dates from the fifteenth century and derives from the verb *slip.* In the sixteenth century *slip-shoe* was also used. *Slipshod,* an adjective to describe a person wearing slip-shoes, was modelled on this term in the second half of the century. Later the word was also applied to people who slopped and shuffled about in shoes that had not been tied or were down at heel. In his poem 'Truth' (TABLE TALK, 1781) William Cowper describes:

The shivering urchin, bending as he goes,
With slip-shod *heels, and dew-drop at*
his nose.

Often the tone of the description was a touch disapproving, so that, in the first half of the nineteenth century, *slipshod* ceased to refer to the condition of a person's footwear and began to denote 'slovenly habits' or 'careless work'.

See **uproar** for another word influenced by Luther's translation of the Bible.

spice

1. powdered flavouring for food, obtained from plants
2. extra excitement

Under these circumstances I remained solitary. I smelt the rich scent of the heating spices, *and admired the shining kitchen utensils, the polished clock, decked in holly, the silver mugs ranged on a tray ready to be filled with mulled ale for supper. . .*

(Emily Brontë, WUTHERING HEIGHTS, 1847)

Come into the garden, Maud,
For the black bat, Night, has flown,
Come into the garden, Maud,
I am here at the gate alone;
And the woodbine spices *are wafted*
abroad,
And the musk of the roses blown.

(Alfred Lord Tennyson, MAUD, 1855)

Boar's head used to be the popular Christmas treat before the advent of turkey, and mince pies were originally made from a mixture of ox tongue, chicken, egg, sugar, raisins, lemon, orange peel, and various spices.

(Peter Gammons, ALL PREACHERS GREAT AND SMALL, 1989)

The Latin word *speciēs*, 'outward appearance, particular kind' (from *specere*, 'to look'), is responsible for both *species* and *spice* in English. A direct borrowing from Latin in the sixteenth century gave *species*; *spice* took a slightly longer route. In late Latin *speciēs* with its notion of 'kind, sort' was extended to refer to ' a particular sort of merchandise' and, more especially, to spices. In this sense it was borrowed into Old French as *espice* and into Middle English as *spice*. Since then its position has been secure, both in the basic sense of 'a flavouring for food' and in the parallel figurative senses that evolved, meaning 'added enjoyment, excitement, zeal'.

In medieval France a dealer in *spices* was known by the derived term *espicier*. This has become modern French *épicier*, 'grocer'. Middle English had the equivalent *spicer* but the word became obsolete in the early seventeenth century.

Instead English developed the word *grocer* (Middle English *grosser*) which, in the early fourteenth century, denoted 'a wholesale dealer in a particular commodity' such as wine or fish. It was especially applied to merchants who traded in spices and imported foodsuffs. The term derived from Old French *grossier* and Medieval Latin *grossārius*, 'wholesale dealer', the latter being a derivative of Latin *grossus*, 'thick, large'.

By the second half of the fifteenth century, however, *grocer* was already begining to lose its exclusive 'wholesale' application and was starting to be used of retailers in spices, dried fruit, sugar and the like. In time it came to supplant *spicer*.

◆ *Special*, in English since the thirteenth century, is a borrowing of Latin *speciālis*, 'individual, of a particular kind', a derivative of *speciēs*.

Latin *grossus* was also responsible for *engross*. One of the particular meanings of the verb at the turn of the fifteenth century was 'to buy up the entire stock for sale at a premium' (Middle English *engrossen*, from Anglo-French *engrosser*, from Old French *en gros* 'wholesale'). From this developed the senses 'to need the entire use of something' and, at the beginning of the eighteenth century, 'to totally absorb one's attention'.◆

spinster

an unmarried woman, often past normal marrying age and considered fussy and prim

The history of the house is plain now. It was once the residence of a country squire, whose family, probably dwindling down to mere spinsterhood, *got merged in the more territorial name of Donnithorne. It was once the Hall; it is now the Hall Farm.*
(George Eliot, ADAM BEDE, 1859)

Colombo is one of the calmest places on earth. . . The asphalt avenues with their very occasional cars are graced, in the evening, by processions of saris whose colours are those of the pastel drawings of the English spinsters *buried in the nearby cemeteries.*
(André Malraux, ANTIMÉMOIRES, 1967)

. . . 14-year-old Sarah arrived at court as a single girl and at once caught the attention of Prince George – future George III. Brother-in-law Henry Fox flung Sarah at the royal feet and she found herself playing a romantic drama to the whole world of the newspaper readers. . . When Prince George made an arranged marriage to Princess Charlotte of Mecklenberg, Sarah's humiliation was public. Aged 15, she despaired of anyone liking her enough to marry her. She seized on Thomas Bunbury, an MP of only moderate means, as the only alternative to a dismal spinster *future and despite his lack of both ardour and wealth, married him.*
(SUNDAY TIMES, 24 April 1994)

A *spinster* is literally 'a woman who spins'. Middle English *spynnester* derives from the verb *spinnen*, 'to spin', and *-ster*, a suffix denoting a female agent. *Spinnen* came from Old English *spinnan* and ultimately from the unattested Indo-European root *spen-* 'to draw out'.

In the fourteenth century, the term *spinster* was applied to any ordinary woman who was regularly employed with her spinning. Perhaps it was an occupation that was particularly well-suited to unmarried daughters who did not carry the main burden of household responsibility or to women without the support of a husband, for in the seventeenth century *spinster* became a recognised legal term to denote 'an unmarried girl or woman'. From then on the term no longer belonged to the lowly echelons of society but was applied across the social board with no consideration of rank. In registers and legal documents the term was simply appended to the woman's name; thus, in Goldsmith's play SHE STOOPS TO CONQUER (1773) we hear of *Constantia Neville,* spinster, *of no place at all.* This use is still regularly heard in churches when the banns of marriage are read aloud by law in the weeks preceding the ceremony: *Janet Perkins,* spinster *of this parish.*

In POOR RICHARD'S ALMANACK (1733) Benjamin Franklin summarises centuries of history in one short verse:

When great Augustus ruled the World and Rome,
The Cloth he wore was spun and wove at Home,
His Empress ply'd the Distaff and the Loom.
Old England's Laws the proudest Beauty name,
When single, Spinster, *and when married, Dame,*
For Housewifery is Woman's noblest Fame.
The Wisest household Cares to Women yield
A large, a useful and a grateful Field.

By the eighteenth century a somewhat derogatory shadow had been cast over *spinster*, when it was popularly used of an unmarried woman who no longer seemed to have any prospects of conjugal bliss and had become, or was destined to be, an old maid. Even today *spinster* conjures up the image of a rather fussy maiden lady; it is not a term to apply to a career woman.

◆ *Spiders* also spin and this is reflected in their name. It comes from *spithra*, an Old English derivative of *spinnan*, 'to spin'. This gave Middle English *spither* or *spithre* and modern English *spider*.

The suffix *-ster* has a long history. In some periods and in some regional varieties, it has meant 'a female agent'. It was replaced in this sense by the French import *-stress*, as in *seamstress, songstress*. From the sixteenth century onwards, surviving words ending in *-ster* and new coinings have not been so specific. *Gamester, jokester, tipster, youngster* and many more are no longer necessarily female.◆

The distaff side

Tools used for spinning – the spindle, the rod used to twist the fibres of wool into yarn, and the distaff – have given rise to a number of terms associated with women.

Distaff has quite a history attached to it. In medieval times running sheep and shearing them was a man's work but washing, carding and spinning the wool was a woman's responsibility. In addition to providing for their own needs, many rural women took in wool and spun extra yarn for the weaving industry, in order to augment their income. Women in medieval illustrations of domestic rural life are invariably pictured with their distaff (the rod which held the wool to be teased out), whether they are feeding the chickens or stirring the pot. Indeed L F Saltzman (ENGLISH LIFE IN THE MIDDLE AGES) tells how the occupation was so widespread that the implement became a symbol of a woman's work and, ultimately, of woman herself. As a reflection of the status of the distaff, the medieval Queens of France were buried with an ornate distaff at their sides.

Since at least the fourteenth century, a number of expressions in English connect the word *distaff* and the areas of work, influence and interest that have belonged specifically to a woman.

The *distaff-side* (and also *spindle-side*, as in other Germanic languages) has long been used to distinguish the female line of the family from the *spear-side* (sometimes the *sword-side*, in imitation of a German compound word), the male branch.

Distaff's day, or *St Distaff's day*, is 7 January, the day after the Twelfth Day or Epiphany. It is so called because the women took up their spinning and ordinary everyday work again, after the Christmas festivities.

See **spinster**.

starboard

the right-hand side of a ship, looking forward

Captain Paul Chavasse, who has died aged 86, was First Lieutenant and Torpedo Officer of the cruiser Jamaica *during the dramatic sinking of the German battlecruiser* Scharnorst *by ships of the Home Fleet. . . Chavasse painted a vivid picture of* Scharnhorst's *last moments: 'By starshell we saw the black mass of the* Scharnhorst *and as we closed with her we let fly with our torpedoes. . . We did another 'swing' and fired three more from our* starboard *tubes. When the smoke cleared we saw the* Scharnhorst *lying on her side. She looked like a whale that had just come up for air, except that she was ablaze from stem to stern.'*
(DAILY TELEGRAPH, 10 October 1994)

Sailing for the blind and visually impaired was pioneered in Britain some 20 years ago, but competing round short courses, using the same racing rules employed in club events to the Admiral's Cup, is still in its infancy.

Dick Fawcett is one of those still involved from the early days. His electronic yacht instrument company, Autohelm, made the first audio compasses, where a change of heading was denoted by change of note, a different sound for port or starboard. *'A blind person can actively navigate the boat,' says Fawcett, 'and get the full satisfaction a sighted person would.'*
(DAILY TELEGRAPH, 11October 1994)

We berthed in the harbour at Carcassonne, the most complete fortified medieval city bar none, with castle, ramparts and towers, stunning without and maybe within, but we did not give it a chance since our restless brood had locked on to the town's McDonald's, starboard *side, north by northeast.*
(GUARDIAN, 14 January 1995)

It might be supposed that this nautical term for the right-hand side of a ship originates in ancient methods of navigating by the stars. In fact starboard evolved from the Old English *stēorbord*. Viking-age ships were not steered by a rudder at the stern but by a special paddle called a *stēor* (from *stēoran*, from unattested Germanic *steurjan*, 'to steer', from *steurō*, 'steering') which was dropped over the right-hand *bord* or ship's side.

The term *larboard* (*laddeborde* in Middle English) – the left-hand side of the ship to which the steersman had his back – was modelled on the earlier *starboard*. *Ladde* is thought to derive from *laden*, 'to load'. When quays were built to make the loading of vessels easier, ships had to be moored with the steering paddle free and cargo was therefore always taken over the left board. The later term *port* (recorded since the sixteenth century) is thought to have arisen for the same reason, the left-hand side of the vessel being the one that was presented to the port. Gradually *port* superseded the use of *larboard* since it was less easily confused with *starboard*. On 22 November 1844, this Order was issued from the Admiralty in England:

The word 'Port' is frequently . . . substituted

A posh tip

An acronym is a word formed from the initial letter of other words (see **Acronyms**, page 148, for examples). However, some words whose origin is commonly claimed to be an acronym almost certainly are not so. *Tip* does not come from *T*o *I*nsure *P*romptness. *Posh* does not come from *P*ort *O*ut, *S*tarboard *H*ome.

. . . for the word 'Larboard', and as . . . the distinction between Starboard' *and 'Port' is so much more marked than that between* Starboard' *and 'Larboard', it is their Lordships direction that the word 'Larboard' shall no longer be used.*

Under fifteen months later, the US Navy put out a Department Notice in very similar terms.

In modern times, of course, much nautical vocabulary has been applied to aircraft, so that *starboard* and *port* now also refer to the right and left sides of a plane.

◆ Also from Germanic *steurō*, 'steering', come the Old Norse *styra*, 'to steer' and *stjorn*, 'steering', from which English derives *stern*. This was formerly the 'steering equipment' of a ship but now refers simply to the 'back part of a vessel'.◆

stationer

a person selling writing materials

The portcullis is the heraldic symbol of Parliament, useful for putting on stationery *and tourist knick-knacks. . .*
(WEEKEND TELEGRAPH, 2 July 1994)

In classical Latin the noun *statiō* meant 'a standing still' (from *stāre*, 'to stand'). Later this was given the more concrete application of 'post, station'. The derived adjective *statiōnārius* therefore meant 'attached to a military station'. This passed into medieval Latin as a noun to distinguish a tradesman who had an established shop from an itinerant vendor. In the Middle Ages the term *staciouner* was particularly applied to booksellers. Most of these were itinerant but there were permanent bookshops at the universities where the governing bodies would license trustworthy vendors to trade. Over time the word *stationer* was loosely applied to anyone who was connected with the booktrade, from publisher to bookseller, or who sold other requirements for study such as paper and pens. In his GLOSSOGRAPHIA (1656) Thomas Blount attempts correction:

Stationer... *is often confounded with Book-seller, and sometimes with Book-binder, whereas they are three several Trades; the* Stationer *sells Paper and Paper-Books, Ink, Wax, etc. The Book-seller deals onely in printed Books, ready bound; and the Book-binder binds them, but sells not. Yet all three are of the Company of* Stationers.

Despite Blount's efforts, it was not until the eighteenth century that *stationer* was applied solely to a vendor of paper and writing materials.

◆ *Station* (Middle English *stacioun*) and *stationary* (Middle English *stationarye*) also derive from *statiō*.◆

stepchild

a son or daughter by one's spouse and a previous partner

I wept on Antonia's wedding day, something I didn't do for any of my other children. It was such a huge thing to be losing her from the family. We were all so close. Divorce had barely happened in my family, so when Antonia was divorced it was difficult, but it was such a long time ago. Antonia's so happy with Harold, who is a wonderful husband and stepfather.
(Lady Longford about Lady Antonia Fraser in THE SUNDAY TIMES MAGAZINE, 18 December 1994)

Economics is not likely to be taken over by some other discipline, but the threat could

well arise. Business economists are in the best position to build relationships, and many are already doing so. There will be ample opportunity for business economists to challenge pure academic superiority by demonstrating that our profession is not the stepchild, *but rather the real, enhanced version of economics.*
(Walter E Hoadley, BUSINESS ECONOMICS, January 1995)

The whole range of step-relationships is based on an Old English prefix *stēop-* which is ultimately related to the Old High German verb *stiufen*, 'to bereave'. *Stēop-* had the sense 'deprived of parents' and so the Old English compounds *stēopbearn* (stepbairn) and *steopcild* (stepchild) originally meant 'orphan'. By extension, in Middle English these two terms and also *stēopsunu* (stepson) and *stēopdohtor* (stepdaughter) came to mean 'a bereaved child who becomes a son or daughter to someone else', while *stēopfæder* (stepfather) and *stēopmōder* (stepmother) had the sense 'one who, through marriage, becomes a father or mother to a child who has lost a parent'. In time the *step-* terms were also applied to new family relationships formed through divorce and remarriage.

sterling

1. connected with British currency, usually pounds
2. of high quality, first class

But elephants are far from cheap in India, where they are becoming scarce, the males, which alone are suitable for circus shows, are much sought, especially as but few of them are domesticated. When therefore Mr. Fogg proposed to the Indian to hire Kiouni, he refused point-blank. Mr. Fogg persisted, offering the excessive sum of ten pounds an hour for the loan of the beast to Allahabad. Refused. Twenty pounds? Refused also. Forty pounds? Still refused. Passepartout jumped at each advance; but the Indian declined to be tempted. Yet the offer was an alluring one, for, supposing it took the elephant fifteen hours to reach Allahabad, his owner would receive no less than six hundred pounds sterling.
(Jules Verne, AROUND THE WORLD IN EIGHTY DAYS, 1873)

The earliest attested reference to *sterling* in English is from the late thirteenth century. However, there are earlier Old French and Medieval Latin examples. The word is thought to be native English and to derive from an unattested late Saxon word *steorling*, meaning 'a little star' (from *steorra*, 'star', and *-ling*, a diminutive suffix), a reference to the tiny star evident on some of the early silver pennies from the reign of William Rufus (c. 1056–1100).

Over the centuries, however, alternative etymologies have been suggested. Silver coins from the reign of Edward the Confessor (c1003-66), for instance, bore an emblem of four birds giving rise to the suggestion that the word derived from Old English *stær*, 'starling'.

The favourite theory until the last century held that the coin was first minted by the *Easterlings*, Hanse merchants and money-lenders with whom England traded, and that it bore their name. Scholars, however, have since established that early contexts where *esterling* appears clearly indicate the currency and there is no suggestion of a link with the people. Indeed, it seems *easterling*, meaning 'inhabitant of the Hanse towns', does not appear in English until the sixteenth century. It is also highly unlikely that a word would be shortened by the loss of a stressed initial syllable: *easterling* reduced to *sterling*.

The term *pound sterling* was originally

pound of sterlings, a clear reference to 'a pound weight of silver pennies'.

The widely recognised qualities of silver were figuratively attributed to character from the seventeenth century onwards. Nathaniel Hawthorne could write in 1850:

With all these sterling *attributes, thought Hester, the evil which she inherited from her mother must be great indeed, if a noble woman do not grow out of this elfish child.*
(THE SCARLET LETTER).

For notes on another currency, see **dollar**.

stickler

a person very insistent on discipline, rules, accuracy, etc.

'I grit my teeth a lot. And I watch while they sometimes elect managers I would never want to work for. But I trust my employees. They're looking for success as strongly as I am.'

A wholesale rejection of his Harvard business school training? Not at all, says Semler. A stickler *for productivity, he relies on the market to police both his employees and his own far-out ideas.*
(FORTUNE, 6 February 1995)

Sticklers are people who insist on a particular point or scruple. They may be *sticklers* for punctuality, politeness, form, etiquette or shiny shoes. In the sixteenth and seventeenth centuries, a *stickler* was 'an umpire', someone who presided over a contest or tournament to guarantee fair play or to come between combatants where necessary. It has been claimed that the name derived from *stick*, the suggestion being that this was the weapon the *stickler* was often forced to resort to when parting quarrelsome contestants. However, an earlier form *stightler* existed in the fifteenth century, showing that the noun derived rather from the now obsolete Middle English verb *stightlen* (itself from Old English *stihtian, stihtan*). It meant 'to arrange', 'to control' and was often applied to the work of a steward given the responsibility of making arrangements and overseeing events. By the sixteenth century this verb had evolved into *stickle* and meant 'to arbitrate'.

One might conjecture that umpires were generally despised for their nit-picking; certainly, the history of *stickler* begins to take a downward turn, gradually sliding into its modern derogatory meaning. In the second half of the sixteenth century the word was often found in political contexts to denote 'one who is actively involved in a matter', often with the implication that such a person was 'a meddler'. By the first quarter of the seventeenth century a *stickler* had also become 'an adversary, an opponent given to raising objections'. Towards the middle of that same century the term was combined with *for* to give the modern sense 'one who advocates a principle', 'one who insists on something (petty)'. The verb *to stickle* has followed the same path and has come to mean 'to contend over (trivial matters)', 'to raise objections'.

sycophant

an obsequious flatterer

. . . I would open the door from the bedroom, a preposterous figure in a dressing-gown, blink, pause, then withdraw again with a mumbled apology. But in that brief instant she would have turned to me with a smile and a look quite different from that reserved for her sycophantic *retinue.*
(Graham Swift, EVER AFTER, 1992)

If the truth be told, Sarah would probably have wished to get married quietly, without the pomp and circumstance of announcements from Buckingham Palace and sycophantic *goodwill messages from mayors and town councils hoping to win re-election today.*
(DAILY MAIL, 5 May 1994)

The literal meaning of Greek *sukophantēs* is 'fig-shower' (from *sukon*, 'fig' and *phantēs*, 'shower', from *phainein*, 'to show'). *Sycophants* in ancient Greece were those who ingratiated themselves by informing against others. There is, however, no evidence from classical texts to support the theory, commonly held since at least the sixteenth century, that the term first applied to those who informed against the illegal exportation of figs from Attica. More probable by far is the suggestion that *fig* relates to an obscene gesture of the 'Up yours!' variety, which originated in ancient times, was once common in England and still prevails in southern Europe. The gesture, which is illustrative of the female genitals, is made by thrusting one's thumb between the first two fingers or into the mouth. It takes its name from *sukon*, 'fig', which the Greeks used euphemistically for 'vulva'. Metaphorically speaking, a *sycophant* was making this gesture of triumphant contempt at those he was informing against.

When the word first entered English by way of Latin *sycophanta* in the first half of the sixteenth century, it had the ancient sense of 'tell-tale, informer' but swiftly came to mean 'flatterer, toady, one who curries favour'.

◆ *Phainein* is a root of a good number of English words, such as:

emphasis (16th cent) from Latin, from Greek *emphasis*, a grammatical term indicating 'the significance behind the words', from *emphainein*, 'to indicate'.

Epiphany (14th cent) 'the manifestation of Christ to the Gentiles', from Greek *epiphaneia*, 'manifestation', from *epiphainein*, 'to manifest'.

phase (19th cent) from *phases* (plural), from New Latin *phasis*, from Greek *phásis*, 'any of the cyclical aspects or appearances of the moon or planets'.

phenomenon (17th cent) from Late Latin *phaenomenon*, from Greek *phainomenon*, from *phainesthai*, 'to appear'.

Phainein was also the source of the Greek derivative *phantazein*, 'to make visible'. From this came the noun *phantasma*, 'spectre, apparition', *phantasma* in Latin. By way of Old French it was taken into Middle English as *fanto(s)me* in the thirteenth century. The spelling *phantom* was revised after the Latin in the seventeenth century. A second common word from the same Greek derivative is *fantasy* which came into English in the fifteenth century.◆

For another word with a similar meaning, see **toady**.

tabloid

a popular newspaper of small format

Formerly seen as a man who liked to paint the town beige before retiring to bed with a glass of milk, Deayton now stands reviled in the tabloids *as a party animal, and not the domesticated variety. Allegedly.*
(TELEGRAPH MAGAZINE, 10 December 1994)

Scandalous behaviour at public schools has become as regular a part of our tabloid *diet as gay vicars and celebrity cocaine confessions, but I wonder how much longer even the great British hack can keep feigning shock and surprise when the children of our wealthier citizens are caught misbehaving.*
(THE SUNDAY TIMES Style, 19 March 1995)

On 14 March 1884, the London-based drug company Burroughs, Wellcome and Co registered *Tabloid* as a trademark for the medicines they prepared and compressed into tablet form. There was nothing new in drugs presented in this way but the small firm had the advantage of new machinery capable of turning out copious quantities of first-class tablets.

Mr Wellcome needed a trade name for marketing purposes and *Tabloid* was coined by adding the suffix *-oid*, meaning 'resemblance, similarity' (from Latin *-oīdēs*, from Greek *-oeidēs*, 'having the form of'), to the existing term *tablet*. *Tablet* itself had come into Middle English in the fourteenth century by way of Old French *tablete*, a diminutive form of *table*. At first it referred to 'a small flat slab', of stone or marble for instance, which could be written or carved upon but its use was extended in the second half of the sixteenth century to 'small compact cakes of compressed medication or soap'.

To the company's annoyance *Tabloid* was seized upon and was soon in general use (now without its initial capital letter) to refer to a compacted form of anything at all, from tea to rocks. The OED has a quotation that illustrates the meaning at its time of transition:

The word Tabloid *has become so well-known . . . in consequence of the use of it by the Plaintiff firm in connection with their compressed drugs that I think it has a acquired a secondary sense in which it has been used and may legitimately be used so long as it does not interfere with their trade rights. I think the word has been so applied generally with reference to the notion of a compressed form or dose of anything.* (Mr Justice Byrne, REPORTS ON PATENT AND TRADE MARK CASES XXI, 20 November–14 December 1903)

Since the turn of the twentieth century even the news has been compressed. The word survives in the world of journalism, a *tabloid* being a popular newspaper of small format which offers concentrated easy-to-read articles and news stories.

taboo

a prohibition, a forbidden thing

By the second half of the 1950s, the extent of royal coverage had become so monumental, and the tone so cloying, as to invite a reaction. I remember well when it happened. One morning in 1957 Kingsley Martin came into my office at the New Statesman *. . . and slapped down on my desk an article he had just been sent by Malcom Muggeridge: 'Read that. It's a crackerjack (his favourite term of praise). The best article I have ever read.' This was Muggeridge's famous piece on the 'Royal Soap Opera', which first broke the* taboo *on criticising royalty.*
(Paul Johnson, WAKE UP, BRITAIN!, 1994)

The world has changed so much that the conditions under which certain taboos *were made do not exist any more. This means we need to modify certain aspects of our* taboos. *One* taboo *says that if a cow moos in the night it must be killed or the owner would die. In the days of old most farmers had several herds of cattle and it did not matter if one or two were killed. These days very few people have cattle. Imagine the plight of the farmer who has to kill his only bullock just because the poor animal got excited and mooed at night.*
(COMMON CAUSE, Autumn/Winter 1994)

Taboo came into English through Captain Cook's accounts of his voyages in the South Seas (1777). It is a Tongan adjective, *tabu*, a term of prohibition to indicate that a particular article, word or action had been declared sacred and was consecrated uniquely for royal or religious purposes, or was forbidden to a particular section of the community. James Cook described it thus:

Not one of them would sit down, or eat a bit of any thing. . . On expressing my surprize at this, they were all taboo, *as they said; which word has a very comprehensive meaning; but, in general, signifies that a thing is forbidden. Why they were laid under such restraints, at present, was not explained.* (VOYAGE TO THE PACIFIC OCEAN, 1777)

Pronouncing *taboo* was not confined to Tonga, however. The practice prevailed throughout the islands of the Pacific where various forms of the word are found; the Maoris, for instance, have *tapu* and the Fijians *tambu*.

Strictly the stress should fall on the first syllable of the word. English, however, accentuates the final syllable and uses the term as a noun, and sometimes a verb, as well as an adjective. Perhaps the most common use today is in the phrase *taboo words*. These are any expressions that allude too directly to sensitive subjects such as copulation, death, old age, sweat and any number of other topics that are viewed as embarrassing and for which people resort to euphemisms.

For another Polynesian word that entered English through Cook's writings, see **tattoo**.

tadpole

the larva of a frog or toad

A spawn of children cluttered the slimy pavement, for all the world like tadpoles *just turned frogs on the bottom of a dry pond.* (Jack London, THE PEOPLE OF THE ABYSS, 1903)

Over the Easter term, the inky tadpoles *changed from commas into exclamation marks.* (Carol Ann Duffy [b 1955], IN MRS TILSCHER'S CLASS)

Pollywiggle
Pollywog
Tadpole
Bullfrog
Leaps on
Long legs
Jug-o'-rum
Jelly eggs. . .

This poem, *Frog* by Mary Ann Hoberman, mentions three of the names that have been given to the larva of the frog or toad. *Tadpole* is the accepted term; *pollywiggle* and *pollywog* (sometimes *polliwog* or *pollywoggle*) are both old dialectal words in English and the latter is current in the United States. *Pol* (or *polle*), a Middle English word meaning 'head', is a common element in each since the creature gives the appearance of being nothing more than a large head with a slim tail attached. Indeed the French word *têtard* (Old French *testard*) is based on the same observation (from French *tête*, 'head'). While the dialectal terms also focus on the frantic wiggle of the tail, the initial element in *tadpole* is *tadde*, a Middle English word meaning 'toad'. The entire word, therefore, means '*toad head*'.

◆ Modern English *poll*, 'the casting or recording of votes', is more literally a 'head count' and derives from *pol*. It has been in use since the seventeenth century.

Pole-axe has only been the accepted spelling of the word from the beginning of the seventeenth century. From its first use in the fifteenth century to that date, its earlier spelling of *pollaxe* or *polaxe* shows its connection to *pol*. It is not clear whether *pol* here refers to the head of the axe, or to the head of enemies on which the axe was used.◆

Fabrics

Fabrics are often named for their place of manufacture, giving rise to a number of quaint or exotic-sounding words:

Calico (16th cent): a hardwearing cotton cloth. In the sixteenth century it was known as *Calicut-cloth* after the town on the southwest coast of India, now known as Kozhikode, from which it was exported.

Cambric (16th cent): a fine cotton or linen fabric which was made in Cambrai. The cloth took its name from *Kameryk* (Latin *camaracum*), the Flemish name for the town, and this was borrowed into English as *cameryk* and corrupted to *cambric.*

Cretonne (19th cent): this heavy, printed cotton furnishing fabric takes its name from *Creton,* the Normandy village where it originated.

Damask (14th cent): this richly patterned cloth was called *pannus de damasco,* 'cloth of Damascus', in Medieval Latin, since the cloth was exported to Europe from that Syrian city.

Denim (late 17th cent): the name is a corruption of *serge de Nîmes*, a term given to a type of serge fabric that was woven in the French town of *Nîmes.* English often referred to it as *serge de Nim* before further corrupting the term by isolating the two last words and blending them together to form *denim.*

Hessian (19th cent): this loosely woven cloth made of jute, which was used to make sacks and wrap bales, takes its name from the West German state of *Hesse* where it was made.

Lawn (15th cent): this word for fine cotton or linen cloth is probably a corruption of *Laon,* a linen-weaving town in northern France.

Muslin (17th cent): Fine, semi-transparent cotton cloth. It was originally manufactured in the Iraqi town of *Al-Mawsil.* The Arabs called it *mūslin,* 'cloth of Mosul', and this word was borrowed into Italian as *moussolina,* into French as *mousseline* and into English as *muslin.*

Poplin (18th cent): came into English via the French *papeline* from Italian *papalina.* This is a feminine form of the adjective *papalino,* which means 'papal'. *Papalina* was used to describe the cloth because it was made in Avignon which had been a papal city in the fourteenth century.

Satin (14th cent): is probably a borrowing of Arabic *zaitūnī,* 'of Zaitun', which came into English as *satin* by way of Middle French: *satin, satanin, zatanin, zatany.* According to Marco Polo, Zaitun was a great oriental sea port of the thirteenth century. It is generally identified as modern Tsinkiang in south east China.

Worsted (13th cent): This closely woven woollen cloth still bears its original Middle English name which derives from *Worthstede,* now known as *Worstead,* the Norfolk parish where it was first produced.

continued over page

Fabrics continued

Other fabrics are named for their appearance or colour:

Brocade (16th cent): fabric with a pattern, often of gold, silver or silky thread, raised against a flat, dull background. Earlier the word *brocado* was used. This was a Spanish or Portuguese borrowing from Italian *broccato*, 'embossed fabric', from *brocco*, 'twisted thread', 'shoot', from late Latin *brocca*, 'spike' and Latin *brocchus*, the adjective used in the phrase *brocchi dentes*, 'projecting teeth'.

Chintz (17th cent): a colourful glazed cotton fabric. When imports of brightly painted calico began, English first took the singular *chint* from the Hindi word *chīnt* – itself a derivation from the Sanskrit *chitra*, meaning 'of many colours' – to refer to the cloth. Vendors describing their wares would speak of their silks, satins, brocades and *chints*. The unfamiliar plural *chints* subsequently was taken to be a singular noun by the public and supplanted the earlier *chint*. It is unclear why in the second half of the eighteenth century *chints* became *chintz*.

Chino (20th cent): this twilled fabric is used for sportswear and uniforms. The term originated in the United States, being an American Spanish word meaning 'toasted', a reference to the light golden brown colour of the original fabric.

Corduroy (18th cent): it is tempting to devise a French etymology for this ribbed cotton fabric linking it with *corde du roy*, 'king's cord'. Instead its derivation is rather less attractive, probably coming from a combination of *cord* and an obsolete term for a type of woollen fabric, *deroy* or *duroy*.

Gingham (17th cent): cotton cloth made up of dyed yarn and woven into stripes or checks. It originally came from Malaya, where it was known as *ginggang*, meaning 'striped', and was imported into Europe by the Dutch, who retained the Malay word *gingang*.

Lace (16th cent): a delicate fabric with its pattern in the weave. The word *lace* (also *laas* or *las*) had various meanings in Middle English, but its figurative meaning of 'a trap', 'a snare' best reflects its ancient origin. It came into English by way of Old French *laz* or *las*. This in turn derived from an unattested late Latin term *lacium* and from Latin *laqueus* meaning 'a noose', 'a snare'. From this history, it is possible to see how the sense of 'thread' or 'string' came about and passed into Middle English. Medieval clothing was fastened with cords and these, too, were referred to as *laces*. The transference of the term to a fabric made of intricately woven threads took place in the mid-sixteenth century.

Velvet (14th cent): a heavy fabric with a downy pile, originally made of silk. The word has its origins in *villus*, a Latin word meaning 'shaggy hair'. This gave *villūtus* in medieval Latin and *velu*, 'hairy', in Old French. The noun *veluotte* derived from this and passed into Middle English as *veluet*.

Some fabrics are named for the raw material used in their manufacture:

Flannel (14th cent): a soft fabric, originally of wool, now also of cotton. Latin *lāna* was ultimately responsible for *gwlān*, the Welsh word for 'wool'. From this Welsh derived *gwlanen*, 'woollen cloth'. Middle English *flanen*, 'sackcloth', is a corruption of this.

The association of the Welsh with the cloth has likely given rise to the recent use of flannel as an informal term for 'wordy, insincere talk'. In Shakespeare's THE MERRY WIVES OF WINDSOR (1598) Falstaff, when scolded by the Welsh parson, Hugh Evans, declares, '*I am dejected; I am not able to answer the Welsh flannel*' (Act 5, scene 5).

Linen (8th cent): is cloth made from the flax plant, and this is reflected in its name. Its origins lie in an ancient Indo-European word for flax which gave Latin *līnum* and an old, unattested Germanic form *linam*. The derived Germanic adjective *līnin* meant 'made of flax' and this was borrowed into Old English as *līnen* or *līnnen*.

And still others have an etymology that defies any category:

Chiffon (18th cent): this sheer silky fabric is etymologically nothing more than a bit of old rag and the term, though French, has English origins. Old English had *cipp*, 'a beam', and Middle English *chip*, 'a fragment cut off'. This was borrowed into Old French as *chipe* and adapted to give the variant *chiffe*, 'old rag'. Modern French uses the further variant, *chiffon*, for 'duster'. A *chiffonier*, a type of 'ornamental cabinet', is etymologically nothing more than a cupboard for storing rags.

Serge (14th cent): the name for this worsted twill cloth probably ultimately derives from *sī*, the Chinese word for silk. The Greeks traded with an oriental people whom they named *Sēres*, 'the silk people'. From this Late Latin had *sērica lāna*, 'wool of the Seres', in other words 'silk'. Vulgar Latin probably had the unattested form *sārica* which was taken into Old French as *sarge* and from there into Middle English.

Silk (9th cent): the name of this fabric, woven from threads produced by the silk-worm, probably originates ultimately from the Chinese word *sī*, 'silk'. Some etymologists hold that the Old English form *sioloc*, which gave Middle English *silk*, came through Greek *Sēres*, 'the oriental people from whom silk was obtained', and *sērikos*, 'silken' (see **serge**), and subsequently through Latin *sēricum*, 'silk'. Others argue that *sī* was picked up by the Slavic and then the Germanic peoples before passing into English.

Taffeta (14th cent): the origins of this stiff silk fabric are Persian. The Persian verb *tāftan* meant 'to weave', the derived adjective *tāftah* meaning 'woven'. This was borrowed into Turkish as *tafta* and into Old Italian as *taffettà*. It came into Middle English as *taffeta* by way of Old French *taffetas*.

Tweed (19th cent): the word was originally a trademark, a misspelling of *tweeled*, that is 'twilled' in Scottish dialect, that arose through confusion with the name of the river *Tweed*.

tailor

a person who makes suits, jackets, etc for men, usually to special order

'Why are women so fond of raking up the past? They're as bad as tailors, *who invariably remember what you owe them for a suit long after you've ceased to wear it.'*
(Saki, REGINALD, 1904)

He said he proposed at once taking an unfurnished top back attic in as quiet a house as he could find, say at three or four shillings a week, and looking out for work as a tailor. . . *The difficulty was how to get him started. It was not enough that he should be able to cut out and make clothes – that he should have the organs, so to speak, of a* tailor; *he must be put into a* tailor's *shop and guided for a little while by someone who knew how and where to help him.*
(Samuel Butler, THE WAY OF ALL FLESH, 1903)

The unattested Vulgar Latin verb *tāliāre*, 'to cut', was derived from Latin *tālea*, an agricultural word which means 'a cutting from a plant'. The verb became *taillier* in Old French and gave the noun *tailleur*, which generally denoted 'a person who cuts'; a *tailleur de bois*, for instance, was a woodcutter and a *tailleur d'images* a sculptor. The *tailleur d'habits* was, literally, the 'cutter out of clothes' (Medieval Latin had the similar term *tāliātor vestium*), although by the thirteenth century, this artisan was already simply referred to as the *tailleur*. The word came into Middle English in the fourteenth century by way of Anglo-French *taillour*. The verb was formed from the noun only about the beginning of the eighteenth century.

◆ Also from Vulgar Latin *tāliāre* come:

detail (17th cent): from French *détail* 'a piece cut off', from *détailler*, 'to cut in pieces', from the intensive *de-* and *tailler*, 'to cut'

retail (14th cent): from Old French *retaille*, 'a piece cut off', from *retaillier*, from intensive *re-* and *taillier*, 'to cut'◆

For a word from the same source, see **tally**.

tally

a reckoning, a score, an account

Just an ordinary man [Stanley Matthews] who played First Division football until the age of 50 and who collected 54 international caps for England (a tally *which would have been trebled but for the selectors' mistrust of his genius). . .*
(THE DAILY TELEGRAPH, 23 January 1995)

Centuries ago merchants and tradesmen used *tallies* as invoices and receipts. The word ultimately derives from Latin *tālea*, an agricultural term meaning a 'cutting' or 'twig'. It came into Middle English as *taly* through Norman French *tallie* and Medieval Latin *talia*. A *tally* was a simple wooden rod with notches cut across one of its faces to represent the amount of money owed or received. The rod was then split in two lengthways, both parties in the transaction receiving half. Brought together the halves corresponded exactly and were legal proof of the debt incurred or payment made.

Tallies were still tendered as receipts by the British Exchequer until the reign of George III and the elmwood sticks were stored in the Palace of Westminster. In 1826, however, the Court of Exchequer was abolished and in 1834 William IV gave orders that the tallies should be burned. Bundles of them were taken to the furnaces beneath the Lord's chamber but their blaze was so intense that the flues caught fire and almost all of the Palace burnt down.

For a word from the same source, see **tailor**.

tantalise

to teasingly offer something but not actually provide it

It is Tabitha who has hatched the notion of writing a family history; Michael finds other members of the family not just uncooperative but hostile, and as Tabitha is locked away in an institution she can give him only sporadic help and tantalising *hints. Tabitha believes that, during the second world war, her brother Lawrence collaborated with the enemy and brought about the death of her brother Godfrey. She may be right but fratricide and treason would be all in a day's work for a bunch like the Winshaws.*
(SUNDAY TIMES, 24 April, 1994)

Tantalus, the mythical king of Phrygia, deeply offended the gods. There are different versions of the crime he committed but it was probably the theft of their food. As a punishment, he was consigned to Hades where he was condemned to stand up to his chin in water whose level receded each time he tried to slake his raging thirst. Fruit trees grew at the edge of the pool, their boughs overhanging the water, but each time he stretched out his hand to pluck a ripe fruit the branches raised it just beyond his reach.

Tantalise, 'to torment someone by showing or promising him things he might have and then withdrawing them', was derived from the king's name in the late sixteenth century, when the story was widely known.

◆ The nineteenth century discovered a new fascination for Tantalus. There was a *Tantalus-cup*, a novelty siphon encased within the figure of a man whose chin came up to the bend of the siphon. Like Tantalus of the fable the figure stood chin-high in water but unable to drink. And there was the *tantalus* or *tantalus-stand*, a receptacle for the display of spirit-decanters. Although not appearing to be so, the decanters were locked into the stand – seemingly available but in fact unobtainable.

In 1802 a Swedish chemist, Anders Ekeberg, named a new element he discovered *tantalum*. He explained his choice as following the custom which favours names from mythology. Certainly that had been the case in Sweden just ten years before when Bergman had given *hartshorn* the name *ammonia* on the same grounds. (See **ammonia**). Ekeberg's choice was apt because when *tantalum* is immersed in acid it is unable to absorb any of it and be saturated by it, just as King Tantalus was incapable of imbibing water. The passion for mythological names was unabated. In 1801, an English chemist Charles Hatchett discovered a metallic element that he called *colombium*. It was found in the mineral that came to be called *tantalite*, from *tantalum*. However, since *colombium* and *tantalum* were very closely related in chemical properties, the German chemist Heinrich Rose in 1844 renamed colombium *niobium*. *Niobe* is the daughter of Tantalus.◆

For another nineteenth century scientific term that originates in the myths of the ancient world, see **ammonia**.

tattoo

1. a signal on a drum or bugle
2. a permanent picture or design on the body

You knew my brother John; but neither you nor, I believe, any human being could distinguish between him and me if we chose to seem alike. Our parents could not; ours is the only instance of which I have any knowledge of so close resemblance as that. I speak of my brother John, but I am not at all sure that his name was not Henry and mine John. We were regularly christened, but afterward, in the very act of tattooing *us with small distinguishing marks, the operator lost his reckoning; and although I bear upon my forearm a small 'H' and he bore a 'J,' it is by no means certain that the letters ought not to have been transposed. . . During all the years that we lived together at home everybody recognized the difficulty of the situation and made the best of it by calling us both 'Jehnry.'*
(Ambrose Bierce, CAN SUCH THINGS BE?, 1909)

To many people dramatic criticism must seem like an attempt to tattoo *soap bubbles.*
(John Mason Brown, 1900–19969)

Even without the tattoos *on his remarkable biceps, he still, in his early fifties, has the look of a marine – close cropped, solid and imperturbable.*
(THE TIMES, 22 January 1994)

When the tavern keepers in seventeenth century Holland heard the bugle or drum recalling the soldiers to barracks, they would turn off the taps on their casks to discourage soldiers from lingering over their drink. The signal was known as *taptoe* from the Dutch *tap*, 'tap' and *toe*, 'shut', 'closed'. The word was borrowed into military English by the middle of the same century and variously spelt as as *taptow*, *taptoo* or *tattoo*. The OED's first quotation well illustrates this use:

If anyone shall bee found tiplinge or drinkinge in any Taverne, Inne, or Alehouse after the houre of nyne of the clock at night, when the Tap-too *beates, hee shall pay 2s. 6d.*
(COLONEL HUTCHINSON'S ORDERS, 1644)

In the eighteenth century the signal formed the basis of an entertainment when it was embellished by military marches and music performed by torchlight. The *Edinburgh Tattoo* is still performed and televised annually. Outside the purely military sphere, the word can be used contemporarily of drum beats from a pop group or of the repetitive rapping of fingers on a surface. In the same sense, Jack London gives a vivid description of a seaman's death in THE SEA WOLF (1904):

The captain, or Wolf Larsen, as men called him, ceased pacing, and gazed down at the dying man. So fierce had this final struggle become that the sailor paused in the act of flinging more water over him, and stared curiously, the canvas bucket partly tilted and dripping its contents to the deck. The dying man beat a tattoo *on the hatch with his heels, straightened out his legs, stiffened in one great, tense effort, and rolled his head from side to side. Then the muscles relaxed, the head stopped rolling, and a sigh, as of profound relief, floated upward from his lips. The jaw dropped, the upper lip lifted, and two rows of tobacco-discolored teeth appeared. It seemed as though his features had frozen into a diabolical grin at the world he had left and outwitted.*

Tattoo in the sense 'a design on the body made by puncturing the skin and inserting indelible dyes' has a totally different etymology. It is from a

Polynesian word for this process, *tatau*. *Ta* means 'a mark, a design'. *Tattoo* was introduced into English by Captain Cook's record of his voyages on the South Seas in 1769. In his JOURNAL DURING HIS FIRST VOYAGE, he writes:

Both sexes paint their Bodys, tattow, *as it is called in their Language. This is done by inlaying the colour of Black under their skins, in such a manner as to be indelible.*

It is perhaps surprising that a word was not coined in English before this time, as the practice to which it refers is very ancient and widespread. The Authorised Version of the Bible of 1611 – over 150 years before Captain Cook's voyage – renders Leviticus Chapter 19, verse 28, as *Ye shall not make any cuttings in your flesh for the dead, nor print any marks upon you.* One of the best modern versions of Scripture, the New International Version of 1973, translates this as *Do not cut your bodies for the dead or put* tattoo *marks on yourselves.* The practice that Leviticus refers to dates back to the divine revelation given to Moses at Sinai, very early indeed in recorded history.

Tattooing was commented on by Columbus amongst West Indians and Central Americans; travellers also found it in some North American Indians and Eskimos. Nor was tattooing unknown in England. There is the legend that King Harold was identified by his sister Edith on the battlefield of Hastings by the tattoo on his neck. Since it had been the practice of Saxons so to mark their soldiers as an aid to identification, there may be some truth in the story.

For another word introduced into English by James Cook, see **taboo**.

tawdry

showy, cheap, of poor quality

It is the biggest Indian reservation on the eastern United States and it was packed from one end to the other with souvenir stores selling tawdry *Indian trinkets, all of them with big signs on their roofs and sides saying: Mocassins! Indian Jewelry! Tomahawks! Polished Gemstones! Crappy Items of Every Description!!*
(Bill Bryson, THE LOST CONTINENT, 1989)

It must be a matter of concern that so much that is trivial, trashy and tawdry *is shaping the ambience in which young lives evolve today.*
(DAILY TELEGRAPH, 4 March 1995)

Some remarkable characters are commemorated in the commonest words. Saint Etheldreda (about 630–679) – known now as *Saint Audrey,* a corruption of her name, but in Old English as Saint Aethelthryth – was one of five daughters of Anna, King of the East Angles in Suffolk. Each one of the sisters became a saint. Audrey had two, apparently unconsummated, marriages, first with Tonbert and then with Egfrith. The latter was some 15 years her junior and, after a decade of marriage, he pressed her for his conjugal rights. Reluctantly he granted her a dissolution of their marriage, so that she could maintain her virginity. At first, in AD 672, she entered the convent at Coldingham; in the following year she founded a religious community at Ely. (The Norman cathedral now stands on the site of the abbey she built.) The rest of her life was spent in a severe regime of penance and prayer.

According to Bede's ECCLESIASTICAL HISTORY (AD 731), St Audrey died of a tumour in her throat, an affliction she looked upon as just punishment for earlier vanity because, in her youth, she had had a penchant for wearing fine necklaces.

St Audrey was well-loved and her shrine a popular visiting place for pilgrims. On 17 October each year her saint's day was marked with a holiday and a fair at Ely. Here were sold laces and fringes for wearing about the neck in her honour. These were known as *St Audrey's laces*, often corrupted to *Tawdry laces* or *tawdries*. Ardent suitors would sometimes buy them to woo their sweethearts. An old ballad pleads:

One time I gave thee a paper of pins,
Another time a tawdry *lace;*
And if thou wilt not grant me love,
In truth I'll die before thy face.

Some sweethearts, however, were more demanding than others:

It was a happy age when a man might have wooed his wench with a pair of kid leather gloves, a silver thimble, or with a tawdry *lace; but now a velvet gown; a chain of pearl, or a coach with four horses will scarcely serve the turn.*
(RICH, MY LADY'S LOOKING-GLASS, 1616)

These quotations show that tawdry laces were worn by rich and poor alike. Nicholas Harpsfield, Archdeacon of Canterbury in the reign of Mary Tudor, says that the necklaces were 'formed of thin and fine silk' (HISTORIA ANGLICANA ECCLESIASTICA). Drayton, however, calls them '*a kind of necklace worn by country wenches*' (margin note, first part of POLY-OLBION, 1612). Certainly those offered at the saint's fair were of the cheap-and-cheerful variety, produced to please the country girls and suit their purses. Not surprisingly then, by the end of the seventeenth century *tawdry*, used as both a noun and an adjective, was applied to any form of inexpensive and showy finery.

tea

the dried leaves of a specific shrub, used to prepare an aromatic drink

'Is there ony hot watter?' asked Mrs Gregson.

'Plenty o' that,' said the red-faced man.

'Teem it in th' big urn,' said Mrs Gregson, 'an'squeeze th' tay-bag. *It'll be thick enoof for th' choir lads.'*

'Couldn't we brew a fresh lot?' asked the vicar's wife.

'We could,' said Mrs Gregson, 'but they wouldn't know th' difference. We allus keep it a bit thin. It's betther for their kidneys.'

'It's a shame,' said Mrs Pyot. 'There's plenty as likes strong tay.*'*
(T Thompson, LANCASHIRE BREW, 1935)

Being interviewed for casual labour on the building site, a candidate was asked by the foreman: 'Can you make a decent cup of tea*?'*

'Oh yes,' came the reply.

'Can you drive a fork-lift truck?' asked the foreman.

A little disconcerted, the job-seeker scratched the back of his head and inquired: 'Just how big is this teapot *then?'*
(DAILY MAIL, April 23 1994)

Tea is prepared from the leaves of the *camellia sinensis.* A Chinese legend dates the discovery of the beverage to the third millennium BC. It tells how falling leaves from a camellia tree drifted into a pot of water which the Emperor Shen-Nung had set to boil, filling the air with their fragrance. Tea was first drunk in China for its medicinal properties and then for pleasure, so that, by the 6th century AD there was a thriving tea trade in East Asia.

In the early seventeenth century the Dutch, who traded extensively in the East, started to import shipments of a herb which the Chinese infused in hot

A taste of India

English involvement in India began largely with the mercantile activities of the East India Company, which was incorporated in 1600. There was severe competition between the British, the French and the Dutch to challenge the Portuguese, the first Europeans to trade in India. It was not until the mid-eighteenth century that British traders predominated. A century later, trading by the East India Company had become political rule throughout virtually all of the subcontinent. It continued until independence in 1947.

British influence on India was obviously great; there was also very considerable impact in the other direction. Specifically with regard to language, English has gained a number of words from that source, including:

bungalow (17th cent): First recorded as *bungale* in the second half of the seventeenth century, the word comes from Hindi *banglā*, meaning 'of Bengal'. It therefore denoted a 'Bengali-style house', that is a flimsy one-storey construction with a thatched roof.

chutney (19th cent): The Hindi word for this spicy relish is *chatni*. An early recipe for it recorded in English lists '*cocoa-nut, lime-juice, garlic, and chilies*' amongst its ingredients.

curry (late 16th cent): from the Tamil word *kari*.

dinghy (late 18th cent) – the Hindi word *ḍeṅgi* or *ḍiṅgi* was a diminutive of *ḍeṅga*, 'boat', and referred to a small open native boat.

dungaree (17th cent): the *Dungrī* district of Bombay gave its name to a stout coarse fabric which was manufactured there. This became *dungaree* in English. In the nineteenth century the name *dungarees* was applied to hardwearing trousers made of this or similar material. (For other Indian cloth imports, see **Fabrics**, page 235).

jungle(18th cent): The Hindi word *jāṅgal* (from Sanskrit *jāṅgala*, 'desert') originally referred to 'uncultivated land, bush'. Anglo-Indian use then applied the term to uncultivated areas that were covered with dense vegetation. By the mid-nineteenth century the word was being applied to similar areas in other parts of the world and had also gained its figurative applications.

kedgeree (17th cent): Hindi *khichrī* was a dish of rice and spiced pulses to which European cookery added fish and eggs.

shampoo (18th cent): The term was originally a verb in English and referred to giving someone a relaxing massage. It is a borrowing of the Hindi *chāmpo*, which came from *chāmpnā* meaning 'to massage, to press'. Its modern use as a verb meaning 'to wash the hair', and as a noun denoting the cleansing agent itself, dates from the 1860s.

It is not surprising that many borrowings cluster round the practicalities of life: a building to live in, food, features of the landscape and products from the country. There are specialist dictionaries on Anglo-Indian words and phrases which record the mutual influence of the two languages.

water to make a drink. The herb was known as *te* in the Amoy Chinese dialect. Under this name, the Dutch introduced it into France in the 1630s, where it was known as *thé*, and into England in the early 1650s where it was originally called *tay*, a form still current in some northern dialects (see the quotation above). *Tay* persisted until the second half of the eighteenth century but was finally ousted by *tea* (sometimes *tee*), a form which arose within a few years of the product's appearance in England. In his diary for 25 September 1660, Samuel Pepys records sending '*for a cup of tee (a China drink) of which I never had drunk before*'. Pepys does not say what he thought of his first cuppa. It is to be hoped that he enjoyed it, for he was a man of modest means and it must have cost him dear. Tea was an extremely expensive commodity, being a monopoly of the East India Company. As such, however, it was fit for a king – in 1664 Charles II was delighted by a presentation of two pounds of tea. It was to be another century before cheaper illegal cargoes were brought in from the continent and the beverage could be enjoyed by all classes.

Although the Dutch were responsible for introducing the English to their national drink, they were not the first to bring news of the Chinese herb into Europe. The Portuguese were also establishing colonies and trading links in the East. They first arrived in Macau, for instance, in 1513 and started officially to trade with China from there in 1553. It was in the late 1550s that they first made mention of tea, calling it *chá*, a word they borrowed from the Mandarin Chinese dialect, *ch'a*. When tea became known in Europe several languages also adopted the term, which even travelled overland to Russia becoming the modern Russian *chai*. Spanish, for instance, had *cha* and Italian *cià*. These became obsolete in favour of words based on *tè*. Modern Portugese, however, retains *chá* and it lingers on in English where it has gradually degenerated into a jocular slang term, *a nice cuppa cha*.

For other seventeenth century taste sensations, see **coffee** and **chocolate**. See also **caddy**.

teetotaller

one who abstains from alcoholic drink of any kind

She talked about the poor blighter as if he wasn't there. Not that Motty seemed to mind. He had stopped chewing his walking-stick and was sitting there with his mouth open. 'He is a vegetarian and a teetotaller *and is devoted to reading. Give him a nice book and he will be quite contented.'*
(P.G.Wodehouse, CARRY ON, JEEVES, 1925)

I greet January the First in a fervour of determined excitement, knowing that this is the year I will become literate, tidy and almost teetotal *(in any table of resolutions, alcohol and its abandonment must surely top the list. . .).*
(GOOD HOUSEKEEPING, January 1995)

The eighteenth and nineteenth centuries saw a marked increase in alcohol consumption in Britain. Rum flowed in from the West Indies and Dutch gin, which had been introduced by William of Orange, was in cheap and abundant supply. By the mid-eighteenth century it was not uncommon for a city dweller to drink a pint of gin a day. Heavy drinking, however, was generally frowned upon only when it lead to rowdy or unsocial behaviour. It was not until the beginning of the nineteenth century when two doctors, one American and one Scottish, published papers in their respective countries suggesting that alcohol could seriously damage health that real concern about this menace grew. By now there were large numbers of taverns and gin palaces in every big town, especially in the poorer areas where those who were ground down by poverty and hard work sought to forget their condition through drink. This pattern was repeated on the other side of the Atlantic. It was time to recognise alcohol abuse as a serious problem.

The first temperance society was founded in Saratoga, New York State, in 1808 but it was to be another twenty years or so before the movement really flourished in Britain. Credit for the word *teetotal*, which served as a rallying cry in both Britain and America, is claimed by both countries.

According to the British story the word's origin had nothing to do with 'tea' as an accepted beverage. The *tee* element is a repetition of the first letter of *total* and is therefore an intensifier. (This is a common linguistic device of emphasis.) In the early days of the movement some reformers were content to preach abstinence from spirits only. Others disagreed, saying that only total abstinence would do. One of this band was Richard (Dicky) Turner, an artisan of Preston, England, who, *'contending for the principle at a temperance meeting about 1833, asserted that "nothing but te-te-total will do"'* (STAUNCH TEETOTALLER, January 1867). The word had immediate appeal. The 1834 issues of the local temperance paper, THE PRESTON TEMPERANCE ADVOCATE, are full of testimonies of 'tee-total abstainers' who have signed the 'tee-total pledge'. Mr Turner became something of a celebrity for his clever coinage. Even his tombstone proclaims the fact. The inscription reads:

Beneath this stone are deposited the remains of Richard Turner, author of the word Teetotal *as applied to abstinence from all intoxicating liquors, who departed this life on the 27th day of October 1846, aged 56 years.*

Possibly a stimulus to Turner's linguistic inventiveness was the word *teetotum*. This was a type of top or spinner, with letters written on the sides. The way it fell decided how the players in the game proceeded. The toy had been in use for over a hundred years by Turner's time and may have been known to him.

The American case for coinage rests on two strands of evidence. Firstly, there is an 1832 example of *teetotally* as an emphatic adverb:

These Mingoes...ought to be essentially, and particularly, and tee-totally *obflisticated off of the face of the yearth.*
(James Hall, LEGENDS OF WEST PHILADELPHIA)

This has no reference to abstinence from strong drink, however, and is surely just a Kentucky backwoodsman creatively intensifying his point.

The second piece of evidence is put by the Rev. Joel Jewell in a letter to the editors of the CENTURY DICTIONARY (1891). The Rev. Jewell became the secretary of a temperance society in Hector, New York. The society had a policy of partial abstinence but in January 1827 it decided to introduce a new pledge for those who wished to commit themselves to total abstinence. The initials that the two pledges bore distinguished them; *O P* signified 'old pledge' and *T* indicated 'total abstinence', so that the new word emerged from the continuous repetition of '*T, Total*'. However, while there is no contemporary evidence to support this claim, letters of the period show that the total abstinence movement in

America came later than and was influenced by the work in Preston – an indication, perhaps, that Dicky Turner can rest in peace. Certainly American lexicographers of the 1840s (Webster and Worcester) and medical professionals ascribed to him the word's origin.

For an entry a teetotaller would not like, see **alcohol**.

temple

a building set apart for the worship of a god

Higher up are the ruins of a Byzantine church built from the stones of a temple *to Adonis, stained grey and brown as the wind has found or overlooked them.*
(Colin Thubron, THE HILLS OF ADONIS, 1968)

As a guide to fruitful contemplation, *the teenagers are encouraged, but not obliged, to think in terms of a circle of eight stones, each representing both a point on the compass and an aspect of one's personalilty or place in life. Topics covered might include dreams and ambitions or self-image.*
(WEEKEND TELEGRAPH, 4 March 1995)

The Latin *templum*, 'temple', originally denoted a consecrated open space that was cut off or set apart by augurs for their observation of the stars and natural phenomena. (Indeed, the word is related to Greek *temnein*, 'to cut'). It was taken into Old English from Latin as *templ* or *tempel*. A variant, *temple*, was later reinforced by the influence of French and became its Middle English form.

The Latin verb *contemplārī*, 'to examine auspices with care', was formed from the intensive prefix *con-* and *templum* to denote the work of the augurs in the temple. The word was then applied more generally with the sense 'to observe carefully'. It was taken into English at the end of the sixteenth century.

For another word involving augurs, see **consider**.

toady

a flatterer, a hanger-on

[Fuegi] was put in charge of the Berliner Ensemble and made to pay for his position by having to toady *to a brutal regime.*
(NATIONAL REVIEW, 21 November 1994)

Charlatans were tricksters, quack doctors who travelled from place to place selling miracle cures for all ills. They relied upon their clever, persuasive patter to sell their wares. This is reflected in the origin of the word *charlatan* which is a borrowing from Italian *ciarlatano*, itself a derivation from the verb *ciarlare*, 'to babble', 'to chatter'. These itinerant quacks also demonstrated 'proof' of the efficacy of their medicines in order to persuade the gullible public to buy them. For example, in the seventeenth century they were often accompanied by a *toad-eater*, an accomplice who would apparently eat a toad. The crowd, believing toads to be poisonous, would gasp with horror as the creature was swallowed and again with amazement as the charlatan effected his cure.

The toad-eater was completely dependent upon his master for his livelihood and performed the trick out of self-interest. In the eighteenth century his role gave rise to the figurative application of *toad-eater* as a 'flatterer' and 'parasite'. The term was reduced to *toady* in the first half of the nineteenth century with the verb *to toady*, meaning 'to fawn', dating from the same period.

For a synonym, see **sycophant**.

toast

1. a grilled piece of bread, crisp and brown
2. wishing someone health and happiness
3. the person whose health is drunk

After five long days, with snowflakes falling in the midnight dusk, we made landfall on tiny, volcanic Deception Island. And sipping whisky, we toasted *in the New Year on the freezing deck, keeping a wary eye on luminous bergs, each with its own flock of penguins.*
(WEEKEND TELEGRAPH, 25 February 1995)

There was a wonderful documentary on the life of Alan Bennett on The South Bank Show a few years ago now. He was reminiscing over the menu of a favourite office cafeteria and looking at the dishes subsequently on offer. 'Avocado with prawns?' he exclaimed. 'You don't want avocado with prawns, you want something on toast*!'*
(THE INDEPENDENT, 28 January 1995)

Ultimately this culinary term has to do with the effect of the burning sun upon the earth. The Latin verb *torrēre* meant 'to dry', 'to parch'. The past participle was *tostus* from which Vulgar Latin derived the unattested verb *tostāre* and the noun *tostāta*, 'a piece of toasted bread'. From these terms Romance languages took their words for 'toast'. Old French had the verb *toster* and the noun *tostée* from which Middle English borrowed *tosten* and *tost* respectively.

From at least the fifteenth century it was common to serve wine or ale with a piece of spiced toast in it. In Shakespeare's THE MERRY WIVES OF WINDSOR (1598), for instance, Falstaff, at the Garter Inn, commands his follower Bardolphe, '*fetch me a quart of Sacke, and put a* toast *in 't.*' The toast served to flavour the drink and collect any sediment in it.

In the seventeenth century this practice gave rise to a figurative application where a *toast* was a lady, usually an admired society beauty, who was said to flavour the wine like spiced toast and to whose health a company was invited to drink. In his comedy THE WAY OF THE WORLD (1700), William Congreve writes of the bitterness of one who is '*More censorious than a decayed Beauty, or a discarded* Toast.' Sir Richard Steele, writing in THE TATLER (4 June 1709), gave the following story for the origin of this use:

Many wits of the last age will assert that the word, in its present sense, was known among them in their youth, and had its rise from an accident at the town of Bath, in the reign of king Charles the Second. It happened that, on a public day, a celebrated beauty of those times was in the Cross Bath, and one of the crowd of her admirers took a glass of the water in which the fair one stood, and drank her health to the company. There was in the place a gay fellow half fuddled, who offered to jump in, and swore, though he liked not the liquor, he would have the toast. *He was opposed in his resolution; yet this whim gave foundation to the present honour which is done to the lady we mention in our liquors, who has ever since been called a* toast.

The application of *toast* to 'a health' may or may not originate in this story but certainly comes from the practice of serving drink with spiced grilled bread.

◆ *Torrid* comes from *torridus*, a Latin adjective derived from *torrēre*. It was used to translate the Latin *zona torrida*, 'torrid zone', from the fourteenth century, but was used as an adjective in its own right meaning 'parched, burning' in the early seventeenth century. Later senses developed from the idea of 'hot in passion', whether the passion of ardent zeal or lust.◆

tobacco

leaves of the tobacco plant dried and prepared for smoking

Her [Virginia Woolf's] cigarettes were made from a special tobacco *called My Mixture. Mr Woolf bought it for her in London and, in the evenings, they used to sit by the fire and make these cigarettes themselves. It was a mild sweet-smelling* tobacco, *and she would not have any other cigarettes, though sometimes she smoked a long cheroot which she enjoyed very much.*
(R J Noble, RECOLLECTIONS OF VIRGINIA WOOLF, 1975)

Tabaco was a New World crop which the Spanish brought back with them from the Indies in the sixteenth century. The word was then borrowed directly into a number of other European languages: *tabaco* (Portuguese), *tabac* (French), *tabak* (German, Dutch, Russian). English originally followed a similar pattern: *tabaco* or *tabacco* were common spellings until the early seventeenth century.

The OED chronicles the debate on the rather disputed origin. A Spanish writer, Oviedo, says that the word is of Haitian origin. His account in his HISTORY OF THE INDIES (1535) states that *tabaco* was the name given to a pipe through which the Indians smoked dried plant leaves and that the term was erroneously transferred to the plant itself by the Spaniards. However, according to Las Casas, another Spaniard who wrote a history of the region in 1552, *tabaco* was the Indian term not for a pipe but for a tight roll of leaves, rather like a cigar in form and use. Which account is correct? It is not known for sure, but a learned paper in the AMERICAN ANTHROPOLOGIST (1889) presents evidence that members of a tribe of South American Indians may have come to northern Haiti towards the end of the fifteenth century. They used a pipe called a *taboca*, similar to the one described by Oviedo, for inhaling various hallucinatory plant substances. Possibly Oviedo mistook the use of this pipe for that of the rolled up leaves, the similarity between *taboca* and *tabacos* compounding his error.

The Spaniards knew that the Indians of the Indies and Central America used tobacco in their religious rituals but they were not averse to smoking it themselves. By 1558 tobacco was being grown in Spain, as well as imported, to feed the new habit. It did not catch on in England, however, until it was introduced to the English court by an Englishman, traditionally said to be Sir Walter Raleigh. Raleigh certainly popularised the habit at court and was a confirmed addict, understandably needing a final smoke to calm his nerves before his execution in 1618. One ballad composer had this to say about the subsequent popularity of the weed:

Though many men crack,
Some of ale, some of sack,
And think they have reason to do it;
Tobacco *hath more,*
That will never give o'er,
The honour they do unto it.
Tobacco *engages*
Both sexes, all ages,
The poor as well as the wealthy;
From the court to the cottage,
From childhood to dotatge,
Both those that are sick, and the healthy.

James 1 detested tobacco which he referred to as 'that most filthy weed', but royal disapproval was not enough to prevent the government from protecting the Virginian tobacco trade. England, as the ballad proclaimed, was hooked.

See also **cigar**.

treacle

molasses, the thick, dark syrup produced in the refining of sugar

When that young man had caught her from stone to stone as she passed over the ford at Bolton, she was almost ready to give herself to him. But then had come upon her the sense of sickness, that faint, overdone flavour of sugared sweetness, which arises when sweet things become too luscious to the eater. She had struggled to be honest and strong, and had just not fallen into the pot of treacle.

(Anthony Trollope, LADY ANNA, 1846)

These palms are, for their family, ugly trees. Their stem is very large, and of a curious form, being thicker in the middle than at the base or top. They are excessively numerous in some parts of Chile, and valuable on account of a sort of treacle *made from the sap.*

(Charles Darwin, THE VOYAGE OF THE BEAGLE, 1839)

As a corps in pale tie-dyed sarongs rose to their feet pretending to be hills among which the Brontës skipped like lambs, I began to feel solid ground turning into treacly *bog.*

(DAILY TELEGRAPH, 8 March 1995)

In classical times physicians taught that the antidote for a bite from a wild animal or venomous reptile was a compound which incorporated the flesh of the creature. The Greek expression for such a compound was *thēriakē* (from *thērion*, 'poisonous beast', diminutive of *thēr*, 'beast'), which gave the Latin *thēriaca*. From here the word progressed into Romance and Germanic languages, first appearing in English as *tyriaca* around the turn of the eleventh century. It subsisted until the eighteenth century in the forms *theriac* and *theriacle*, meaning 'antidote'.

Latin *thēriaca* had a second path of development. *Triaca* was a popular Late Latin form of *thēriaca* and yielded a crop of variants in the Romance languages, coming into Old French as *triacle*, a form which was then borrowed into Middle English. In the fourteenth century, then, *triacle* was an ointment containing venom to destroy venom. Some translations of the Bible, the Great Bible of 1539, for instance, used *treacle* or *triacle* as a rendering for 'balm'. Later the term also denoted an efficacious remedy for the healing of diseases in general. Some plants held to have medicinal qualities had *treacle* incorporated into their local country names: *rue*, *valerian* and *garlic*, for instance, were all known as *countryman's treacle* in various counties. Naturally any remedy that was intended to be swallowed was made more palatable if it was sweetened; the syrup that came from sugar during the refining process proved a useful agent for this, so that by the end of the seventeenth century *treacle* was applied not only to the medicine but also to the syrup itself. Figuratively, *treacle* – or, more commonly its adjective *treacly* – denotes 'cloying sentimentality'.

It is not only in the context of treacle that the idea surfaces of incorporating the flesh of the animal by which one has been bitten into a remedy. Sixteenth and seventeenth century medical treatments regularly recommended putting a hair from a dog that had bitten you into the wound, to assure healing. From this came the subsequent saying '*Take the hair of the dog that bit you*', in the sense of having a drink the following morning of the same beverage that had caused the hangover the night before.

For another sticky confection, see **marmalade**.

trivial

unimportant, insignificant, slight

Habitual attitudes and behaviour often receive reinforcement from external circumstances. To take a trivial *example, anyone who has attempted to give up smoking comes to realize that the wish for a cigarette often depends upon cues from the environment which recur at intervals. Finishing a meal; sitting down to work at a familiar desk; reaching for a drink after work is over – such* trivial *reinforcing stimuli are well known to everyone who has struggled with the habit.*
(Anthony Storr, SOLITUDE, 1988)

My son, who has always shown manly scorn for such a trivial *piece of nonsense, receives stacks of [Valentine] cards and sends none. He does write to his girlfriend and buy her flowers but not when advertisers nag him to and certainly not when the prices are seasonally hiked.*
(WEEKEND TELEGRAPH, 11 February 1995)

The Latin noun *trivium* meant 'a place where three roads meet' (from *tri-*, 'three' and *via*, 'way'). People invariably bump into one another and exchange gossip at a busy crossroads and so the derived adjective *triviālis*, which literally meant 'belonging to the crossroads', carried the sense 'commonplace, ordinary'. In the English of the late sixteenth century *trivial* was used with the sense 'ordinary, common' which soon developed into 'unimportant, trifling'.

Trivial was not new to the sixteenth century, however. Medieval learning had been divided into seven liberal arts. Four of these – music, arithmetic, geometry and astronomy – were regarded as the higher disciplines and were known as the *quadrivium* (from *quadri-*, 'four' and *via*, 'way'). The remaining three – grammar, rhetoric and logic – were the lower disciplines and comprised the *trivium*. When *trivial* was first used in English in the fifteenth century, then, it denoted anything concerning the *trivium* and its subjects. However, the fact that the adjective referred to the lower disciplines, together with growing contempt for antiquated medieval scholarship in the light of the Renaissance, possibly further influenced the derogatory use of *trivial* in the late sixteenth century.

umpire

an arbiter, a judge, a referee

A black spot happened to cross the eye of the ancient umpire *just as the baker put all his feet and legs and pads in front of a perfectly straight ball, and, as he plaintively remarked over and over again, he had to give the batsman the benefit of the doubt, hadn't he? It wasn't as if it was his fault that a black spot had crossed his eye just at that moment.*
(A G Macdonell, ENGLAND THEIR ENGLAND, 1933)

Modern English is more familiar with *umpire* as 'one who enforces rules and fair play' in certain sports such as cricket, baseball or tennis. Originally, however, an *umpire* was a person who was chosen as an arbitrator in any context where the services of a fair and impartial moderator were required. The first attested use of *umpire* in a sporting context was with reference to wrestling in 1714, some three hundred years after its use as 'judge, arbiter'.

The word originated in Old French as *nonper* or *nomper*, literally 'non-peer': that is 'not equal', 'a third, and therefore impartial, party' (from *non*, 'not' and *per*, 'equal', from Latin *pār*, 'equal'). The word was borrowed into Middle English quite correctly as *a noumpere*. However, the initial *n* was wrongly understood to belong to the indefinite article, so that *an oumpere* soon became current. Spellings such as *umpere*, *umpeer* and *umpyre* followed, *umpire* becoming finally established around the end of the seventeenth century.

◆ Also from Old French *per* and Latin *pār*, 'equal', comes English *peer* meaning 'one's equal'. Studies in child development, for instance, are much concerned with *peer pressure* – pressure on children and teenagers by others of their own age. In the cases where one's equal was a fellow nobleman, the term *peer* came to mean lord. It is particularly found today in the phrase *peers of the realm*.

Pār is also evident in *compare* while its derivative *paria*, 'equal things', is the source of English *pair*, through Old French *paire*.◆

For details of an old game where an umpire was required, see **handicap**.

Mind your indefinite article

A few common English words, at some stage in their development, lost an initial letter *n* to the indefinite article. *Apron*, for instance, was originally spelt *napron*, being a fourteenth-century borrowing of Old French *naperon* (a diminutive of *nape*, 'tablecloth'). Modern French retains *napperon* but in English *a napron* became *an apron*. The error was already in evidence by the mid-fifteenth century but not until the end of the sixteenth century was the initial *n* lost for ever.

Another borrowing from Old French, *noumpere*, suffered the same fate in the fifteenth century, eventually to emerge as *umpire*. (Full details are given in that entry.) But the error was indiscriminate and attacked English words as well. Old English *nædre*, 'snake', became *naddre* in Middle English but between 1300 and 1500 lost its initial *n* to become *adder*.

Sometimes the error was reversed. The entry for *idiot* shows how, in the sixteenth century, the word was sometimes spelt as *nidiot*, the initial *n* having been transferred from the end of the indefinite article. This form gave rise to the variant *nidget* which persisted into the nineteenth century.

The various forms which Old English *efeta* passed through to emerge as *newt* are difficult to account for, but in the fifteenth century an *n* was transferred to the intermediate form *ewt*.

Nickname has a similar history. Middle English had *an ekename*, that is 'an additional name', until around the mid-fifteenth century when the form *nekename* began to appear.

Such misinterpretations are not unique to English, however. The long and complicated history of *omelette* is marked by a similar error in French – this time with the definite article. See **omelette**.

uncouth

1. awkward, ungainly
2. unrefined, uncultured

A few would at once emerge on its being found after their first examination that they were likely to be ornaments to the college; these would win valuable scholarships that enabled them to live in some degree of comfort, and would amalgamate with the more studious of those who were in a better social position, but even these, with few exceptions, were long in shaking off the uncouthness *they brought with them to the University, nor would their origin cease to be easily recognisable till they had become dons and tutors.*
(Samuel Butler, THE WAY OF ALL FLESH, 1903)

English has retained a number of adjectives whose negative form is current while the positive has become either obsolete or rare. *Uncouth* is one of these.

The Old English adjective *cūth* (*couth*) meant 'well-known, familiar', being a derivative of the verb *cunnan.* Originally, then, its negative, *uncūth* (*uncouth*), meant 'unknown', 'unfamiliar'. But whereas *couth* barely managed to survive into the eighteenth century (until it reappeared as a back-formation of *uncouth* in the late nineteenth century, often in humorous contexts), *uncouth* remained a well-used word. It developed various shades of meaning over the centuries all seemingly stemming from the notion that what is unknown and unfamiliar is also strange, suspect and therefore ultimately unacceptable. Swift is clearly not impressed by the Scots' way of talking:

There are some people who think they sufficiently acquit themselves and entertain their company with relating of facts of no consequence, nor at all out of the road of such common incidents as happen every day; and this I have observed more frequently among the Scots than any other nation, who are very careful not to omit the minutest circumstances of time or place; which kind of discourse, if it were not a little relieved by the uncouth *terms and phrases, as well as accent and gesture, peculiar to that country, would be hardly tolerable.*
(HINTS TOWARDS AN ESSAY ON CONVERSATION, 1710)

The modern senses 'awkward, clumsy' developed in the sixteenth century and 'crude and unrefined' in the eighteenth.

◆ *Unruly* is another example of a negative form that has outlasted the positive. It is of more recent coinage and quite transparent in its meaning and origin. The adjective *ruly* now survives only as a back formation of *unruly.* It was coined around the turn of the fifteenth century and meant 'obedient to rule', 'orderly'. *Unruly,* meaning 'ungovernable', 'disorderly' dates from the same period.◆

See also **unkempt** and **unwieldy**

unkempt

1. dishevelled, uncombed
2. neglected, uncared for

The wedding reception was in full swing in the adjacent hall. . . On the stage an unkempt *group of hairy musicians played soaring, swirling music.*
(WEEKEND TELEGRAPH, 4 March 1995)

Unkempt and *uncombed* both mean the same thing; they are cousins and can be traced to the unattested Germanic form *kamboz,* 'comb'. In the case of *uncombed*, *kamboz* was responsible for the Old English word *camb* which became *comb* in Modern English.

As for *unkempt*, *kamboz* spawned the derivative *kambjan*. From this the Old English verb *cemban*, 'to comb', was derived, and this in turn yielded the Middle English word *kemb*, 'to comb'. From this came *unkembed*, 'uncombed', which was the common form from the fourteenth to nineteenth century. The variant *unkempt* is found from the sixteenth century onwards, but only at first applied to language and not to hair or appearance. In his SHEPHERDS CALENDER (1579), Edmund Spenser laments '*howe my rymes bene rugged and unkempt*', and in the FAIRIE QUEENE (1590) he writes of '*vncourteous and vnkempt*' words. Not until the eighteenth century did *unkempt* come to be used to mean 'uncombed', when it supplanted *unkembed*. Having established itself, in the following century it went on to develop the wider sense of 'neglected, uncared for' with regard to the whole appearance, not just the hair.

Unkempt is one of those words that is much more common with a negative prefix. The positive *kempt*, however, has been around for nearly a thousand years, but was little used up to the second half of the nineteenth century. It may well have come back into use because of the rise of *unkempt* around that time. *Kempt* originally referred to well-combed hair or wool but it now enjoys the extended sense 'well-tended'.

◆ *Kamboz* can be traced to an unattested prehistoric Germanic form *gombhos* which is related to words which mean 'tooth' in various languages. A *comb*, therefore, is named for its teeth. ◆

See also **uncouth** and **unwieldy** for words that begin with a negative prefix.

With and without

Some words like to do without, for they accept the suffix *-less*, 'without', but not its contrary *-ful*:

ageless
countless
feckless
hapless
leafless
lifeless
loveless
peerless
priceless
rootless
sleepless
stainless
strapless
timeless
toothless
voiceless

unwieldy

difficult to handle, unmanageable

A cynical columnist once compared marriage to an overgrown courgette. While falling in love is sweet, tender and tasty, ran the article, living together turns romance into something much more unwieldy *and unpalatable, more like a marrow. And who wants a marrow?*
(GOOD HOUSEKEEPING, August 1994)

The verb *wield* can be traced back to an unattested Germanic base *walth-*, 'to possess power' and probably still further to an Indo-European root *wal*, 'to be strong' (source of Latin *valēre*). Originally in Saxon times *wield* meant 'rule, govern, command' but by the eleventh century an extended sense 'to manage a tool or weapon with skill' was emerging. This, of course, is the current meaning of the verb.

The derived Middle English adjective *wieldy*, now rarely used, meant 'strong, vigorous, capable of handling a heavy weapon'. Its opposite, *unwieldy*, therefore meant 'weak and feeble in body', through age, perhaps, or infirmity.

In the sixteenth century *wieldy* was also applied to the object wielded, to give the sense 'easily handled or controlled'. It might be applied to a horse, a boat or a weapon, for instance. Its opposite, *unwieldy*, duly followed suit with the sense 'difficult to control or handle', because of the object's size or shape.

◆ If indeed *wield* does ultimately stem from *wal*, it is a distant relative of words deriving from Latin *valēre*, such as *valiant*, *valid* and *value*.◆

For other words that begin with a negative prefix, see also **uncouth** and **unkempt**.

Negative prefixes

It seems that some words have bias to the negative – they prefer to appear with a negative prefix and look odd without it.

UN

- uncouth
- ungainly
- unkempt
- unruly
- unscathed
- untoward
- unwieldy
- unwonted

DIS

- disabled
- disconsolate
- disgruntled
- dismayed
- disparate
- dishevelled

IN

- inalienable
- incessant
- indelible
- indomitable
- ineffable
- inept
- inestimable
- inexorable
- innocent
- innocuous
- inordinate
- insatiable
- insufferable
- inviolate

P G Wodehouse is one writer to break this rule for humorous effect:

He spoke with a certain what-is-it in his voice, and I could see that, if not actually disgruntled, he was far from being gruntled.
(THE CODE OF THE WOOSTERS, 1938).

See also entries for **uncouth, unkempt.**

uproar

commotion, hubbub, tumult

I went down to Greenway Lane Farm by the quiet meadows fragrant with the incense of evening prayers. How sweet and still and pure after the noise and dust and crowd and racket of the town, the fine and smart dresses, the tawdry finery, the flaunting ribbons and the uproar *of the cheese market where the band was thundering and the dancers whirling. Here the sweet flowers were blossoming and the only sound was the birds singing very quietly.*
(Francis Kilvert, DIARY, Whit Monday, 25 May 1874)

But later, in bed, I became anxious. Never before had I heard the wind quite so violent in Fairacre. . .I pulled the bedclothes up round my ears, thanked heaven that I was schoolteacher and not a sailor, and slept amidst the uproar.
(Miss Read, THE FAIRACRE FESTIVAL, 1968)

. . .the future George IV, was drunk on his wedding night, parted with his wife soon after and attempted – and failed – to get rid of her in a sensational case in the House of Lords which kept the entire country in uproar *for six months.*
(Paul Johnson, WAKE UP BRITAIN!, 1994)

Appearances can be deceptive. *Uproar,* in spite of its form and meaning, does not derive from the same source as *roar. Roar* is an old imitative word: Old English had *rarian,* which finds its parallel in early German and Dutch words. *Uproar,* on the other hand, derives from the Middle Dutch *oproer* which means 'confusion', 'insurrection' (from *op,* 'up' and *roer,* 'confusion'). It was introduced into English by William Tyndale. Tyndale, a leader of the Reformation in England, had plans to translate the Bible into English. These met with considerable opposition, however, and so he undertook the task in Germany. Here he made his translations of the New Testament (1526) from the original Greek and Hebrew but also drew upon the work of other translators. One of these was Martin Luther, who used the German word *Aufruhr* when referring to certain scenes of confusion in the original text. Tyndale's work reflects this use for, where Luther has *aufruhr,* Tyndale has *uproar.* He renders Acts 21:38, for instance, as: *That Ægipcian whych. . . made an* vproure, *and ledde out into the wildernes about iiij. thousande men.*

When Miles Coverdale made his translation of the Bible nine years later in 1535, he did not draw on the original texts at all but on the Vulgate Bible together with Luther's and Tyndale's renditions, so that *uproar* features in his text also. Such was the impact of these versions of the Bible in the vernacular that *uproar* became a familiar word from the 1540s onwards. Besides its sense of 'commotion and disorder', it developed the related meaning of 'deafening clamour and outcry', which was obviously influenced by the etymologically unrelated *roar.* The early English spelling was either *uprour(e)* or *uprore* but, by the end of the sixteenth century, *uproar* had made an appearance, about the same time that the spelling of *roar* also settled into its modern form.

For another instance of a word influenced by an etymologically unrelated word, see **blindfold**. For another word that entered English through Bible translation, see **slippery**.

utopia

an ideal state, a country of perfection, that is probably unattainable

An acre in Middlesex is better than a principality in Utopia.
(T.B. Macaulay, ESSAYS: LORD BACON, 1837)

I know perfectly well I'll be called a utopian. *It's true! And I say: Why not? We must have* utopias *so that one day they may become realities. Less than a century ago, social security, unemployment benefits, and paid vacations were* utopias; *today we have them and everyone takes it for granted. The same is true for everything: what for the moment seems unattainable will be tomorrow's reality.*
(Emilie Carles, tr Avriel H Goldberger, A WILD HERB SOUP,1991)

Sir Thomas More was a leading scholar and humanist in Renaissance England. He numbered Erasmus, Colet and Lily amongst his friends and, at court, was greatly favoured by his king, Henry VIII. In 1516 More published a political work entitled UTOPIA, the name he gave to an imaginary island where a perfect form of government and society had been achieved. The work is divided into two parts: Book One is a discourse on the economic, legal, social and moral failings of contemporary Europe, while Book Two details the perfection of *Utopia* where principles dear to the humanists, such as education for all, religious tolerance and community of goods, are given full rein and result in a state that is happy, stable and just. More was too much of a realist to imagine that such perfection was ultimately possible or had ever been reached: he coined *Utopia* from the Greek *ou*, 'not', and *topos*, 'place' so that the island was called 'nowhere'.

The work was widely acclaimed. From the original Latin it was translated into French, German, Italian and Spanish and, in 1551, into English, and so, in all these languages, *Utopia* describes ideal, albeit unattainable, political or social reform. The cynicism of the modern age has meant that *utopian* is now a term of condemnation; the implication is that whatever or whoever is so described may be praiseworthy but is quite impractical and unrealistic.

Possibly More might be heartened to hear that Utopia now officially exists – it is the place on Mars where the Viking II spacecraft landed.

vaccine

a substance containing antibiotics which is injected into the bloodstream to protect a person from disease

CHICKEN AND EGG VACCINE
An automatic system for injecting eggs is rapidly replacing the traditional practice of vaccinating *chicks by hand in the US poultry industry. . . The machine first punches a tiny hole in the shell at the large end of the egg and then injects* vaccine *through the hole into the chick embryo. Injecting chicks by machine is much cheaper and easier than employing people to grab newly hatched chicks and* vaccinate *them by hand. . .. The system is being used first in the US to* vaccinate *against Marek's disease, which causes nervous system tumours in the birds. In Europe, the poultry industry is most interested in a novel* vaccine *against Gumboro disease, which destroys the birds' immune system.*
(FINANCIAL TIMES, February 1994)

Smallpox was once dreaded. Epidemics were frequent, the mortality rate was high and survivors were left badly scarred, although safe in the knowledge that they were now protected from reinfection. The observation that cowhands and milkmaids who had been infected with cowpox also appeared to have later immunity from smallpox is sometimes attributed to a Dorset farmer, Benjamin Jesty, although it appears that there was quite a tradition to this effect amongst country folk. Dr Edward Jenner's interest and subsequent research into the rumour are undisputed, however. The culmination of Jenner's investigations came in 1796 when he inoculated an eight-year-old boy, James Phipps, with matter from cowpox pustules and afterwards inoculated him with smallpox. The boy remained healthy. Jenner was then able to demonstrate that matter drawn from a vesicle on the boy's body was effective in inoculating others. In this way resistance could be passed on.

Jenner published his findings in an article INQUIRY INTO THE CAUSE AND EFFECTS OF THE VARIOLAE VACCINAE in 1798. They were not well received and met with fierce opposition initially until a number of eminent physicians and surgeons declared their confidence in his work. In 1853 vaccination against smallpox was made compulsory in Britain. Nevertheless the order was often ignored, while outrageous rumours circulated amongst the uneducated that vaccinated patients risked becoming like cows themselves. The case was cited of a youngster from Peckham who displayed bovine behaviour, moving on all fours, mooing and butting. An entry in Francis Kilvert's diary dated 27 February 1871, reads:

Clyro Petty Sessions. Fifteen people summoned for neglecting to have their children vaccinated, but they got off by paying costs.

The following year the order was enforced.

Vaccine entered English as an adjective derived from Latin *vaccinus*, 'belonging to a cow' (from *vacca*, 'cow'), possibly by way of the French (*virus*) *vaccine*. Jenner used it in couplings such as *vaccine disease*, *vaccine matter*, *vaccine virus* and *vaccine inoculation*. The latter was the source of the verb *vaccinate* and the noun *vaccination*, both of which were coined at the beginning of the nineteenth century. Initially *vaccination* referred uniquely to the preventative treatment of smallpox. Later, in honour of Jenner's pioneering work, the French microbiologist and chemist Louis Pasteur (1822–95) applied the term more widely to the prevention of different diseases with other types of inoculation. The earliest recorded use of *vaccine* standing alone as a noun to denote 'matter for inoculation' dates from 1846.

vanilla

1. a type of orchid
2. flavouring obtained from the orchid's dried pods

Instead of promoting vanilla's *unique taste, too many bland ice creams and yogurts have degraded the name, and virtually given it the status of a non-flavour.*

Another nonentity is cheap vanilla *'flavouring', which nevertheless lures home cooks with a sense of convenience, though it stems more from a laboratory than a* vanilla *pod. You can take a chemical formula out of a pod, but you can't take the artificiality out of the flavour. With* vanilla *it has to be the real thing...*

(WEEKEND TELEGRAPH, 8 August 1994)

Vanilla pods come from a species of climbing orchid indigenous to the tropics of Mexico. The Aztecs used them with other ingredients such as chilli water, powdered flowers and honey to enhance the flavour of their chocolate drink. When the conquering Spaniards adapted the chocolate recipe to their taste, they replaced the chilli with nutmeg and cinnamon but retained the vanilla and took pods home with them to Spain.

The Spanish avoided the difficult Aztec word *tlixochitl* with some justification and instead called the pod *vainilla*, 'little sheath', with an eye to its elongated shape. *Vainilla* was a diminutive form of *vaina* which, in turn, came from Latin *vāgīna*, meaning 'sheath, scabbard'.

Vanilla came into English in the seventeenth century along with the recipe for chocolate which, for almost a century, had been jealously guarded by the Spanish (see **chocolate**).

◆ The Romans used the term *vāgīna* as a euphemism for the 'female genital canal', hence English *vagina*.◆

ventriloquist

someone appearing not to speak, yet producing the speech for a dummy, another person, etc.

'John Major is more a ventriloquist's *dummy than a Prime Minister. . .'*
(Sir Nicholas Fairbairn on BBC in Scotland, April 1994)

According to the etymology, a *ventriloquist* is 'one who is skilled in speaking from his belly' (although speech is, in fact, produced quite normally). The word derives from Late Latin *ventriloquus*, 'speaking from the stomach' (from Latin *venter*, 'stomach' and *loquī*, 'to speak'). The word was modelled on a Greek word *eggastrimuthos* (*engastrimyth* in English), which was similarly derived.

Ancient texts contain many hints of the use to which ventriloquism was put in oracles and the like. In the Middle Ages it was regarded as a device of sorcery or evidence of possession by an evil spirit and was punishable by death. In the fourteenth century, for instance, the French magician Meskyllene was executed for touring with a box which uttered judgements and predictions. Not until the Renaissance did ventriloquism begin to be perceived as a skill. The Renaissance prince Francis I of France (1494–1547) is said to have had the first ventriloquist entertainer at court. Gradually ventriloquism shook off its evil associations and gained respectability until the art was perfected in the eighteenth century.

◆ Latin *loqui*, 'to speak' is the source of:

colloquy (16th cent) and *colloquial* (18th cent), from Latin *colloquī*, 'to speak together, to converse'

elocution (16th cent), *eloquent* and *eloquence* (14th cent), from Latin *ēloquī*, 'to speak out'

loquacious (17th cent) from Latin *loquāx* (stem- *loquāc-*), from *loquī*, 'to speak'

Latin *venter* is the source of:

ventral (18th cent) and *ventricle* (15th cent), from Latin *ventriculus*, diminutive of *venter*.◆

villain

a rogue, a criminal

[Miss Long]was infatuated and would not listen to those friends who told her that he was a villain *and only wanted her money. . . At length Lady Catherine gave way and consented to the marriage, which*

Miss Long never ceased to regret, for her husband treated her in the most brutal manner and squandered the estate.
(Francis Kilvert, DIARY, Friday, 12 December 1873)

The villain *of the piece is Bulstrode, a banker and philanthropist of the sort that was the backbone of provincial English towns.*
(THE TIMES, 22 January 1994)

According to the Yorkshire Evening Press a remand prisoner is suing Doncaster Prison, on the very proper grounds that they have cut his hair too short and made him look like a villain.
(THE GUARDIAN, 25 January 1995)

This is an instance of public opinion making corrupt endings of honest beginnings. The medieval Latin word for a farm worker was *vīllānus* (from *villa*, meaning 'farm' or 'farming estate'). The word came into Middle English as *vilein* or *vilain* by way of Old French and denoted a peasant or a serf who, under the feudal system, was bound to serve a lord or property in exchange for the right to hold a parcel of land. Such social inferiors were generally despised by those of a higher class. Low-birth meant base instincts, lack of moral judgement and a natural inclination to wrongdoing. Interestingly the two Middle English variants *vilein* and *vilain* soon parted company, the former retaining the meaning of 'serf' and the latter taking on the derogatory overtones of 'scoundrel'.

◆ *Villas* are these days ubiquitous; any domestic residence can be given a gloss of style and called a *villa*. The smallest and most unprepossessing time-shares throughout the Mediterranean basin almost universally share the name. The Latin word retains more of its positive character in *village*.

The suffix *-anus* is very commonly found in the slightly different guise of *-an*. It means 'of, coming from, pertaining to', as in *urban* ('belonging to a city'), *Roman* ('coming from Rome'), *Lutheran* ('pertaining to Luther').◆

For other words for scoundrel, see **cad** and **blackguard**.

viper

a type of poisonous snake

Of reptiles there are many kinds: one snake (a Trigonocephalus, or Cophias), from the size of the poison channel in its fangs, must be very deadly. Cuvier, in opposition to some other naturalists, makes this a sub-genus of the rattlesnake, and intermediate between it and the viper. *In confirmation of this opinion, I observed a fact, which appears to me very curious and instructive. . . This Trigonocephalus has, therefore, in some respects the structure of a* viper, *with the habits of a rattlesnake.*
(Charles Darwin, THE VOYAGE OF THE BEAGLE, 1839)

In ancient times it was believed that vipers gave birth to live young – the baby was supposed to eat its way out from the female at birth, so killing her. The Latin *vīpera*, 'viper, snake', is a contracted form of *vivipara* (from *vīvus*, 'alive, living' and *parere*, 'to give birth, to produce'). The zoological adjective *viviparus* obviously comes from the same source. *Vīpera* passed into Old French as *vipere* and from there into English in the sixteenth century.

The most efficacious cure for the viper's bite was a compound containing its flesh (see **treacle**), but the flesh on its own was also valued for its medicinal properties.

Not surprisingly, many writers have built on the infamy of the *viper* for their own figurative extensions. The most common is to apply it to a viciously vindictive, spiteful person; in similar vein, the phrase *a viper in one's bosom* alludes to the old fable of the viper nurtured in a person's bosom that turns and poisons its host. Both these uses have been current since the sixteenth century.

◆ *Vīvus* comes from the verb *vīvere*, 'to live'. This verb is apparent in many other words denoting life, living and liveliness, such as: *convivial, revive, survive, vital, vivacious, vivid, vivisection.*

Latin derived *parēns*, 'parent', from *parere.* Its stem *parent-* was responsible for *parent* in Old French and then English.◆

wanton

1. excessive and pointless
2. capricious, wilful, arbitrary
3. immoral, lewd, lascivious
4. abundant, profligate

A man shall see, where there is a house full of children, one or two of the eldest respected, and the youngest made wantons; *but in the midst, some that are as it were forgotten, who many times, nevertheless, prove the best.* (Francis Bacon, OF PARENTS AND CHILDREN, Essays,1601)

I discovered that a lot of imported drainage-pipes for the settlement had been tumbled in there. There wasn't one that was not broken. It was a wanton *smash-up.* (Joseph Conrad, THE HEART OF DARKNESS, 1902)

A lack of firm discipline in the formative years is at the etymological heart of this word. The Middle English form *wantowen* shows that the word was formed from the prefix *wan-*, meaning 'lacking, wanting', and *towen,* which came from Old English *togen,* the past participle of *teon* 'to draw', and therefore meant 'to bring up', 'to educate', 'to take in hand'. The other side of the coin was the Middle English adjective *welitowen,* which meant 'well-brought-up'.

Not surprisingly, from its earliest uses *wanton* often described unruly children. Indeed in the sixteenth and seventeenth centuries the word was used as a noun to denote 'a spoilt brat': *I am enforced to thinke . . . that thy parents made thee a* wanton *with too much cockering.* (John Lyly, EUPHUES AND HIS ENGLAND, 1580)

From the seventeenth to the nineteenth centuries the adjective often singled out cruel boys:

As flies to wanton *Boyes are we to*
th' Gods,
They kill us for their sport.
(Shakespeare, KING LEAR, Act 4, scene 1, 1605)

But the Middle English adjective was also extended to describe unruly, rebellious people or behaviour in general, and its many subsequent shades of meaning sprang from the basic notion of lack of discipline and self-control which manifests itself in thoughtless excess. By the end of the thirteenth century, for instance, lustful, unchaste women and lewd behaviour in general also came within its scope. Francis Bacon epigrammatically puts it thus:

Nuptial love maketh mankind; friendly love perfecteth it; but wanton *love corrupteth, and embaseth it.* ('Of Love', ESSAYS, 1625)

More popular works were free with the adjective in much less elevated settings. It is hardly surprising that it is found repeatedly in John Cleland's FANNY HILL (1748–9). Here is one instance:

Then his touches were so exquisitely wanton, *so luxuriously diffus'd and penetrative at times, that he had made me perfectly rage with titillating fires.*

Other modern senses of 'gratuitous cruelty or neglect' and 'arbitrary destruction' emerged in the seventeenth century. The Spanish conquerors of the New World were noted for their brutality – but it was not wanton destructiveness in the case of Cortés, it appears:

It may seem slight praise to say that the followers of Cortés used no blood-hounds to hunt down their wretched victims, as in some other parts of the continent, nor exterminated a peaceful and submissive population in mere wantonness *of cruelty, as in the Islands.* (William Hickling Prescott, THE HISTORY OF THE CONQUEST OF MEXICO, 1843)

wedlock

matrimony, the state of marriage

Pedro: For all your Character of Don Vincentio she is as like to marry him as she was before.

Hellena: Marry Don Vincentio! hang me, such a Wedlock *would be worse than Adultery with another Man: I had rather see her in the Hostel de Dieu, to waste her Youth there in Vows, and be a Handmaid to Lazers and Cripples, than to lose it in such a Marriage.*

(Aphra Behn, THE ROVER; OR THE BANISH'D CAVALIERS, PART 1, 1677)

The two elements of this word seem to suggest the permanency of the marriage bond, that one is 'locked' into the relationship. In fact *wedlock* was once *wedlāc*, where *wedd* meant 'a pledge' and *-lāc* was an Old English suffix giving the sense of 'carrying out' or 'putting into action' the noun that preceded it. Thus the compound had the sense 'the activity of making a pledge'. Old English had a number of such compounds – *rēaflāc*, for instance, was 'robbery' and *feohtlāc* 'warfare' – but, of these, only *wedlock* remains. It has been used commonly since AD 1100 and, because of its importance in the fabric of social life, finds eloquent expression in the greatest writers:

Boweth youre nekke under that
blisful yok
Of soveraynetee, noght of servyse,
Which that men clepeth spousaille or
wedlock;
(Chaucer, The Clerkes Tale, CANTERBURY TALES, 1387)

Shakespeare, of course, recognises the pain or the pleasure wedlock can bring:

For what is wedlock *forced but a hell,*
An age of discord and continual strife?
Whereas the contrary bringeth bliss,
And is a pattern of celestial peace.
(Shakespeare, HENRY VI, PART ONE, Act 5, scene 5, 1592)

The term is somewhat old fashioned to modern ears but remains familiar through the words of the marriage service in the BOOK OF COMMON PRAYER that date back to 1549 ('*Forasmuche as N. and N. haue consented together in holye* wedlocke . . .'), and also through the thirteenth-century expressions *born in* and *born out of wedlock*, to denote legitimate and illegitimate offspring. However, modern forms of the marriage service and a diminishing of the taboo over illegitimacy may well mean the days of this lone surviving compound are numbered.

◆ *Wedding* is the gerundive of the verb *wed*, 'to pledge' and hence 'to marry'. Originally, it meant 'the action of marrying' and also 'the state of wedlock' but around the turn of the fourteenth century began to be applied as a noun to the marriage ceremony itself.

Wed comes from the unattested Old Germanic noun *wadhjam*, 'pledge', which is also the source of *gage*, *engage*, *wage* and *wager*.

window

an opening in a wall to admit light and air

Lafeu: Do not plunge thyself too far in anger, lest thou hasten thy
trial; which if-Lord have mercy on thee for a hen! So, my good
window *of lattice, fare thee well; thy casement I need not open,*
for I look through thee. Give me thy hand.
(Shakespeare, ALL'S WELL THAT ENDS WELL, Act 2, Scene 3, 1604)

Mowgli was uneasy, because he had never been under a roof before. But as he looked at the thatch, he saw that he could tear it out any time if he wanted to get away, and that the window *had no fastenings. . . .*

There was a difficulty at bedtime, because Mowgli would not sleep under anything that looked so like a panther trap as that hut, and when they shut the door he went through the window.
(Rudyard Kipling, THE JUNGLE BOOK, 1894)

Then came a hundred yards' dash to the lighted parchment window, *which told its own story of the home cabin, the roaring Yukon stove, and the steaming pots of tea.*
(Jack London, SON OF THE WOLF, 1900)

Perhaps she knew with her intelligence that the chains she forged only aroused his instinct of destruction, as the plate-glass window *makes your fingers itch for half a brick; but her heart, incapable of reason, made her continue on a course she knew was fatal.*
(W Somerset Maugham, THE MOON AND SIXPENCE, 1919)

Window derives from an Old Norse word *vindauga* which was introduced into English by the Vikings. It is a compound of *vindr*, meaning 'wind' and *auga*, 'eye' and is literally, therefore, 'an eye to admit the wind'. It gradually replaced the existing Old English word *eagthyrel* 'eyethurl', 'eyehole', (from *eage*, 'an eye' and *thyrel*, 'a hole'). The early Middle English book of devotions the ANCRENE WISSE OR ANCRENE RIWLE (C. 1225), written by a chaplain for three sisters, contains both the last recorded mention of *eagthyrel* and the first of *window*.

But the acceptance of *window* was not plain sailing from then on; it had to jostle for prominence with *fenester*, an Old French borrowing, first recorded in 1290 and still in use in the mid-sixteenth century. Indeed Edward Hall, in his chronicle THE UNION OF THE NOBLE AND ILLUSTRE FAMILIES OF LANCASTRE AND YORKE (1542), found himself unable to decide in favour of one term over the other as he struggled to make his meaning clear: '*In the* Fenestres *and* wyndowes *were images resemblynge men of warre.*' By the end of the century, however, *window* was established and had royal approval; for Elizabeth I, in her pursuit of religious tolerance, declared she did not wish '*to open* windows *into men's souls.*'

The open window, on the other hand, has played a significant role in the literature of romance. Romeo, most famously, woos Juliet at her balcony; Cyrano de Bergerac does the same to Roxanne; Belvile (in Behn's THE ROVER, 1677) stations himself at Florinda's chamber-window. Few, however, can have been as direct as Diana to Bertram:

When midnight comes, knock at my chamber window;
I'll order take my mother shall not hear.
Now will I charge you in the band of truth,

When you have conquer'd my yet
maiden bed,
Remain there but an hour, nor speak
to me.
(Shakespeare, ALL'S WELL THAT ENDS WELL, Act 4, scene 2, 1604)

◆ In Modern English the Old English *thyrel* still survives in *nostril* (Old English *nosthyrel*, from *nosu*, 'nose' and *thyrel*, 'hole') and as *thirl* in some northern dialects to denote 'an opening'.

Fenester (from Old French *fenestre*, Latin *fenestra* and ultimately Greek *phainein*, 'to show') is found in the Modern English *defenestration*, usually only with reference to the historical DEFENESTRATION OF PRAGUE (1618), and its derived verb *defenestrate*, 'to throw out of a window', which is confined to humorous contexts.◆

See also **sycophant** for another word deriving from *phainein*.

Viking conquests

The period of 'Viking' invasion and settlement in England dates from the middle of the eighth century to the beginning of the eleventh. It began with short, swift coastal raids followed by large-scale attacks in the 860s which brought much of eastern England under Viking control. Alfred the Great secured Wessex against the invaders through battle and negotiation, and his successors succeeded in regaining much of the eastern territory. Then, in 991, came a new Scandinavian invasion. Years of marauding and pillaging ended in 1014 with the seizure of the throne by the Danish king Canute (Cnut). There followed a quarter century of Danish rule.

Throughout these centuries of upheaval and invasion, large numbers of Scandinavians settled in England, integrating themselves into communities in their adopted country. This assimilation left a store of Scandinavian words in the English language. Since the language already spoken in England (brought in by earlier invasions of Angles, Saxons and Jutes – see **Early Latin influences**, page 86) as well as the language of the Vikings was from the same Germanic source, they already had many everyday words in common, so that it is sometimes difficult to distinguish whether a word was already in English before the Vikings or was introduced by them.

Sometimes it is possible to distinguish, however. One group of words that came in with the Danes has an *sk* pronunciation:*sky, skin, skirt, whisk*, etc, whereas that *sk* sound in Old English words had usually softened to a *sh* pronunciation (written *sc*), as in *ship, fish*. This led to pairs in which an original Old Norse root gave two different products through separate development: Old English *scyrte* produced *shirt* while Viking *skyrta* became *skirt*. Their common root was *skyrta*. Similarly, the *g* and *k* sounds in words such as *leg, get, girth, egg, take, kid, meek*, and *link* indicate an Old Norse origin.

world

the earth

Nothing is more certain than that worlds *on* worlds, *and spheres on spheres, stretch behind and beyond the actually seen.*
(Edward Carpenter, The Drama of Love and Death, 1912)

The concept behind this word is uniquely Germanic. The word is a compound noun and the meaning expressed by its two elements is 'the life of man'. It is made up of Germanic *weraz*, 'man' and *aldh-* 'age' (both unattested). The Old English derivatives *wer* and *eald* are evident in the Old English form *weoruld*. In other languages of Germanic origin the same two elements can be distinguished in modern forms of the word. German, for instance, has *welt*, Swedish *verld* and Dutch *wereld*.

By the second half of the ninth century the term was no longer confined to an expression of human existence but was also evolving its modern sense of 'the earth and all that is in it'.

worry

1. to trouble, distress
2. to bother, annoy, pester

. . .that good dog, more thoughtful than its master, had, it seemed, been watching the old gentleman in his sleep. . . and he still attended on him very closely, worrying *his gaiters in fact, and making dead sets at the buttons.*
(Charles Dickens., The Cricket on the Hearth, 1845)

The great western middle class is worried *sick. It is witnessing its own demise: the collapse of socialism has coincided with the advance of a new proletariat.*
(Weekend Financial Times, 14 January 1995)

Since the Soviet Union dissolved, its nuclear remains have been a worry, *at least for those whose* worry-beads *aren't fully occupied already.*
(The Times, 14 January 1995)

Worry is a violent verb coming from the Old Germanic *wurgjan* which was responsible for words in a number of related languages, all of which meant 'to strangle'. In Old English it became *wyrgan* and in Middle English *worien* or *wirien*, 'to throttle'. In the late fourteenth century the term was also applied to dogs and, in those days, to wolves, which had the habit of seizing their prey by the throat in order to kill it. This use is still current – farmers have the right to shoot any dog which *worries* their sheep – and all the subsequent senses of *worry* spring from it.

Later uses appear to arise from the dog's tenacity as it harasses its victim. In the sixteenth century *worry* was used to mean 'to torment or fret someone by aggressive treatment'. When this sense was employed in a lighter vein in the following century it took on the modern meaning 'to pester', 'to plague', 'to annoy' – by repeated demands, for instance, or constant chatter.

In a similar way concerns and fears work away unrelentingly in our imaginations to make us anxious. For William Hazlitt it was the '*small pains*' that plagued. They are, he says, '*more within our reach; we can fret and* worry *ourselves about them*' (Table Talk, 1822). Trollope, on the other hand, wrote of the persistence of fear: '*Men, when they are* worried *by fears . . . become suspicious*' (Last Chronicle of Barsetshire, 1867). And so, instances such as these from the first quarter of the nineteenth century onwards linked worry to anxiety and care.

write

to form letters and symbols on paper or other surface with an instrument such as a pen or pencil

A Writer *Is A Person Who* Writes

Once the late Sinclair Lewis arrived at Harvard, drunk as usual (alcoholism is our main occupational disease) to talk about writing. *'Hands up, all those who want to be* writers!' *he yelled. Everyone's hand went up. 'Then why the hell aren't you at home* writing? *he asked, and staggered off the platform.*

I begin with this anecdote because it illustrates a simple but profound truth: a writer *is a person who* writes.

(John Braine, Writing a Novel, 1974)

In today's highly literate society it is difficult enough to imagine a time when records had to be hand written, let alone cut out of material, but that is the ultimate meaning of the verb *write.* The word goes back to an Old English term *writan,* meant 'to write by cutting' (as one might score marks into bark or engrave characters into stone). Ultimately it goes back to the unattested Germanic *writan,* 'to tear'.

It is thought that early inscriptions amongst Germanic tribes were scratched upon beech wood tablets, or that the bark of beech trees was used, since the unattested Old Germanic words for *book* and *beech* appear to be connected: *bōks,* 'writing tablet' and source of 'book' in many Germanic languages, is probably related to *bōkā,* 'beech'. Derivatives of these two words in modern Germanic languages also demonstrate the similarity: German, for instance, has *Buch,* 'book' and *Buche,* 'beech', while Dutch has *bock* and *beuk.* The modern English words book and beech come via Old English *bōc,* 'written account' and *bece* respectively.

In some ways it is perhaps surprising that the origins of this important word should remain unclear. It has certainly been the object of intense study over the centuries. The OED has a very extensive entry on the word, with a large number of quotations from the earliest times, as it charts its varied history. The basic meaning has long been clear, 'to set down on paper, etc with a special instrument for the purpose'. The spelling, however, took a long time to settle down, with many alternative forms. Even today in dialects and spoken forms there remains considerable variation.

yacht

a light, fast boat, usually propelled by sails and used for pleasure or racing

Impaired eyesight leads to extraordinary spatial awareness, a sense of knowing exactly where you are in any environment. In a small yacht, *where your head touches the cabin top and outstretched arms can reach both sides of the hull at once, space is neatly defined.*

Putting that same yacht *on a stretch of water like the Solent, where the tide moves the water sideways at walking pace, and trying to cross a short-line start is a skill sighted sailors spend years mastering.*

At Britain's inaugural Visually Impaired National Sailing Championships at Lymington over the weekend, 33 competitors showed unerring accuracy in handling their boats.

(Daily Telegraph, 11 October 1994)

Few yachts *have sailed so far south. Winds hurtle down the icy mountains at more*

than 100 knots and icebergs loom up in the fog, not to mention growlers and brash, which could all sink our delicate glass-fibre boat. But my head was full of stories of Shackleton, Scott and Amundsen.
(WEEKEND TELEGRAPH, 25 February 1995)

English regard for Dutch nautical prowess is evident from the large number of words and idioms to do with ships and sailing that the English borrowed from their rivals across the Channel in the sixteenth and seventeenth centuries. In the sixteenth century the Dutch designed a swift, light, sailing vessel known as a *jaghte*, a shortened form of the compound *jaghtschip* which was literally 'a ship for chasing' (from *jagen*, 'to chase, hunt' and *schip*, 'ship'). The craft, as its name implies, was designed to pursue illegal shipping off the Dutch coast. In the early seventeenth century the Dutch used the vessel to convey royalty or as a pleasure craft on canals and sheltered waters. Here the exiled English king, Charles II, was introduced to *yachting* and upon his Restoration in 1660 the city of Amsterdam presented him with a pleasure yacht named the MARY. Charles and his brother James, Duke of York, had other yachts built and in 1662 raced the KATHERINE and the ANNE on the Thames from Greenwich to Gravesend and back for a £100 wager. This royal endorsement made yachting fashionable and orders from wealthy gentlemen kept the boatyards busy. Surprisingly, however, it was not until the second half of the eighteenth century that yacht racing was organised to any degree.

The speedy Dutch vessel attracted wide international attention, for the word was extensively borrowed into the languages of neighbouring countries. An early spelling in English, *yeagh* (1557) demonstrates the difficulty writers here had in adapting the unfamiliar guttural *gh* of the foreign word. There is great variation in spelling throughout the seventeenth century; *yoath, yolke, yaugh, zaught, jacht, yach* and *yott* are just a few examples, until *yacht* was finally settled upon in the mid-eighteenth century.

> *Cruiser, hooker, sloop, smack* – these terms came into English by way of Dutch in the seventeenth century, when the Dutch were a prominent maritime nation.

For another conveyance which attracted international attention, see **coach**. For another Dutch nautical borrowing, see **aloof**.

yellow

a luminous primary colour, between green and orange; the colour of butter and gold

Ten blue tickets equalled a red one, and could be exchanged for it; ten red tickets equalled a yellow *one; for ten* yellow *tickets the superintendent gave a very plainly bound Bible (worth forty cents in those easy times) to the pupil. . .*

And now at this moment, when hope was dead, Tom Sawyer came forward with nine yellow *tickets, nine red tickets, and ten blue ones, and demanded a Bible. This was a thunderbolt out of a clear sky. Walters was not expecting an application from this source for the next ten years.*
(Mark Twain, THE ADVENTURES OF TOM SAWYER, 1876)

After journeying on for some distance the narrow path they were following turned into a broad roadway, paved with yellow

brick. By the side of the road Tip noticed a sign-post that read: Nine Miles to the Emerald City.
(L Frank Baum, THE MARVELOUS LAND OF OZ, 1904)

She had a little thin face and a little thin body, thin light hair and a sour expression. Her hair was yellow, *and her face was* yellow *because she had been born in India and had always been ill in one way or another.*
(Frances Hodgson Burnett, THE SECRET GARDEN, 1911)

The Indo-European root *ghel-* is responsible for *yellow* in English. Our present-day colour term came from this by way of Old English *geolu* and Middle English *yelwa* and *yelow.*

◆ The same Indo-European root yielded words for a number of things which are notable for their yellowness, such as:

gall, 'bile' (from Middle English *gall(e)*, from Old English *gealla*). This word has been used in figurative applications (*to dip one's pen in gall*) and commonly in a wider sphere because the medieval mind thought that rancour and bitterness of spirit were housed in the gall-bladder. The expression *to have the gall,* meaning 'to have the impudence', arose as a nineteenth-century American slang term.

gold (from Old English *gold*)

yolk of an egg (from Middle English *yolke,* from Old English *geoloca, geolca,* from *geolu,* 'yellow').◆

zany

way out, eccentric, bizarre

. . . he was going to tell them they were staying, and that was that. Wives, obey your husbands. It did not matter what zany *ideas she had. All these wild cards she was dealing, like a croupier on crack. . .*
(Jeremy Vine, THE WHOLE WORLD IN MY HANDS, 1994)

The children took to [the Family Pager] instantly, loving the way the adult operators. . .treated them with inscrutable politeness no matter how zany *the messages.*
(WEEKEND TELEGRAPH, 3 April 1995)

John, and its variants, was a common name in all Christian countries and was therefore frequently used to refer to the man-in-the-street generally, or to a fool or simpleton in particular. French, for instance, has *Gros Jean* and *Jack* is commonly used in this way in English. Venetian and Lombardic dialects transformed the Italian name *Gianni* (the short form of *Giovanni,* 'John') into *Zanni.* This variant became the name of a character in the commedia dell'arte, taking the role of a servant who imitates his master in a farcical way. The word *Zanie* came into English, possibly through French, in the second half of the sixteenth century to denote the 'playful sidekick of a clown, an acrobat or a charlatan'. Shakespeare wrote of *Zanies* in both LOVE'S LABOUR'S LOST (1588) and TWELFTH NIGHT (1601) and Ben Jonson describes '*a* Zanito *a Tumbler, That tries trickes after him to make men laugh*' (EVERY MAN OUT OF HIS HUMOUR, 1599). The meaning was extended in the seventeenth century to refer to 'a person who acts the fool to keep others amused' but all uses of the word as a noun are now obsolete.

Zany's first appearance as an adjective in the first quarter of the seventeenth century was shortlived but it reappeared as such in the second half of the nineteenth century with the sense of 'clownishly bizarre, crazy', the very meanings it still has today.

Back to front

Some words do double duty: they mean one thing when you read them forwards and another when you read them backwards. Here are a few examples. Crossword dictionaries and reverse dictionaries will provide many more examples.

deliver
devil
doom
knits
maps
repaid
revel
reward
sleep
smart
strap
straw
stressed

A variant of this game is the palindrome, in which it is the same word (or phrase or even sentence) that can be read forwards and backwards. The race is on the find the longest – *redivider* is a favourite, though with a little cheating *sensuousnes(s)* does better, and the technical *detartrated* is a good outsider. Beyond the word level, ingenuity knows no bounds. Napoleon is credited with saying *Able was I ere I saw Elba.* Best of all is this bilingual palindrome that goes back to the mid-nineteenth century:

English: Anger? 'Tis safe never. Bar it! Use love!
Latin: Evoles ut ira breve nefas sit; regna.

Even more amazing is that the sense is roughly the same in the two languages.

zest

1. gusto, enthusiasm
2. outer skin of citrus fruits, used to flavour food

Zest. *Originally the tough outer skin of the walnut, but now used to denote the outer skin of citrus fruits, especially of lemon and orange, which contains the essential flavouring oils.*
(Tom Stobart, The Cook's Encyclopaedia, 1980)

. . . *the gods were ridiculed with uninhibited* zest *but with little real malice.*
(A Dictionary of Ancient History, ed Graham Speake, 1994)

She has a rare zest *for life, a passion for looking at things, for knowing what is going on. She has a magical attraction for young people who adore her enthusiasm.*
(Julia Neuberger, Mothers By Daughters, 1995)

Zest is a refreshing word with a hint of mystery. Many modern recipes call for the addition of citrus *zest*, that is the brightly coloured layer in orange, lemon or lime peel that contains the flavoursome oil. These days an effective little gadget called a *zester* can be purchased to pare it away. Even tonic water now comes ready flavoured with the *zest* of lemon or lime – the gin is all that is needed. Not surprisingly it was the French who introduced this taste sensation into British cookery in the seventeenth century. The French called it *zest* (*zeste* in modern French), but no one has been able to discover how they derived this energetic word. The fact that French also applies the term to the membrane or film within a walnut that divides the kernel into four parts has lead to fanciful attempts to connect it with the Latin *schistus*, 'divided'.

In French the word has remained a

culinary term but the British have been more imaginative, so that, by the beginning of the eighteenth century, *zest* was also figuratively used to denote something that adds spice or sparkle to an enjoyment. Mrs Manley, in one of her scurrilous memoirs (1709), informed the world that '*Monsieur St. Amant lov'd nothing so tenderly as he did the Baron, . . . he was the* Zest *to all his Pleasures*'. Towards the end of the eighteenth century *zest* had also come to mean 'great enthusiasm', 'keen pleasure'. In MARTIN CHUZZLEWIT (1844), Dickens described the midwife, Mrs Sarah Gamp, as one who '*went to a lying-in or a laying-out with equal* zest'.

zodiac

a part of the celestial sphere which is divided into twelve parts, each with a distinctive sign

I see that the astrologers have got the signs of the Zodiac *all wrong. . .apparently, there is a 13th sign of the* zodiac, *applying to those born between November 30 and December 17. . . It is called Ophiuchus, and is depicted as a man with a coiled snake. So! I am an Ophiuchan, and not a Sagittarian after all.*
(THE DAILY TELEGRAPH, 21 January 1995)

In astrology the *zodiac* was the name given to an imaginary zone in the heavens through which the sun appears to move during the course of the year. In ancient times astrologers divided the zone into twelve areas, each containing a major constellation. Ancient and medieval astrologers predicted events by observing the position of the sun, moon and other known planets in relation to each other.

The constellations were given names, all of which are still familiar through the popularity of 'star' columns in newspapers and magazines, and many of which relate to animals. The Greek for 'animal' was *zōion* and this gave the diminutive *zōidion*, which denoted the 'carved figure of an animal' and thence 'a sign of the zodiac'. *Zōidion* yielded the adjective *zōidiakos* and the heavenly zone which contained these signs was known as the *zōidiakos kuklos*, 'zodiac circle'. The term was abbreviated to *zōidiakos*, with the adjective becoming a noun. This passed into Latin as *zōdiacus* and, from there, the word and superstition were taken into the Romance languages. The Middle English *zodiaque* was borrowed directly from Old French in the fourteenth century.

For another word deriving from *zōion*, see **zoo**.

zoo

a place where usually wild animals are kept for breeding and showing to the public

A few decades ago, cases of stuffed animals and birds took pride of place in small-town museums. This appealed particularly to children – a sort of static zoo *where the animals were never so anti-social as to skulk in their pens all day.*
(THE TIMES MAGAZINE, 11 March 1995)

The word is derived from the Greek *zōion*, which meant 'animal'. From this, the modern scientific Latin term *zoologia* was coined to describe the study of animals in terms of their usefulness to medical science. This is also the sense in the earliest references to *zoology* in English, which occur in seventeenth-century translations of foreign treatises on the subject. In time the sense broadened to cover the study of animals within natural history, distinct from botany, the study of plants.

The adjective *zoological* appeared in the early nineteenth century. In 1826 it was incorporated into the name of the *Zoological Society of London* which was founded '*for the advancement of* Zoology *and Animal Physiology, and for the introduction of new and curious subjects of the animal kingdom.*' In 1829 the *Zoological Gardens,* the Society's collection of animals in Regent's Park, London, were opened to the public. Within two years, however, the gardens were popularly referred to as *the Zoological* and by the 1840s their name had been clipped to *zoo.* The names of similar animal collections opening in other cities and rejoicing in the cumbersome title *Zoological Gardens* immediately met the same fate – a new word had evolved.

For another word deriving from *zōion,* see **zodiac**.

Bibliography

All lexicographers must admit to a dependence on the work of others. We are no exception. We owe a huge debt of gratitude to the many dictionaries and general reference sources that we have consulted. It would have been quite impossible to have produced this book without the OXFORD ENGLISH DICTIONARY, for example, and there are many other standard dictionaries of British and American English (and of French, Spanish , Latin, Greek, etc) that we have regularly referred to. Then there are more specifically dictionaries of etymology, such as Skeat's, that have aided us immensely. And given the historical nature of this book, dictionaries from previous centuries have been a rich source, such as Dr Johnson's DICTIONARY OF THE ENGLISH LANGUAGE, Grose's DICTIONARY OF THE VULGAR TONGUE, Halliwell's ARCHAIC WORDS and Nares' GLOSSARY OF WORDS, PHRASES, NAMES AND ALLUSIONS. Books about language have ranged from the encyclopedias on language, to textbooks such as Baugh and Cable's splendid HISTORY OF THE ENGLISH LANGUAGE and Hughes' WORDS IN TIME. Contemporary specialist dictionaries on slang, jargon, abbreviations, eponyms, etc. have also figured significantly in our researches.

The following bibliography includes a sample of some of these various categories of books; it does not give a comprehensive listing of them all. Neither does it mention books and articles of interest primarily to the historical linguist, such as Malkiel's ETYMOLOGY. Instead it gives a taster of books that the word lover rather than the professional lexicographer might like to pursue. Many of them are out of print, but most word lovers are also regular visitors to second-hand bookshops, so the chase might add an extra piquancy to the prey when they run it to earth! In virtually all cases, just some of an author's books on words are listed, giving a flavour of their work. If these satisfy, there are plenty more from the pens of Brown, Evans, Partridge and Weekley. Further explorations might lead to journals on language such as NOTES AND QUERIES and AMERICAN NOTES AND QUERIES and then to VERBATIM. Contemporary commentators on language well worth looking out for are Philip Howard, Fritz Spiegl and Nigel Rees.

Ayto, J. (1990). DICTIONARY OF WORD ORIGINS. London, Bloomsbury.

Baugh, A. C. and T. Cable (1993). *A History of the English Language.* London, Routledge.

Beeching, C. L. (1989). A DICTIONARY OF EPONYMS. London, Clive Bingley.

Brandreth, G. (1987). THE JOY OF LEX. London, Futura.

Brown, I. (1942). A WORD IN YOUR EAR. London, Cape.

Brown, I. (1948). NO IDLE WORDS. London, Cape.

Brown, I. (1969). A RHAPSODY OF WORDS. London, Bodley Head.

Brown, I. (1971). RANDOM WORDS. London, Bodley Head.

Brown, I. (1973). WORDS ON THE LEVEL. London, Bodley Head.

Cochrane, J. (1992). STIPPLE, WINK & GUSSET. London, Century.

Crystal, D. (1987). THE CAMBRIDGE ENCYCLOPEDIA OF LANGUAGE. London, Cambridge University Press.

Dunkling, L. (1994). THE GUINNESS BOOK OF CURIOUS WORDS. Enfield, Guinness.

Espy, W. R. (1971). THE GAME OF WORDS. Newton Abbot, Readers' Union.

Espy, W. R. (1978). O THOU IMPROPER, THOU UNCOMMON NOUN. New York, Clarkson.

Evans, B. (1963). COMFORTABLE WORDS. London, Andre Deutsch.

Greenough and Kittredge (1902). WORDS AND THEIR WAYS IN ENGLISH SPEECH. London, Macmillan.

Halliwell, J. H. (1850). ARCHAIC WORDS. London, John Russell Smith.

Hargrave, B. (1911). ORIGINS AND MEANINGS OF POPULAR PHRASES & NAMES. London, Laurie.

Hellweg, P. (1986). THE INSOMNIAC'S DICTIONARY. New York, Facts on File.

Hendrickson, R. (1987). THE ENCYCLOPEDIA OF WORD AND PHRASE ORIGINS. New York, Facts On File.

Hoare, D. (1883). EXOTICS OR ENGLISH WORDS FROM LATIN ROOTS. London, Hodges, Smith & Co.

Hughes, G. (1988). WORDS IN TIME. Oxford, Basil Blackwell.

Hunt, C. (1949). WORD ORIGINS. New York, Philosophical Library.

Lederer, R. (1992). CRAZY ENGLISH. Sittingbourne, Sawd.

Manser, M. (1990). A DICTIONARY OF WORD AND PHRASE ORIGINS. London, Sphere.

Merriam-Webster (1991). NEW BOOK OF WORD HISTORIES. Springfield, Massachusetts, Merriam-Webster.

Paisner, M. (1982). ONE WORD LEADS TO ANOTHER. New York, Dembner.

Palmer, A. S. (1907?). SOME CURIOS FROM A WORD COLLECTOR'S CABINET. London, Routledge.

Partridge, E. (1949). NAME INTO WORD. London, Secker & Warburg.

Room, A. (1991). DICTIONARY OF WORD ORIGINS. Lincolnwood, Illinois, National Textbook Company.

Schur, N. W. (1987). A DICTIONARY OF CHALLENGING WORDS. New York, Facts On File.

Shipley, J. T. (1945). DICTIONARY OF WORD ORIGINS. New York, Philosophical Library.

Smith, L. P. (1925). WORDS AND IDIOMS. London, Constable.

Stimpson, G. (1948). INFORMATION ROUNDUP. New York, Harper.

Walsh, W S. (1892). A HANDY BOOK OF LITERARY CURIOSITIES. Philadelphia, Lippincott.

Weekley, E. (1912). A ROMANCE OF WORDS. London, Murray.

Index

Entries in *italics* refer to headwords.